The COVID-19 Reader

MW00389404

This reader offers some of the most important writing to date from the science of COVID-19 and what science says about its spread and social implications. The readings have been carefully selected, introduced, and interpreted for an introductory or graduate student readership by a distinguished medical sociology and political science team. While some of the early science was inaccurate, lacking sufficient data, or otherwise incomplete, the author team has selected the most important and reliable early work for teachers and students in courses on medical sociology, public health, nursing, infectious diseases, epidemiology, anthropology of medicine, sociology of health and illness, social aspects of medicine, comparative health systems, health policy and management, health behaviors, and community health. Global in scope, the book tells the story of what happened and how COVID-19 was dealt with. Much of this material is in clinical journals, normally not considered in the social sciences, which are nonetheless informative and authoritative for student and faculty readers. Their selection and interpretation for students makes this concise reader an essential teaching source about COVID-19. An accompanying online resource on the book's Routledge web page will update and evolve by providing links to new readings as the science develops.

William C. Cockerham is Distinguished Professor of Sociology and Chair Emeritus, University of Alabama at Birmingham, and Research Scholar of Sociology, College of William & Mary, USA. He is author of *Medical Sociology*, 15th ed. (Routledge, forthcoming); *Sociological Theories of Health and Illness* (Routledge, 2021); *Sociology of Mental Disorder*, 11th ed. (Routledge, 2021); *Social Causes of Health and Disease*, 3rd ed. (2021); Associate Editor-in-Chief, *The International Encyclopedia of Public Health* (2017); and Editor-in-Chief, *Wiley Blackwell Encyclopedia of Health, Illness, Behavior, and Society* (2014).

Geoffrey B. Cockerham, Associate Professor of Political Science at Utah Valley University, USA, is author of *Global Governance and Public Health* (2018) and *Health and Globalization* (2010).

The COVID-19 Reader
The Science and What It Says About the Social

Edited By William C. Cockerham and Geoffrey B. Cockerham

Routledge
Taylor & Francis Group

NEW YORK AND LONDON

First published 2021
by Routledge
52 Vanderbilt Avenue, New York, NY 10017

and by Routledge
2 Park Square, Milton Park, Abingdon, Oxon, OX14 4RN

Routledge is an imprint of the Taylor & Francis Group, an informa business

© 2021 Taylor & Francis

Library of Congress Cataloging-in-Publication Data
Names: Cockerham, William C., editor. | Cockerham, Geoffrey B., editor.
Title: The COVID-19 reader : the science and what it says about the social /
    [edited by] William C. Cockerham and Geoffrey B. Cockerham.
Description: New York, NY : Routledge, 2021.
Identifiers: LCCN 2020038610 | ISBN 9780367693305 (hardback) |
    ISBN 9780367682286 (paperback) | ISBN 9781003141402 (ebook)
Subjects: LCSH: COVID-19 (Disease)—History. | COVID-19 (Disease)—
    Social aspects. | COVID-19 (Disease)—Transmission.
Classification: LCC RA644.C67 C684 2021 | DDC 362.1962/414—dc23
LC record available at https://lccn.loc.gov/2020038610

ISBN: 978-0-367-69330-5 (hbk)
ISBN: 978-0-367-68228-6 (pbk)
ISBN: 978-1-003-14140-2 (ebk)

Typeset in Bembo
by Apex CoVantage, LLC

Visit the eResources: www.routledge.com/9780367682286

Contents

Part I

Introduction to the COVID-19 Pandemic

The purpose of this book is to provide background readings on the 2019–21 COVID-19 pandemic. COVID-19 unleashed itself on the world in the fall of 2019. It originated in Wuhan, China, and subsequently spread across the globe as the most widely contagious pandemic yet to come since the Spanish flu of 1918. By the fall of 2020, over 42 million people were confirmed as infected, more than 1.1 million died, and trade and travel were severely disrupted on a global basis. The number of cases, however, is likely much more than reported as some people had either mild or no symptoms and did not seek medical care or testing yet still may have been contagious (Havers et al. 2020). Final tallies on the disease's deadly and varied effects are not available as the pandemic is ongoing as this book goes to press. Nevertheless, as the virus passes through human populations on its way to resolution, enough information is available to examine the basic parameters of the pandemic from a social science perspective.

The book is organized into six parts beginning with this introduction as Part I, followed by Part II examining the origin of COVID-19 in China. Next is Part III on Europe, which was the pandemic's next explosive site. The book concludes with Part IV on the United States, the country most affected by the virus, and Canada, Part V on Africa and Latin America, and Part VI on the route to a resolution.

COVID-19 belongs to the coronavirus family of viruses. The term "coronavirus" comes from the Latin word "corona," meaning "crown" or "halo" for the crown-like spikes of glycoprotein on the virus's surface (Hempel 2018:63). The spikes bind the virus to receptors on host cells, from which it attacks the cell. Coronaviruses were once considered to be inconsequential pathogens associated mostly with the common cold (Paules, Marston, and Fauci 2020). They usually caused only mild upper respiratory ailments. But three coronaviruses became particularly dangerous: SARS, MERS, and COVID-19. That these three coronaviruses are "a pathogen from a viral family formerly thought to be benign underscores the perpetual challenge of emerging infectious diseases and the importance of sustained preparedness" (Paules et al. 2020:708).

In the late 1960s it was thought infectious diseases were possibly declining as a significant health hazard (Armelagos, Brown, and Turner 2005; Oldstone 2010). Smallpox, measles, yellow fever, and polio were under control. It appeared that some infectious diseases were becoming extinct, and others were controllable through antibiotics. But this is not at all the situation today, as new diseases and some old ones keep appearing (Armelagos et al. 2005; Armelagos and Harper 2016; Barrett 2021; Oldstone 2010). Some viruses have been able to resist antibiotics, certain disease-transmitting insects (i.e., mosquitoes in the case of malaria and Zika) remain active, and humans have encountered new infectious diseases through expansion, climate change, and ecological disturbances. The globalization of trade and travel have made the worldwide transmission of new diseases easier and faster (Cockerham and Cockerham 2010).

There had been early warnings about the possibility of a future pandemic of major proportions sweeping the world (Garret 1994; Osterholm 2005). Evidence pointing to the probability of such an occurrence included the continuing sequence of little known or previously unknown viral diseases infecting humans in various geographic areas. Typically vaccines providing immunity when these outbreaks first occurred were not readily available, increasing concerns. The parade of newly emerging diseases included HIV/AIDS (1983–2008), H5N1 avian influenza (1996), West Nile (1999), the severe acute respiratory syndrome or SARS (2002–03), Middle East respiratory syndrome or MERS (2012), H7N9 avian influenza (2013), Ebola (2014), and Zika (2016). These viruses infected millions of people, causing many deaths, and different viruses appeared year after year. Although they usually came from out-of-the-way places in the world and were not recognized as significant health hazards until they spread into major metropolitan areas, they carried with them the message that newly emerging diseases were repetitive threats to future global health.

The first reading in Part I is a chapter by epidemiologist Michael Osterholm (2005) on a future pandemic. Osterholm produced this paper in 2005 after the SARS contagion, which he viewed at that time as the closest the world has come in the present era to a devastating global pandemic. He notes how quickly an infectious agent can spread around the world through international travel and the possibility of a new pandemic—with SARS as the model—causing worldwide social and economic disruption. He called attention to the need for stockpiling medical supplies, food, and other consumer commodities, nationalizing resources for developing a vaccine and distributing it, and the necessity for governments to take action to prevent what eventually was to occur in 2019–21 with the COVID-19 pandemic. Of course, we know now that little was actually accomplished beforehand, but the article forecasts what would happen and what should have been done to prepare for it—but was not.

SARS as a Precursor

SARS is of particular interest as an example of what was yet to come not only because it was the first viral pandemic of the 21st century, but also is a coronavirus like MERS and COVID-19 (Cavanagh 2010; Hempel 2018; Oldstone 2010). SARS was officially designated SARS-CoV, while MERS was labeled MERS-CoV. MERS was passed from bats to camels and then to humans, and there were few cases outside the Middle East. COVID-19 is a far different story. It ravaged the world. COVID-19 was originally SARS-CoV-2 or severe acute respiratory syndrome coronavirus 2, but differed from SARS in that it caused fewer upper respiratory and gastrointestinal symptoms (Xie and Chen 2020). But COVID-19 is particularly fatal for people who have already existing medical conditions.

Like COVID-19 some 18 years in the future, SARS originated in horseshoe bats who were found to be natural hosts for the virus (Poon and Peiris 2010). The bats produced antibodies that prevented them from becoming sick but nevertheless allowed the virus to live in their bodies. How bats are able to accommodate coronaviruses and still survive is an important question yet to be answered. Nevertheless, bats become the natural reservoir within which these viruses live and spread to other species. In this instance, SARS was transmitted from bats to masked palm civets, a cat-like animal that is an exotic food in Chinese culture. Civets are often smuggled into China from Southeast Asia, where they are more plentiful. Some were infected by eating fruit particles with bat saliva, then trapped alive, and transported to Chinese "wet" markets (named for the large quantities of water used to wash the floors) that are open-air markets where live wild animals are sold and processed for food. Sanitary conditions in such markets are poor. The markets are typically crowded with both people and animals who would not usually have close contact with one another, with the animals eating, urinating, and defecating in cramped outdoor cages and processed as food on nearby tables or buckets. Viruses and bacteria thrive in such environments.

Subsequent RNA (ribonucleic acid) genetic mapping of SARS in humans was determined to be almost identical to that of SARS in infected civets in the wet market in Guangdong Province in southern China, where the pandemic began (Oldstone 2010:228). This evidence confirmed that it was civets who passed the virus on to humans. About half of the early SARS patients were food handlers from the market, and others were family members and health care workers treating the sick. Typical symptoms were fever, fatigue, coughing, shortness of breath, and for some, respiratory failure.

SARS spread out of this market into nearby neighborhoods and rural areas. The first hospitalized case was a farmer diagnosed as having a novel form of pneumonia in November 2002. The virus continued to spread and was carried to a Hong Kong hotel in January 2003 by an infected physician attending a wedding who had been treating SARS patients in Guangdong Province. He became sick and died, infecting other hotel residents, including a Chinese-American businessman, who traveled to Hanoi, Vietnam, spreading it there. Another hotel guest, a 78-year-old woman from Toronto, Canada, returned home where she died. Some 400 people became sick in Toronto, of whom 44 died. It had taken about 24 hours for the SARS virus to spread to five countries; within two weeks, the virus reached 18 countries (Hempel 2018; Shah 2016). Altogether, some 8,098 people were known to have been infected in 32 countries with 774 deaths (Hempel 2018).

The first report that such a virus existed came from an Italian physician, Carlo Urbani, working for the World Health Organization (WHO) in Vietnam. He investigated what appeared to be a new disease in patients at the French Hospital of Hanoi and notified WHO in February 2003, of its existence. WHO, in response, issued a worldwide alert. Urbani later died from SARS but is credited with saving thousands of lives by calling attention to the disease. The Chinese government had kept quiet about SARS up until this time and apologized later for its delay in not reporting the outbreak until mid-March of 2003. Local Chinese officials were removed from office, civets were hunted down and killed, selling wild animal meat in wet markets was banned, and a computerized automatic reporting system for infectious diseases was established. There are no reports of SARS since 2004. Nevertheless in 2012, the United States declared SARS to still be a serious potential threat to public health. As it turned out, SARS serves as a model for COVID-19 because both are (1) a coronavirus, (2) originated among bats, (3) likely featured animal-to-human transmission, (4) emerged in a wet animal market in China, (5) cause similar symptoms in humans, and (6) spreads quickly.

Despite being banned, wild animal meat remained for sale in Chinese wet markets. A loophole in the regulations allowed such meat to be sold if the animal was bred in captivity rather than in the wild. In 2011, American science journalist Sonia Shah (2016) traveled to Guangzhou, the capital of Guangdong Province, to find a wet market. A security guard told her no such markets existed but directed her to speak with a passerby. The person gave her directions to the market that was around the corner and it turned out to consist of various covered stalls on a walkway with pungent smells where many different kinds of animals were caged in close proximity and on sale for human consumption, including bats, civets, snakes, frogs, ferrets, and others. A lack of hygiene was obvious from the smells and scattered wastes. The wet markets in China awaited their recurring role in a future pandemic.

If the coronaviruses remained in the wild, namely in the bat caves where they subsisted, the likelihood of transmission to humans would be slim. But they did not. Rather, the "social" enters in at this point as a significant causal factor for the coronavirus pandemics originating in China. This is because of the demand for *yewei* ("wild beast") cuisine in traditional Chinese culture. Eating wild animals is considered a luxury because of their rarity and cost, which China's growing affluence has energized. Often these foods are prized because it is believed they can pass the animal's natural energy on to the person eating it as a restorative substance for their health or stimulant (Shah

2016). It is also thought that consuming exotic creatures can cure various ailments and enhance male vitality. Snake wine, for example, is made from high-proof liqueur in which a poisonous species of snake is marinated for a long period of time and then drunk as a tonic for invigorating the body. Bats are used to make soup and civet meat is favored for its musky smell. This cultural practice, combined especially with the unhygienic conditions of the wet markets, brought the coronavirus into play.

Society Under Siege

COVID-19 is an event of historic proportions. Not only have thousands of people died or are yet to die, but travel by air and sea were shut down, public gatherings canceled, businesses and schools closed or operated remotely online, children home-schooled, stay-at-home and social distancing orders issued, rates of unemployment soared as people were unable to go to their usual place of work, restaurants and bars served food and drink outdoors on sidewalks and in parking lots or take-out only, the 2020 Olympics postponed for a year, fall team sports at all levels in the United States and other countries canceled, postponed, or televised from empty stadiums, and borders between countries closed. Much of human society was in "lockdown."

The social effects are profound. People were supposed to limit social contacts, especially in public through "social distancing" and "staying at home" if possible, and wear masks when among non-family members. Those who could worked from home electronically, performing their job by computer and telephone. While economic activities largely shifted onto electronic platforms, so did education, religious gatherings, routine health care, and some public services. Suggestions have come forward that the changes may be permanent, but this is far from certain as an effective vaccine could return social life to normal with public events and travel resuming. In this case, COVID-19 would likely fade into history as a bad experience. Or, conversely, the virus may continue to mutate and circulate on an annual basis. Either way, some adjustments in social relations may nevertheless remain. Employers may find, for example, that it is less expensive for their employees to work at home rather than providing commercial office space. Teleconferencing may emerge as the standard mode for face-to-face meetings, not only in business but between family members in far-flung locations. Telemedicine may become a routine form of medical practice, and motion picture theatres become extinct as "streaming" movies in one's home takes their place. Online shopping and home delivery may become even more common, thereby further reducing shopping in retail "brick and mortar" stores and forcing closure. Also, new occupations may emerge and existing ones change, consumption patterns of goods and services may likewise be altered, and so on. Social life may indeed be different in some yet to be recognized ways.

Airborne Transmissions and Asymptomatic Individuals

COVID-19 appears to spread more quickly than MERS and SARS, and it does so through the airborne transmission of droplets from the mouth and nose to nearby people (Zhang et al. 2020). Halting it is particularly challenging because some 20 to 45 percent of those infected are initially asymptomatic, particularly younger persons. That is, they have no observable symptoms but can infect others (Gandhi, Yokoe, and Havlir 2020). They might even be surprised to learn they are infected. Among confirmed cases, most individuals (80 percent) have only mild to moderate forms of the disease. While this might not seem so bad, the remainder have severe symptoms. According to the leading American epidemiologist, Anthony Fauci, about 2.4 percent of those infected in the United States die from it (Burling 2020). Moreover, it is not known whether people who have had COVID-19 have lasting immunity or can be infected multiple times, or whether they will suffer long-term effects, such as persistent fatigue, after recovery.

The second reading in this section is by Renyi Zhang and his associates (2020) that identifies airborne transmission as the dominant means of spreading COVID-19 between humans. It examines the difference between wearing and not wearing masks, while taking social distancing into account. The third reading by Monica Gandhi, Deborah Yokoe, and Diane Havlir (2020) discusses the complexities of trying to control COVID-19 when some people who are infected are asymptomatic; that is, they do not overtly show any symptoms and require testing to discover whether or not the virus is present in their bodies. We find out that COVID-19 is an upper-level respiratory infection that takes longer to become symptomatic. SARS, a lower-level respiratory infection took about 5 days for symptoms to appear, while COVID-19 symptoms do not surface for about 14 days on average but the virus can nonetheless spread to other people during this time. What this indicates is that symptom-based screening is not sufficient in determining who is and who is not infected and requires that testing includes asymptomatic persons.

Box 1.1 Becoming Sick

One person who became ill with COVID-19 and described the experience was a British infectious disease professor in Liverpool, Paul Garner (2020). He did not need hospitalization. But he was sick. At first, in mid-March of 2020, he reported simply feeling "strange." Then he lost his sense of smell and had a runny nose, followed by extreme fatigue and tightness in his chest. Every day there was a symptom of some type: dizziness, breathlessness, sweating, and headaches. Some individuals also have a fever, but he apparently did not as the virus can affect different people differently. Although his symptoms were supposed to go away after two weeks, they lasted seven weeks. Other individuals, known as "long-haulers" in the United States, were sick for as long as 100 days. Some people are sick enough to be hospitalized and the worst cases put on ventilators in intensive care wards so they can breathe, and not all survive.

COVID-19: Comorbid Conditions, Age, Race, Gender, and Class

Five variables relevant in understanding the social pattern of COVID-19 are those of (1) comorbid health conditions, (2) age, (3) race, (4) gender, and (5) social class:

- *Comorbid conditions.* The term "comorbid conditions" refers to simultaneous but separate health problems that a person may have, such as heart disease, hypertension, diabetes, and severe asthma, as well as obesity. When COVID-19 is added to such conditions, the health status of less healthy persons is further jeopardized, and deaths are more likely to result in individuals with already compromised immune systems and breathing problems. Comorbid conditions are especially important because they act as an intervening variable causing adverse changes in age, race, gender, and class when COVID-19 is introduced. While comorbid conditions would seem to be exclusively biological in nature, they have social connotations in that they are most common among African Americans and lower social strata (Abrams and Szefler 2020). As fundamental cause theory in medical sociology makes clear, socioeconomic status is a causal factor in health disparities because of differing class-based resources in avoiding risks and adopting protective measures (Phelan and Link 2013; Phelan, Link, and Tehranifar 2010). This would include the risk of COVID-19.
- *Age.* COVID-19 also produces a distinct age-based gradient of mortality that progresses upwards step-by-step with increasing virulence through successively older age groups until the most affected 80-plus-year-old age is reached. It is a notable and the only positive feature of the pandemic that young children from infancy to age 18 are least likely to get sick from COVID-19 and die from it (Davies et al. 2020; Williamson et al. 2020). The exception is children with comorbid conditions, although there are cases of some previously healthy children ill with the coronavirus. Of those infected, some are asymptomatic (without overt symptoms), and the degree to which they can spread the disease to adults is unknown. The idea that children are immune from COVID-19 is wrong.

  Whereas adults over the age of 60 were most likely to be infected by COVID-19 initially, the second wave in the United States largely consisted of young adults in the 20–29-year-old age group and also some children. Many lived in states like Florida, Texas, Arizona, and California who did not social distance after a few weeks in isolation and prematurely socialized in crowds at parties, in bars, and elsewhere. Overall, however, the older the age group, the higher the mortality. People in their 80s are most likely to die and children least likely. Comorbid conditions are increasingly common as age advances. Research in England on over 17 million deaths from different causes shows that people older than 80 were about 20 times more likely to die from COVID-19 than those in their 50s and hundreds of times more likely than those below the age of 40 (Williamson et al. 2020).

- *Race.* Racial minorities are more likely to be infected and die than whites, as seen in the higher mortality rates for blacks and Hispanics in the United States and blacks and South Asians in Britain (Williamson et al. 2020; Yancy 2020). In Chicago, for example, blacks constitute 30 percent of the population but had 50 percent of the COVID-19 cases and almost 70 percent of the COVID-19 deaths by mid-May 2020 (Reyes et al. 2020). Another study in New Orleans of patients served by a local health care system, of whom 31 percent were black, found in May 2020 that some 76.9 percent of those hospitalized and 70.6 percent of deaths were black (Price-Hayward et al. 2020). Before COVID-19, non-Hispanic blacks had the worse health profile of any racial–ethnic group in the United States, with the highest overall rates of age-adjusted mortality (National Center for Health Statistics 2018). Particularly striking are the exceptionally high death rates for non-Hispanic blacks for heart disease, stroke, cancer, homicide, and HIV/AIDS. COVID-19 exacerbates this situation, making a bad outcome even worse because of the high prevalence of comorbid conditions.

  In addition to the effects of underlying health ailments, low incomes, less access to medical care, and high risk jobs as front-line health care workers, bus drivers and mass transit workers, food industry and public service employees, and similar positions making it harder to social distance and work at home are all important factors promoting exposure to COVID-19 on the part of racial minorities.

- *Gender.* While males and females tend to become infected from COVID-19 at approximately the same rate, males have a somewhat higher likelihood (about 2.5 percent) in the United States of dying from it than females of the same age, with comorbid conditions exerting an important influence. In Britain as a whole, some 60 percent of males were found in one study to die compared to 40 percent of females (Williamson et al. 2020). Why females have less risk of mortality is not known, although women may have stronger immune systems or the divergence may rest in hormonal, chromosomal, or genetic differences.

- *Social Class.* The idea that COVID-19 is a great equalizer because it affects all social classes the same is erroneous. Instead, social disparities in health are magnified by the virus. Those persons toward the bottom of the socioeconomic ladder are less likely to be able to engage in social distancing because of jobs requiring face-to-face interaction. They are also more likely to live crowded circumstances making such distancing more difficult, along with a greater likelihood of having comorbid aliments. Research in England showed that people lowest on the social scale had the highest mortality from COVID-19 (Williamson et al. 2020). The history of pandemics shows the poor always fare the worst (Cantor 2001). To be poor means having less of the good things in life, including health and longevity.

Critical Thinking Questions

1. What are the similarities between SARS and COVID-19? What lessons for the future can be learned from these similarities?
2. How has COVID-19 affected society?
3. In what ways do comorbid conditions, age, race, gender, and social class intersect with one another to produce pandemic-related social patterns?

References

Abrams, Elissa M. and Stanley J. Szefler. 2020. "COVID-19 and the Impact of Social Determinants of Health." *Lancet Respiratory Medicine* 8(7):659–61.

Armelagos, George J. and Kristin N. Harper. 2016. "Emerging Infectious Diseases, Urbanization, and Globalization in a Time of Global Warming." Pp. 291–311 in William Cockerham (ed.), *The New Blackwell Companion to Medical Sociology*. Oxford, UK: Wiley Blackwell.

Armelagos, George J., Peter J. Brown, and Bethany Turner. 2005. *Social Science & Medicine* 61:755–65.

Barrett, Ron. 2021. "Emerging Infectious Diseases." Forthcoming in William Cockerham (ed.), *The Wiley Blackwell Companion to Medical Sociology*. Oxford, UK: Wiley Blackwell.

Burling, Stacey. 2020. "No End in Sight, Fauci Tells Doctors at Conference." *Philadelphia Inquirer* (July 21):1.

Cantor, Norman F. 2001. *In the Wake of the Plague*. New York: Simon and Schuster.

Cavanagh, Dave (ed.). 2010. *Methods in Molecular Biology, vol. 454, SARS and Other Coronaviruses: Laboratory Protocols*. New York: Humana Press.

Cockerham, Geoffrey B. and William C. Cockerham. 2010. *Health and Globalization*. Cambridge, UK: Polity.

Davies, Nicholas G., Petra Klepac, Yang Liu, Kiesha Prem, Mark Jit, CMMID COVID-19 Working Group, and Rosalind M. Eggo. 2020. "Age-Dependent Effects in the Transmission and Control of COVID-19 Epidemics." *Nature Medicine*. https://doi.org/10.1038/s41591-020-0962-9.

Gandhi, Monica, Deborah S. Yokoe, and Diane V. Havlir. 2020. "Asymptomatic Transmission, the Achilles' Heel of Current Strategies to Control Covid-19." *New England Journal of Medicine* 382:2158–60.

Garner, Paul. 2020. "For 7 Weeks I Have Been Through a Roller Coaster of Ill Health, Extreme Emotions, and Utter Exhaustion." *BMJ Opinion* (May 5). https://bit.ly/3b6z8XO.

Garrett, Laurie. 1994. *The Coming Plague – Newly Emerging Diseases in a World Out of Balance*. New York: Farrar, Straus, and Giroux.

Havers, Fiona P., Carrie Reed, Travis Lim, Joel M. Montgomery et al. 2020. "Seroprevalence of Antibodies to SARS-CoV-2 in 10 Sites in the United States, March 23–May 12, 2020." *JAMA Internal Medicine* (July 21). https://jamanetwork.com/

Hempel, Sandra. 2018. *The Atlas of Disease*. London: White Lion.

National Center for Health Statistics. 2018. *Health, United States, 2018*. Washington, DC: US Government Printing Office.

Oldstone, Michael B. A. 2010. *Viruses, Plagues, and History: Past, Present and Future*. Oxford, UK: Oxford University Press.

Osterholm, Michael T. 2005. "Preparing for the Next Pandemic." *Foreign Affairs* (Jul/Aug):24–37.

Paules, Catherine, Hillary Marston, and Anthony Fauci. 2020. "Coronavirus Infections—More Than Just the Common Cold." *JAMA* 323(February 25):707–8.

Phelan, Jo C. and Bruce G. Link. 2013. "Fundamental Cause Theory." Pp. 105–26 in William Cockerham (ed.), *Medical Sociology on the Move: New Directions in Theory*. Dordrecht: Springer.

Phelan, Jo C., Bruce G. Link, and Parisa Tehranifar. 2010. "Social Conditions as Fundamental Causes of Health Inequalities: Theory, Evidence, and Policy Implications." *Journal of Health and Social Behavior* 51(Extra Issue):S28–S40.

Poon, Leo L. and J. S. Malik Peiris. 2010. "Detection of Group 1 Coronaviruses in Bats Using Universal Coronavirus Reverse Transcription Polymerase Chain Reactions." Pp. 13–26 in D. Cavanagh (ed.), *Methods in Molecular Biology, vol. 454, SARS – and Other Coronaviruses: Laboratory Protocols*. New York: Humana Press.

Price-Hayward, Eboni G., Jeffrey Burton, Daniel Fort, and Leonardo Seoane. 2020. "Hospitalization and Mortality among Black Patients and White Patients with COVID-19." *New England Journal of Medicine* 382(June 25):2534–43.

Reyes, C., N. Husain, C. Gutowski, S. St. Clair, and G. Pratt. 2020. "Chicago's Coronavirus Disparity: Black Chicagoans are Dying at Nearly Six Times the Rate of White Residents, Data Show." *Chicago Tribune* (April 7).

Shah, Sonia. 2016. *Pandemic*. New York: Picador.

Williamson, Elizabeth J., Alex J. Walker, Krishnan Bhaskaran et al. 2020. "OpenSafely: Factors Associated with COVID-19 Death in 17 Million Patients." *Nature*. https://doi.org/10.1038/s41586-020-2521-4.

Xie, Mingxuan and Qiong Chen. 2020. "Insight into 2019 Novel Coronavirus—An Updated Interim Review and Lessons from SARS-CoV and MERS-CoV." *International Journal of Infectious Disease* 94:119–24.

Yancy, Clyde W. "COVID-19 and African Americans." *JAMA* 323(19):1891–92.

Zhang, Renyi, Yixin Li, Annie L. Zhang, Yuan Wang, and Mario J. Molina. 2020. "Identifying Airborne Transmission as the Dominant Route for the Spread of COVID-19." *PNAS* 117(26):14857–63.

1   Preparing for the Next Pandemic

Michael T. Osterholm

Fear Itself

Dating back to antiquity, influenza pandemics have posed the greatest threat of a worldwide calamity caused by infectious disease. Over the past 300 years, 10 influenza pandemics have occurred among humans. The most recent came in 1957–58 and 1968–69, and although several tens of thousands of Americans died in each one, these were considered mild compared to others. The 1918–19 pandemic was not. According to recent analysis, it killed 50 to 100 million people globally. Today, with a population of 6.5 billion, more than three times that of 1918, even a "mild" pandemic could kill many millions of people.

A number of recent events and factors have significantly heightened concern that a specific near-term pandemic may be imminent. It could be caused by H5N1, the avian influenza strain currently circulating in Asia. At this juncture scientists cannot be certain. Nor can they know exactly when a pandemic will hit, or whether it will rival the experience of 1918–19 or be more muted like 1957–58 and 1968–69. The reality of a coming pandemic, however, cannot be avoided. Only its impact can be lessened. Some important preparatory efforts are under way, but much more needs to be done by institutions at many levels of society.

The Backdrop

Of the three types of influenza virus, influenza type A infects and kills the greatest number of people each year and is the only type that causes pandemics. It originates in wild aquatic birds. The virus does not cause illness in these birds, and although it is widely transmitted among them, it does not undergo any significant genetic change. Direct transmission from the birds to humans has not been demonstrated, but when a virus is transmitted from wild birds to domesticated birds such as chickens, it undergoes changes that allow it to infect humans, pigs, and potentially other mammals. Once in the lung cells of a mammalian host, the virus can "reassort," or mix genes, with human influenza viruses that are also present. This process can lead to an entirely new viral strain, capable of sustained human-to-human transmission. If such a virus has not circulated in humans before, the entire population will be susceptible. If the virus has not circulated in the human population for a number of years, most people will lack residual immunity from previous infection.

Once the novel strain better adapts to humans and is easily transmitted from person to person, it is capable of causing a new pandemic. As the virus passes repeatedly from one human to the next, it eventually becomes less virulent and joins the other influenza viruses that circulate the globe each year. This cycle continues until another new influenza virus emerges from wild birds and the process begins again.

Some pandemics result in much higher rates of infection and death than others. Scientists now understand that this variation is a result of the genetic makeup of each specific virus and the presence of certain virulence factors. That is why the 1918–19 pandemic killed many more people than either the 1957–58 or the 1968–69 pandemic.

A Critical Difference

Infectious diseases remain the number one killer of humans worldwide. Currently, more than 39 million people live with HIV, and last year about 2.9 million people died of AIDS, bringing the cumulative total of deaths from AIDS to approximately 25 million. Tuberculosis (TB) and malaria also remain major causes of death. In 2003, about 8.8 million people became infected with TB, and the disease killed more than 2 million. Each year, malaria causes more than 1 million deaths and close to 5 billion episodes of clinical illness. In addition, newly emerging infections, diarrheal and other vector-borne diseases, and agents resistant to antibiotics pose a serious and growing public health concern.

Given so many other significant infectious diseases, why does another influenza pandemic merit unique and urgent attention? First, of the more than 1,500 microbes known to cause disease in humans, influenza continues to be the king in terms of overall mortality. Even in a year when only the garden-variety strains circulate, an estimated 1–1.5 million people worldwide die from influenza infections or related complications. In a pandemic lasting 12 to 36 months, the number of cases and deaths would rise dramatically.

Recent clinical, epidemiological, and laboratory evidence suggests that the impact of a pandemic caused by the current H5N1 strain would be similar to that of the 1918–19 pandemic. More than half of the people killed in that pandemic were 18 to 40 years old and largely healthy. If 1918–19 mortality data are extrapolated to the current U.S. population, 1.7 million people could die, half of them between the ages of 18 and 40. Globally, those same estimates yield 180–360 million deaths, more than five times the cumulative number of documented AIDS deaths. In 1918–19, most deaths were caused by a virus-induced response of the victim's immune system—a cytokine storm—which led to acute respiratory distress syndrome (ARDS). In other words, in the process of fighting the disease, a person's immune system severely damaged the lungs, resulting in death. Victims of H5N1 have also suffered from cytokine storms, and the world is not much better prepared to treat millions of cases of ARDS today than it was 85 years ago. In the 1957–58 and 1968–69 pandemics, the primary cause of death was secondary bacterial pneumonias that infected lungs weakened by influenza. Although such bacterial infections can often be treated by antibiotics, these drugs would be either unavailable or in short supply for much of the global population during a pandemic.

The arrival of a pandemic influenza would trigger a reaction that would change the world overnight. A vaccine would not be available for a number of months after the pandemic started, and there are very limited stockpiles of antiviral drugs. Plus, only a few privileged areas of the world have access to vaccine-production facilities. Foreign trade and travel would be reduced or even ended in an attempt to stop the virus from entering new countries— even though such efforts would probably fail given the infectiousness of influenza and the volume of illegal crossings that occur at most borders. It is likely that transportation would also be significantly curtailed domestically, as smaller communities sought to keep the disease contained. The world relies on the speedy distribution of products such as food and replacement parts for equipment. Global, regional, and national economies would come to an abrupt halt—something that has never happened due to HIV, malaria, or TB despite their dramatic impact on the developing world.

The closest the world has come to this scenario in modern times was the SARS (severe acute respiratory syndrome) crisis of 2003. Over a period of five months, about 8,000 people were infected by a novel human coronavirus. About 10 percent of them died. The virus apparently spread to humans when infected animals were sold and slaughtered in unsanitary and crowded markets in China's Guangdong Province. Although the transmission rate of SARS paled in comparison to that of influenza, it demonstrated how quickly such an infectious agent can circle the globe, given the ease and frequency of international travel. Once SARS emerged in rural China, it spread to five countries within 24 hours and to 30 countries on six continents within several months.

The SARS experience teaches a critical lesson about the potential global response to a pandemic influenza. Even with the relatively low number of deaths it caused compared to other infectious diseases, SARS had a powerful negative psychological impact on the populations of many countries. In a recent analysis of the epidemic, the National Academy of Science's Institute of Medicine concluded: "The relatively high case-fatality rate, the identification of super-spreaders, the newness of the disease, the speed of its global spread, and public uncertainty about the ability to control its spread may have contributed to the public's alarm. This alarm, in turn, may have led to the behavior that exacerbated the economic blows to the travel and tourism industries of the countries with the highest number of cases."

SARS provided a taste of the impact a killer influenza pandemic would have on the global economy. Jong-Wha Lee, of Korea University, and Warwick McKibbin, of the Australian National University, estimated the economic impact of the six-month SARS epidemic on the Asia-Pacific region at about $40 billion. In Canada, 438 people were infected and 43 died after an infected person traveled from Hong Kong to Toronto, and the Canadian Tourism Commission estimated that the epidemic cost the nation's economy $419 million. The Ontario health minister estimated that SARS cost the province's health-care system about $763 million, money that was spent, in part, on special SARS clinics and supplies to protect health-care workers. The SARS outbreak also had a substantial impact on the global airline industry. After the disease hit in 2003, flights in the Asia-Pacific area decreased by 45 percent from the year before. During the outbreak, the number of flights between Hong Kong and the United States fell 69 percent. And this impact would pale in comparison to that of a 12- to 36-month worldwide influenza pandemic.

The SARS epidemic also raises questions about how prepared governments are to address a prolonged infectious disease crisis—particularly governments that are already unstable. Seton Hall University's Yanzhong Huang concluded that the SARS epidemic created the most severe social or political crisis encountered by China's leadership since the 1989 Tiananmen crackdown. China's problems probably resulted less from SARS' public health impact than from the government's failed effort to allay panic by withholding information about the disease from the Chinese people. The effort backfired. During the crisis, Chinese Premier Wen Jiabao pointed out in a cabinet meeting on the epidemic that "the health and security of the people, overall state of reform, development, and stability, and China's national interest and image are at stake." But Huang believes that "a fatal period of hesitation regarding information-sharing and action spawned anxiety, panic, and rumor-mongering across the country and undermined the government's efforts to create a milder image of itself in the international arena." Widespread infection and economic collapse can destabilize a government; blame for failing to deal effectively with a pandemic can cripple a government. This holds even more for an influenza pandemic. In the event of a pandemic influenza, the level of panic witnessed during the SARS crisis could spiral out of control as illnesses and deaths continued to mount over months and months. Unfortunately, the public is often indifferent to initial warnings about impending infectious-disease crises—as with HIV, for example. Indifference becomes fear only after the catastrophe hits, when it is already too late to implement preventive or control measures.

Ready for the Worst

What should the industrialized world be doing to prepare for the next pandemic? The simple answer: far more. So far, the World Health Organization and several countries have finalized or drafted useful but overly general plans. The U.S. Department of Health and Human Services has increased research on influenza-vaccine production and availability. These efforts are commendable, but what is needed is a detailed operational blueprint for how to get a population through one to three years of a pandemic. Such a plan must involve all the key components of society. In the private sector, the plan must coordinate the responses of the medical community, medical suppliers, food providers, and the transportation system. In the government sector, the plan should take into account officials from public health, law enforcement, and emergency management at the international, federal, state, and local levels.

At the same time, it must be acknowledged that such master blueprints may have their drawbacks, too. Berkeley's Aaron Wildavsky persuasively argued that resilience is the real key to crisis management—overly rigid plans can do more harm than good. Still, planning is enormously useful. It gives government officials, private-sector partners, and the community the opportunity to meet, think through potential dilemmas, purchase necessary equipment, and set up organizational structures for a 12- to 36-month response. A blueprint forces leaders to rehearse their response to a crisis, preparing emotionally and intellectually so that when disaster strikes the community can face it.

Influenza-vaccine production deserves special attention. An initiative to provide vaccine for the entire world must be developed, with a well-defined schedule to ensure progress. It is laudable that countries such as the United States and Vietnam are pursuing programs with long-term goals to develop and produce H5N1 vaccine for their respective populations. But if the rest of the world lacks supplies, even the vaccinated will be devastated when the global economy comes to an abrupt halt. Pandemic-influenza preparedness is by nature an international issue. No one can truly be isolated from a pandemic.

The pandemic-related collapse of worldwide trade and its ripple effect throughout industrialized and developing countries would represent the first real test of the resiliency of the modern global delivery system. Given the extent to which modern commerce relies on the precise and readily available international trade of goods and services, a shutdown of the global economic system would dramatically harm the world's ability to meet the surging demand for essential commodities such as food and medicine during a crisis. The business community can no longer afford to play a minor role in planning the response to a pandemic. For the world to have critical goods and services during a pandemic, industry heads must stockpile raw materials for production and preplan distribution and transportation support. Every company's senior managers need to be ready to respond rapidly to changes in the availability, production, distribution, and inventory management of their products. There is no model for how to revive the current global economy were it to be devastated.

To truly be complete, all planning on international, regional, national, and local levels must consider three different scenarios: What if the pandemic begins tonight? What if it starts one year from now? What if the world is so fortunate as to have an entire decade to prepare? All are possible, but none is certain.

Starting Tonight

What would happen today in the office of every nation's leader if several cities in Vietnam suffered from major outbreaks of H5N1 infection, with a five percent mortality rate? First, there would be an immediate effort to try to sort out disparate disease-surveillance data from a variety of government and public health sources to determine which countries might have pandemic-related cases. Then, the decision would likely be made to close most international and even some state or provincial borders—without any predetermined criteria for how or when those borders might be reopened. Border security would be made a priority, especially to protect potential supplies of pandemic-specific vaccines from nearby desperate countries. Military leaders would have to develop strategies to defend the country and also protect against domestic insurgency with armed forces that would likely be compromised by the disease. Even in unaffected countries, fear, panic, and chaos would spread as international media reported the daily advance of the disease around the world.

In short order, the global economy would shut down. The commodities and services countries would need to "survive" the next 12 to 36 months would have to be identified. Currently, most businesses' continuity plans account for only a localized disruption—a single plant closure, for instance—and have not planned for extensive, long-term outages. The private and public sectors would have to develop emergency plans to sustain critical domestic supply chains and manufacturing and agricultural production and distribution. The labor force would be severely affected when it was most needed. Over the course of the year, up to 50 percent of affected populations could become ill; as many as five percent could die. The disease would hit senior management as hard as the rest of the work force. There would be major shortages in all countries of a wide range of commodities, including food, soap, paper, light bulbs, gasoline, parts for repairing military equipment and municipal water pumps, and medicines, including vaccines unrelated to the pandemic. Many industries not critical to survival—electronics, automobile, and clothing, for example—would suffer or even close. Activities that require close human contact—school, seeing movies in theaters, or eating at restaurants—would be avoided, maybe even banned.

Vaccine would have no impact on the course of the virus in the first months and would likely play an extremely limited role worldwide during the following 12 to 18 months of the pandemic. Despite major innovations in the production of most other vaccines, international production of influenza vaccine is based on a fragile and limited system that utilizes technology from the 1950s. Currently, annual production of influenza vaccine is limited to about 300 million trivalent doses—which protect against three different influenza strains in one dose—or less than one billion monovalent doses. To counter a new strain of pandemic influenza that has never circulated throughout the population, each person would likely need two doses for adequate protection. With today's limited production capacity, that means that less than 500 million people—about 14 percent of the world's population—would be vaccinated within a year of the pandemic. In addition, because the structure of the virus changes so rapidly, vaccine development could only start once the pandemic began, as manufacturers would have to obtain the new pandemic strain. It would then be at least another six months before mass production of the vaccine. Even if the system functions to the best of its ability, influenza vaccine is produced commercially in just nine countries: Australia, Canada, France, Germany, Italy, Japan, the Netherlands, the United Kingdom, and the United States. These countries contain only 12 percent of the world's population. In the event of an influenza pandemic, they would probably nationalize their domestic production facilities, as occurred in 1976, when the United States, anticipating a pandemic of swine influenza (H1N1), refused to share its vaccine.

If a pandemic struck the world today, there would be another possible weapon against influenza: antiviral medicine. When taken daily during the time of exposure to influenza, antivirals have prevented individuals from becoming ill. They have also reduced the severity of illness and subsequent complications when taken within 48 hours of onset. Although there is no data for H5N1, it is assumed antivirals would also prevent H5N1 infection if taken before exposure. There is no evidence, however, that current antiviral influenza drugs would help if the patient developed the kind of cytokine storm that has characterized recent H5N1 infections. But barring this complication, H5N1 should be treatable with Tamiflu (oseltamivir phosphate), which is manufactured by the Roche pharmaceuticals company in a single plant in Switzerland.

In responding to a pandemic, Tamiflu could have a measurable impact in the limited number of countries with sizable stockpiles, but for most of the world it would not be available. Although the company plans on opening another facility in the United States this year, annual production would still cover only a small percentage of the world's population. To date, at least 14 countries have ordered Tamiflu, but the amount of these orders is enough to treat only 40 million people. The orders take considerable time to be processed and delivered—manufacturing can take up to a year—and in an emergency the company's ability to produce more would be limited. As with vaccines, countries would probably nationalize their antiviral supplies during a pandemic. Even if the medicine were available, most countries could not afford to buy it. Critical antibiotics, for treatment of secondary bacterial infections, would also be in short supply during a pandemic. Even now, supplies of eight different anti-infective agents are limited in the United States due to manufacturing problems.

Aside from medication, many countries would not have the ability to meet the surge in the demand for health-care supplies and services that are normally taken for granted. In the United States, for example, there are 105,000 mechanical ventilators, 75,000 to 80,000 of which are in use at any given time for everyday medical care. During a routine influenza season, the number of ventilators being used shoots up to 100,000. In an influenza pandemic, the United States may need as many as several hundred thousand additional ventilators.

A similar situation exists in all developed countries. Virtually every piece of medical equipment or protective gear would be in short supply within days of the recognition of a pandemic. Throughout the crisis, many of these necessities would simply be unavailable for most health-care institutions. Currently, two U.S.-based companies supply most of the respiratory protection masks for health-care workers around the world. Neither company would be able to meet the jump in demand, in part because the component parts for the masks come from multiple suppliers in multiple countries. With travel and transportation restricted, masks may not even be produced at all.

Health-care providers and managed-care organizations are also unprepared for an outbreak of pandemic influenza today. There would be a tremendous demand for skilled health professionals. New "hospitals" in high school gymnasiums and community centers would have to be staffed for one to three years. Health-care workers would probably get sick and die at the same rate as the general public—perhaps at an even higher rate, particularly if they lack access to protective equipment.

If they lack such fundamental supplies, it is unclear how many professionals would continue to place themselves in high-risk situations by caring for the infected. Volunteers who are naturally immune as a result of having survived influenza infection would thus have to be found and employed. That means that the medical community's strong resistance to using lay volunteers, which is grounded in both liability concerns and professional hubris, would need to be addressed.

Other unpleasant issues would also need to be tackled. Who would have priority access to the extremely limited antiviral supplies? The public would consider any ad hoc prioritization unfair, creating further dissent and disruption during a pandemic. In addition, there would not even be detailed plans for handling the massive number of dead bodies that would soon outstrip the ability to process them. Clearly, an influenza pandemic that struck today would demand an unprecedented medical and nonmedical response. This requires planning well beyond anything devised thus far by any of the world's countries and organizations.

A Year From Now

Even if an H5N1 pandemic is a year away, the world must plan for the same problems with the same fervor. Major campaigns must be initiated to prepare the nonmedical and medical sectors. Pandemic planning must be on the agenda of every school board, manufacturing plant, investment firm, mortuary, state legislature, and food distributor in the United States and beyond. There is an urgent need to reassess the vulnerability of the global economy to ensure that surges in demand can be met. Critical health-care and consumer products and commodities must be stockpiled. Health professionals must learn how to better communicate risk and must be able to both provide the facts and acknowledge the unknowns to a frightened or panicked population.

If there is a year of lead-time before an H5N1 pandemic, vaccine could play a more central role in the global response. Although the world would still have a limited capacity to manufacture influenza vaccine, techniques that could allow scientists to get multiple doses from a current single dose may increase the supply. In addition to further research on this issue, efforts are needed to ensure the availability of syringes and equipment for delivering vaccine. There must also be an international plan for how the vaccine would be allocated. It is far better to struggle with the ethical issues involved in determining such priorities now, in a public forum, rather than to wait until the crisis occurs.

Prevention must also be improved. Priority should be placed on early intervention and risk assessment. And an aggressive and comprehensive research agenda must be launched immediately to study the ecology and biology of the influenza virus and the epidemiologic role of various animal and bird species.

Ten Years Later

If developed countries begin to transform radically the current system of influenza-vaccine production, an influenza pandemic 10 years from now could have a much less devastating outcome. The industrialized world must initiate an international project to develop the ability to produce a vaccine for the entire global population within several months of the start of a pandemic. The initiative must be a top priority of the group of seven industrialized nations plus Russia (G-8), because almost nothing could inflict more death and disruption than a pandemic influenza.

The current BioShield law and additional legislation recently submitted to Congress will act to enhance the availability of vaccines in the United States. This aim is laudable, but it does little to address international needs. The ultimate goal must be to develop a new cell-culture vaccine or comparable vaccine technology that works on all influenza subtypes and that can be made available on short notice to all the people of the world.

What Course to Take?

The world must form a better understanding of the potential for the emergence of a pandemic influenza strain. A pandemic is coming. It could be caused by H5N1 or by another novel strain. It could happen tonight, next year, or even 10 years from now.

The signs are alarming: the number of human and animal H5N1 infections has been increasing; small clusters of cases have been documented, suggesting that the virus may have come close to sustained human-to-human transmission; and H5N1 continues to evolve in the virtual genetic reassortment laboratory provided by the unprecedented number of people, pigs, and poultry in Asia. The population explosion in China and other Asian countries has created an incredible mixing vessel for the virus. Consider this sobering information: the most recent influenza pandemic, of 1968–69, emerged in China, when its population was 790 million; today it is 1.3 billion. In 1968, the number of pigs in China was 5.2 million; today it is 508 million. The number of poultry in China in 1968 was 12.3 million; today it is 13 billion. Changes in other Asian countries are similar. Given these developments, as well as the exponential growth in foreign travel over the past 50 years, an influenza pandemic could be more devastating than ever before.

Can disaster be avoided? The answer is a qualified yes. Although a coming pandemic cannot be avoided, its impact can be considerably lessened. It depends on how the leaders of the world—from the heads of the G-8 to local officials—decide to respond. They must recognize the economic, security, and health threat that the next influenza pandemic poses and invest accordingly. Each leader must realize that even if a country has enough vaccine to protect its citizens, the economic impact of a worldwide pandemic will inflict substantial pain on everyone. The resources required to prepare adequately will be extensive. But they must be considered in light of the cost of failing to invest: a global world economy that remains in a shambles for several years.

This is a critical point in history. Time is running out to prepare for the next pandemic. We must act now with decisiveness and purpose. Someday, after the next pandemic has come and gone, a commission much like the 9/11 Commission will be charged with determining how well government, business, and public health leaders prepared the world for the catastrophe when they had clear warning. What will be the verdict?

2 Identifying Airborne Transmission as the Dominant Route for the Spread of COVID-19

*Renyi Zhang, Yixin Li, Annie L. Zhang,
Yuan Wang, and Mario J. Molina*

The novel coronavirus outbreak, coronavirus disease 2019 (COVID-19), which was declared a pandemic by the World Health Organization (WHO) on March 11, 2020, has infected over 4 million people and caused nearly 300,000 fatalities over 188 countries (1). Intensive effort is ongoing worldwide to establish effective treatments and develop a vaccine for the disease. The novel coronavirus, named as severe acute respiratory syndrome coronavirus 2 (SARS-CoV-2), belongs to the family of the pathogen that is responsible for respiratory illness linked to the 2002–2003 outbreak (SARS-CoV-1) (2). The enveloped virus contains a positive-sense single-stranded RNA genome and a nucleocapsid of helical symmetry of −120 nm. There exist several plausible pathways for viruses to be transmitted from person to person. Human atomization of virus-bearing particles occurs from coughing/sneezing and even from normal breathing/talking by an infected person (3–6). These mechanisms of viral shedding produce large droplets and small aerosols (3), which are conventionally delineated at a size of 5 μm to characterize their distinct dispersion efficiencies and residence times in air as well as the deposition patterns along the human respiratory tract (3, 7). Virus transmission occurs via direct (deposited on persons) or indirect (deposited on objects) contact and airborne (droplets and aerosols) routes (3). Large droplets readily settle out of air to cause person/object contamination; in contrast, aerosols are efficiently dispersed in air. While transmission via direct or indirect contact occurs in a short range, airborne transmission via aerosols can occur over an extended distance and time. Inhaled virus-bearing aerosols deposit directly along the human respiratory tract.

Previous experimental and observational studies on interhuman transmission have indicated a significant role of aerosols in the transmission of many respiratory viruses, including influenza virus, SARS-CoV-1, and Middle East Respiratory Syndrome coronavirus (MERS-CoV) (8–11). For example, airborne coronavirus MERS-CoV exhibited strong capability of surviving, with about 64% of microorganisms remaining infectious 60 min after

atomization at 25 °C and 79% relative humidity (RH) (9). On the other
hand, rapid virus decay occurred, with only 5% survival over a 60-min
procedure at 38 °C and 24% RH, indicative of inactivation. Recent experimental studies have examined the stability of SARS-CoV-2, showing that
the virus remains infectious in aerosols for hours (12) and on surfaces up to
days (12, 13).

Several parameters likely influence the microorganism survival and
delivery in air, including temperature, humidity, microbial resistance
to external physical and biological stresses, and solar ultraviolet (UV)
radiation (7). Transmission and infectivity of airborne viruses are also
dependent on the size and number concentration of inhaled aerosols,
which regulate the amount (dose) and pattern for respiratory deposition. With typical nasal breathing (i.e., at a velocity of -1 m·s^{-1}) (4),
inhalation of airborne viruses leads to direct and continuous deposition into the human respiratory tract. In particular, fine aerosols (i.e.,
particulate matter smaller than 2.5 μm, or PM$_{2.5}$) penetrate deeply into
the respiratory tract and even reach other vital organs (14, 15). In addition, viral shedding is dependent on the stages of infection and varies between symptomatic and asymptomatic carriers. A recent finding
(16) showed that the highest viral load in the upper respiratory tract
occurs at the symptom onset, suggesting the peak of infectiousness on
or before the symptom onset and substantial asymptomatic transmission
for SARS-CoV-2.

Significance

We have elucidated the transmission pathways of coronavirus
disease 2019 (COVID-19) by analyzing the trend and mitigation measures in the three epicenters. Our results show that
the airborne transmission route is highly virulent and dominant for the spread of COVID-19. The mitigation measures
are discernable from the trends of the pandemic. Our analysis
reveals that the difference with and without mandated face
covering represents the determinant in shaping the trends of
the pandemic. This protective measure significantly reduces
the number of infections. Other mitigation measures, such
as social distancing implemented in the United States, are
insufficient by themselves in protecting the public. Our work
also highlights the necessity that sound science is essential
in decision-making for the current and future public health
pandemics.

The COVID-19 outbreak is significantly more pronounced than that of the 2002–2003 SARS, and the disease continues to spread at an alarming rate worldwide, despite extreme measures taken by many countries to constrain the pandemic (1). The enormous scope and magnitude of the COVID-19 outbreak reflect not only a highly contagious nature but also exceedingly efficient transmission for SARS-CoV-2. Currently, the mechanisms to spread the virus remain uncertain (17), particularly considering the relative contribution of the contact versus airborne transmission routes to this global pandemic. Available epidemiological (1) and experimental (12, 18) evidence, however, implicates airborne transmission of SARS-CoV-2 via aerosols as a potential route for the spreading of the disease.

Distinct Pandemic Trends in the Three Epicenters

To gain insight into the mechanism of the virus transmission routes and assess the effectiveness of mitigation measures, we analyzed the trend of the pandemic worldwide from January 23 to May 9, 2020 (Figure 2.1). The COVID-19 outbreak initially emerged during December 2019 in Wuhan, China (1). The numbers of confirmed infections and fatalities in China dominated the global trend during January and February 2020 (Figure 2.1*A*), but the increases in the newly confirmed cases and fatalities in China have exhibited sharp declines since February (Figure 2.1*B*). In contrast to the curve flattening in China, those numbers in other countries have increased sharply since the beginning of March. The epicenter shifted from Wuhan to Italy in early March and to New York City (NYC) in early April. By April 30, the numbers of confirmed COVID-19 cases and deaths, respectively, reached over 200,000 and 27,000 in Italy and over 1,000,000 and 52,000 in the United States, compared to about 84,000 and 4,600 in China (Figure 2.1*B*). Notably, the curves in Italy exhibit a slowing trend since mid-April, while the numbers in the world and the United States continue to increase. Remarkably, the recent trends in the numbers of infections and fatalities in the world and in the United States exhibit striking linearity since the beginning of April (Figure 2.1*C*).

We interpreted the differences in the pandemic trends by considering the mitigation measures implemented worldwide. The curve flattening in China can be attributed to extensive testing, quarantine, and contact tracing; other aggressive measures implemented in China include lockdown of all cities and rural areas in the whole country, isolation of residents having close contact with infected people, and mandated wearing of face masks in public. However, the effectiveness of those mitigation measures has yet to be rigorously evaluated. Differentiation of the effects of those mitigation measures in China is challenging (19), since the implementation occurred almost simultaneously in January 2020. While similar quarantine, isolation,

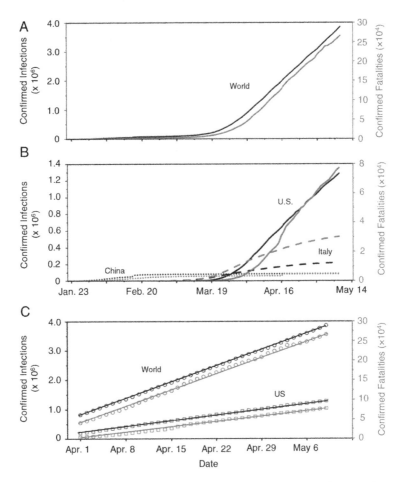

Figure 2.1 Distinct global trends of the COVID-19 pandemic. (*A*) Confirmed infections and fatalities worldwide. (*B*) Comparison of the confirmed infections and fatalities between China, Italy, and United States. (*C*) Linear regression of the confirmed infections and fatalities worldwide and in United States from April 1 to May 9, 2020; the linear regression is, respectively, $y = 79,398x + 810,167$ ($R^2 = 0.999$) for infections and $y = 6,075x + 39,409$ ($R^2 = 0.998$) for fatalities worldwide and $y = 28,971x + 201,187$ ($R^2 = 0.999$) for infections and $y = 2,059x + 243$ ($R^2 = 0.995$) for fatalities in the United States. The left axis and black color correspond to the numbers of confirmed infections, and the right axis and gray color represent the confirmed fatalities.

and city lockdown measures were also implemented on March 9 in Italy after the country became the second epicenter, the curve of infections has yet to show complete flattening. In the United States, guidelines for social distancing, quarantine, and isolation were issued by the federal government on March 16, and stay-at-home orders were implemented by many state and local governments starting, for example, on March 19 and April 3 and on March 22 in NYC. The social distancing measures implemented in the United States include staying at least 6 feet (–2 m) away from other people, no gathering in groups, staying out of crowded places, and avoiding mass gatherings (20). Obviously, the continuous rise in the US infected numbers casts doubt on the effectiveness of those preventive measures alone (Figure 2.1 *B* and *C*).

In contrast to China, wearing of face masks was not mandated and was unpopular in most of the western world during the early outbreak of the pandemic. Advice on the use of face masks was not issued until April 6, 2020, by the WHO (1), claiming that it is important only to prevent infected persons from viral transmission by filtering out droplets but that it is unimportant to prevent uninfected persons from breathing virus-bearing aerosols. The regions heavily plagued by COVID-19 in northern Italy, such as Lombardy, ordered face covering in public starting on April 6, and the Italian authorities required nationwide mandatory use of face masks on May 4. All New Yorkers were mandated to use face covering in public starting on April 17, when social distancing was not possible. With measures implemented in the United States seemingly comparable to those in China, social distancing, quarantine, and isolation exhibited little impact on stopping the spreading of the disease in the United States, as reflected by the linearity from April 1 to May 9 (Figure 2.1*C*). It is possible, however, that these measures likely alter the slope of the infection curve, that is, by reducing the rate of infections during the early stage of the pandemic (Figure 2.1). Notably, the recommended physical separation for social distancing is beneficial to prevent direct contact transmission but is insufficient (without face masks) to protect inhalation of virus-bearing aerosols (or even small droplets at intermediate proximity), owing to rapid air mixing (7).

Understanding the Impacts of Face Covering

Compared to the simultaneous implementation of measures in China, intervention measures were successively implemented in the western world (Figure 2.2*A*), providing an opportunity for assessing their relative effectiveness. We quantified the effects of face covering by projecting the number of infections based on the data prior to implementing the use of face masks in Italy on April 6 and NYC on April 17 (Figure 2.2*A*; see *Methods*). Such projections are reasonable considering the excellent linear correlation for the data prior to the onset of mandated face covering (Figure 2.2 *B* and *C*). Our analysis indicates that face covering reduced the number of infections by over 78,000 in Italy from April 6 to May 9 and by over 66,000 in NYC from April 17 to May 9. In addition, varying the correlation from 15 to 30 days prior to the onset of the implementation reveals little difference in the projection for both places. Notably, the trends of the infection curves in Italy and NYC contrast to those in the world and in the United

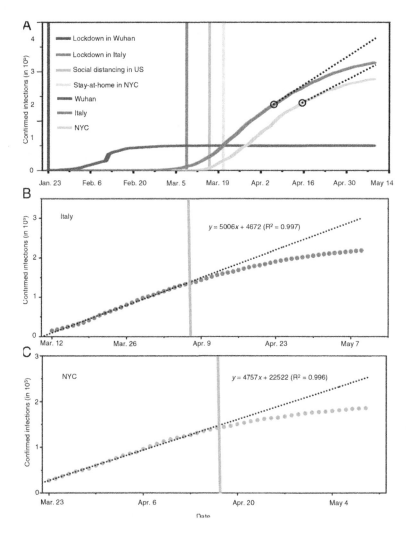

Figure 2.2 The evolving epicenter from Wuhan, to Italy, to NYC. (*A*) Comparison of the trends and mitigation measures between Wuhan, Italy, and NYC in 2020. The vertical lines mark the date for implementing mitigation measures. The two black circles label the dates when face covering was implemented: April 6 in northern Italy and April 17 in NYC. The black dashed lines represent the projection without face covering based on linear regression of 26-day data prior to implementing this measure. (*B*) Linear regression of the number of confirmed infections for 26-day data prior to implementing face covering in Italy. The shaded vertical line denotes the date when face covering was implemented on April 6 in northern Italy. (*C*) Linear regression of the number of confirmed infections for 26-day data prior to implementing face covering in NYC. The shaded vertical line denotes the date when face covering was implemented on April 17 in NYC. In *B* and *C*, the circles are reported values, and the dotted line represents fitting and projection of the confirmed infections before and after face covering, respectively.

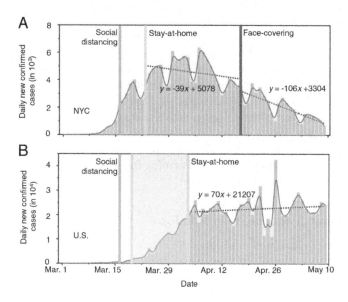

Figure 2.3 Contrasting the trends of new infections between NYC and the United States. Daily new confirmed infections in (*A*) NYC and (*B*) the United States. The dotted lines represent linear fitting to the data between April 17 and May 9 in NYC and between April 4 and May 9 in the United States. In *B*, the number in NYC was subtracted from that in the United States. The vertical lines label the dates for social distancing, stay-at-home orders, and mandated face covering.

States (Figure 2.1*C*), which show little deviation from the linearity due to the nonimplementation of face-covering measures globally and nationally, respectively. The inability of social distancing, quarantine, and isolation alone to curb the spread of COVID-19 is also evident from the linearity of the infection curve prior to the onset of the face-covering rule in Italy on April 6 and in NYC on April 17 (Figure 2.2 *B* and *C*). Hence, the difference made by implementing face covering significantly shapes the pandemic trends worldwide.

We further compared the numbers of daily new cases between NYC and the United States (excluding the data in NYC) from March 1 to May 9 (Figure 2.3). The daily numbers of newly confirmed infections in NYC and the United States show a sharp increase in late March and early April. There exists a slower increase in the number after implementation of the stay-at-home order (about 14 d in New York and shortly after April 3 in the United States), which is attributable to the impacts of this measure. After April 3, the only difference in the regulatory measures between NYC and the United States lies in face covering on April 17 in NYC. We applied linear regression to the data between April 17 and May 9 in NYC and between

April 5 and May 9 in the United States. While the daily numbers of newly confirmed infections fluctuate considerably, the slope of the regression unambiguously reflects the trend in both data. The daily new infection rate in NYC decreases with a slope of 106 cases per day after April 17, corresponding to a decreasing rate of −3% per day (relative to April 17). For comparison, the daily new infections in the United States (excluding NYC) increase, with a slope of 70 cases per day after April 4, corresponding to an increasing rate of −0.3% per day (relative to April 5). Hence, the decreasing rate in the daily new infections in NYC with mandated face covering is in sharp contrast to that in the United States with only social-distancing and stay-at-home measures, further confirming the importance of face covering in intervening the virus transmission.

Dominant Airborne Transmission

We further elucidated the contribution of airborne transmission to the COVID-19 outbreak by comparing the trends and mitigation measures during the pandemic worldwide and by considering the virus transmission routes (Figure 2.4). Face covering prevents both airborne transmission by blocking atomization and inhalation of virus-bearing aerosols and contact transmission by blocking viral shedding of droplets. On the other hand, social distancing, quarantine, and isolation, in conjunction with hand sanitizing, minimize contact (direct and indirect) transmission but do not protect against airborne transmission. With social distancing, quarantine, and isolation in place worldwide and in the United States since the beginning

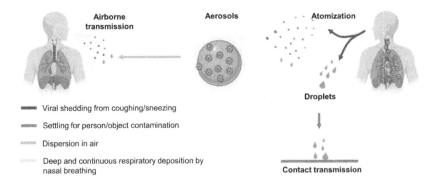

Figure 2.4 Transmission of COVID-19. Human atomization of viruses arises from coughing or sneezing of an infected person, producing virus-containing droplets (>5 μm) and aerosols (<5 μm). Virus transmission from person to person occurs through direct/indirect contact and airborne aerosol/droplet routes. Large droplets mainly settle out of air to cause person/object contamination, while aerosols are efficiently dispersed in air. Direct and airborne transmissions occur in short range and extended distance/time, respectively. Inhaled airborne viruses deposit directly into the human respiration tract.

of April, airborne transmission represents the only viable route for spreading the disease, when mandated face covering is not implemented. Similarly, airborne transmission also contributes dominantly to the linear increase in the infection prior to the onset of mandated face covering in Italy and NYC (Figure 2.2 *B* and *C*). Hence, the unique function of face covering to block atomization and inhalation of virus-bearing aerosols accounts for the significantly reduced infections in China, Italy, and NYC (Figs. 2.1–2.3), indicating that airborne transmission of COVID-19 represents the dominant route for infection.

Recent measurements identified SARS-Cov-2 RNA on aerosols in Wuhan's hospitals (18) and outdoors in northern Italy (21), unraveling the likelihood of indoor and outdoor airborne transmission. Within an enclosed environment, virus-bearing aerosols from human atomization are readily accumulated, and elevated levels of airborne viruses facilitate transmission from person to person. Transmission of airborne viruses in open air is subject to dilution, although virus accumulation still occurs due to stagnation under polluted urban conditions (7, 22). Removal of virus-bearing particles from human atomization via deposition is strongly size dependent, with the settling velocities ranging from 2.8×10^{-5} m·s^{-1} to 1.4×10^{-3} m·s^{-1} for the sizes of 1 and 10 µm, respectively (7). For comparison, typical wind velocity is about 1 m·s^{-1} to 3 m·s^{-1} indoors (23) and is -1 m·s^{-1} horizontally and 0.1 m·s^{-1} vertically in stable air (7, 22). Under those indoor and outdoor conditions, the residence time of virus-bearing aerosols reaches hours, due to air mixing (7).

We also examined ambient conditions relevant to the outbreaks in Wuhan, Italy, and NYC. The initial outbreak of COVID-19 in Wuhan coincided with the winter haze season in China (7, 22), during which high levels of $PM_{2.5}$ were prevalent in the air. On the other hand, the daily average $PM_{2.5}$ concentrations were much lower during the outbreaks in Rome, Italy, and in NYC. The airborne transmission pathways (i.e., indoor or outdoor) as well as the effects of ambient $PM_{2.5}$ levels on virus transmission may be variable among urban cities. For example, the winter haze conditions in China likely exacerbated outdoor virus spreading (24, 25), because of low UV radiation, air stagnation (lacking ventilation on the city scale), and low temperature (7, 22). Also, there may exist a synergetic effect of simultaneous exposure to the virus and $PM_{2.5}$ to enhance the infectivity, severity, and fatalities of the disease (14, 26). In addition, nascent virus-bearing aerosols produced from human atomization likely undergo transformation in air, including coagulation with ambient preexisting PM and/or growth on a time scale of a few hours in typical urban air (27–29). Such transformation, as recently documented on coarse PM in Italy (21), may mitigate virus inactivation (9, 12), by providing a medium to preserve its biological properties and elongating its lifetimes. However, key questions remain concerning transformation and transmission of virus-bearing aerosols from human atomization in air. Specifically, what are the impacts of transformation of human-atomized aerosols on viral survival and infectivity in air?

While the humidity effect on viral surviving is uncertain (3, 9), the conditions during the outbreaks in Wuhan, Rome, and NYC correspond to high RH yet low absolute humidity because of low temperature. Early experimental work (9) showed remarkable survival for the analogous coronavirus MERS-CoV at the RH level characteristic of the COVID-19 outbreaks in Wuhan, Rome, and NYC. For comparison, indoor temperature and RH typically range from 21 °C to 27 °C and 20% to 70%, respectively (23).

Of particular importance are the considerations that render airborne SARS-CoV-2 the most efficient among all transmission routes. Even with normal nasal breathing, inhalation of virus-bearing aerosols results in deep and continuous deposition into the human respiratory tract, and this transmission route typically requires a low dose (8). Also, airborne viruses have great mobility and sufficiently long surviving time for dispersion (9, 12), and residents situated in densely populated environments are highly vulnerable. In addition, nascent micrometer-size aerosols produced from coughing/sneezing of infected people have the potential of containing many viruses, particularly for asymptomatic carriers (16).

Future research is critically needed to assess the transmission, transformation, and dispersion of virus-bearing aerosols from human atomization under different environmental conditions, as well as the related impacts on virus infectivity. It is equally important to understand human atomization of airborne viruses: What are the number and size distributions of nascent aerosols as well as the viral load per particle from coughing/sneezing? It is also imperative to evaluate human inhalation of airborne viruses: How are aerosols deposited along the respiratory tract, and what is the minimum dose of airborne viruses required for infection? It is also important to evaluate the performance of face masks to quantify the efficiency to filtrate airborne viruses relevant to human atomization and inhalation. Elucidation of these mechanisms requires an interdisciplinary effort.

A Policy Perspective

The governments' responses to the COVID pandemic have so far differed significantly worldwide. Swift actions to the initial outbreak were undertaken in China, as reflected by nearly simultaneous implementation of various aggressive mitigation measures. On the other hand, the response to the pandemic was generally slow in the western world, and implementation of the intervention measures occurred only consecutively. Clearly, the responsiveness of the mitigation measures governed the evolution, scope, and magnitude of the pandemic globally (Figs. 2.1 and 2.2).

Curbing the COVID-19 relies not only on decisive and sweeping actions but also, critically, on the scientific understanding of the virus transmission routes, which determines the effectiveness of the mitigation measures (Figure 2.5). In the United States, social distancing and stay-at-home measures, in conjunction with hand sanitizing (Figure 2.5, path a), were implemented

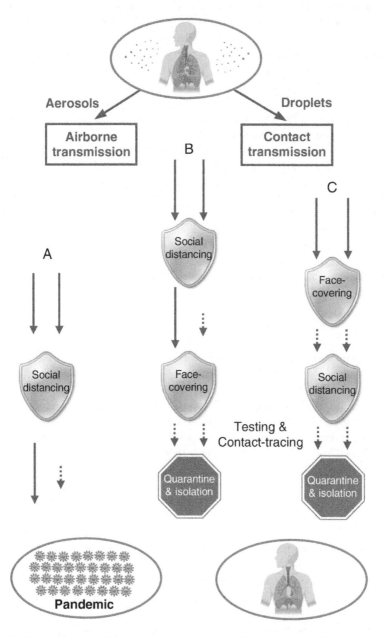

Figure 2.5 Mitigation paradigm. Scenarios of virus transmission under the distancing/quar-
antine/isolation measure only (path a), the measures with distancing/quarantine/
isolation followed by face covering (path b), and the measures with simultaneous face covering and distancing/quarantine/isolation (path c). The short-dashed
arrows label possible remnants of virus transmission due to circumstances when
the measure is not possible or disobeyed and/or imperfection of the measure.

during the early stage of the pandemic (March 16) (20). These measures minimized short-range contact transmission but did not prevent long-range airborne transmission, responsible for the inefficient containing of the pandemic in the United States (Figs. 1 and 3). Mandated face covering, such as those implemented in China, Italy, and NYC, effectively prevented airborne transmission by blocking atomization and inhalation of virus-bearing aerosols and contact transmission by blocking viral shedding of droplets. While the combined face-covering and social distancing measures offered dual protection against the virus transmission routes, the timing and sequence in implementing the measures also exhibited distinct outcomes during the pandemic. For example, social distancing measures, including city lockdown and stay-at-home orders, were implemented well before face covering was mandated in Italy and NYC (Figure 2.5, path b), and this sequence left an extended window (28 d in Italy and 32 d in NYC) for largely uninterrupted airborne transmission to spread the disease (Figs. 2 and 3). The simultaneous implementation of face covering and social distancing (Figure 2.5, path c), such as that undertaken in China, was most optimal, and this configuration, in conjunction with extensive testing and contact tracing, was responsible for the curve flattening in China (Figure 2.1). Also, there likely existed remnants of virus transmission after the implementation of regulatory measures, because of circumstances when the measures were not practical or were disobeyed and/or imperfection of the measures. Such limitations, which have been emphasized by the WHO (1), spurred on controversial views on the validity of wearing face masks to prevent the virus transmission during the pandemic (30). However, it is implausible that the limitations of mitigation measures alone contributed dominantly to the global pandemic trend, as exemplified by the success in China. Our work suggests that the failure in containing the propagation of COVID-19 pandemic worldwide is largely attributed to the unrecognized importance of airborne virus transmission (1, 20).

Conclusions

The inadequate knowledge on virus transmission has inevitably hindered development of effective mitigation policies and resulted in unstoppable propagation of the COVID-19 pandemic. In this work, we show that airborne transmission, particularly via nascent aerosols from human atomization, is highly virulent and represents the dominant route for the transmission of this disease. However, the importance of airborne transmission has not been considered in establishment of mitigation measures by government authorities (1, 20). Specifically, while the WHO and the US Centers for Disease Control and Prevention (CDC) have emphasized the prevention of contact transmission, both WHO and CDC have largely ignored the importance of the airborne transmission route (1, 20). The current mitigation measures, such as social distancing, quarantine, and isolation implemented in the United States, are insufficient by themselves in protecting the public. Our analysis reveals that the difference with and without mandated face covering represents the determinant in shaping the trends of the pandemic worldwide. We conclude that wearing of face masks in public corresponds to the most effective means to prevent interhuman transmission, and this inexpensive practice, in conjunction with extensive testing, quarantine, and contact tracking, poses the most probable fighting opportunity to stop the COVID-19 pandemic, prior to the development of a vaccine. It is also important to emphasize that sound science should be effectively communicated to policy makers and should constitute the prime foundation in decision-making amid this pandemic. Implementing policies without a scientific basis could lead to catastrophic consequences, particularly in light of attempts to reopen the economy in many countries. Clearly, integration between science and policy is crucial to formulation of effective emergency responses by policy makers and preparedness by the public for the current and future public health pandemics.

Methods

Projection of the pandemic trend without implementing face covering in Italy and NYC was performed first by establishing the linear correlation between the infection number and date. The slope and the reported infection number were used for the projections. The avoided infection number due the face covering was determined from the difference between the projected and reported values on May 9, 2020.

The data for accumulative confirmed infections and fatalities in Wuhan, Italy, and NYC were taken from the reports by Wuhan Municipal Health Commission (http://wjw.wuhan.gov.cn/), European CDC (www.ecdc.europa.eu/en), and NYC government (www1.nyc.gov/site/doh/covid/covid-19-data.page), respectively. The data of accumulative confirmed infections and fatalities worldwide were taken from WHO COVID-19 situation report (www.who.int/emergencies/diseases/novel-coronavirus-2019/situation-reports) (1), and the numbers in China, Italy, and United States were from taken from European CDC.

Ground-based measurements of $PM_{2.5}$ and RH in Wuhan were taken from the China National Environmental Monitoring Centre (http://beijingair.sinaapp.com/). The $PM_{2.5}$ data in NYC were taken from US Environmental Protection Agency (www.epa.gov/outdoor-air-quality-data). The $PM_{2.5}$ data in Rome were taken from Centro Regionale della Qualità dell'aria (www.arpalazio.net/main/aria/). The RH data in Rome and NYC were taken from the 6-hourly interim reanalysis of the European Centre for Medium-range Weather Forecasts (www.ecmwf.int/en/forecasts/datasets/reanalysis-datasets/era5).

We used spaceborne measurements of aerosol optical depth (AOD) to characterize the regional aerosol pollution during the COVID-19 outbreak

(January 23 to February 10, 2020) in China. The green band AODs at
0.55 μm are available from Terra and Aqua combined Moderate Resolution
Imaging Spectroradiometer Version 6 Multiangle Implementation of Atmo-
spheric Correction (https://lpdaac.usgs.gov/products/mcd19a2v006/). The
Level-2 product has daily global coverage with 1-km pixel resolution. The
AOD retrieval is only available for the clear sky.

Acknowledgments

This work was supported by the Robert A. Welch Foundation (Grant
A-1417). We are grateful to Fang Zhang for the $PM_{2.5}$ data in Wuhan, China.

References

1. World Health Organization, Coronavirus disease (COVID-2019) situation reports.
www.who.int/emergencies/diseases/novel-coronavirus-2019/situation-reports/.
Accessed 9 May 2020.

2. A. R. Fehr, S. Perlman, Coronaviruses: An overview of their replication and pathogenesis. *Methods Mol. Biol.* 1282, 1–23 (2015).

3. J. S. Kutter, M. I. Spronken, P. L. Fraaij, R. A. Fouchier, S. Herfst, Transmission
routes of respiratory viruses among humans. *Curr. Opin. Virol.* 28, 142–151 (2018).

4. J. W. Tang *et al.*, Airflow dynamics of human jets: Sneezing and breathing – potential
sources of infectious aerosols. *PLoS One* 8, e59970 (2013).

5. N. H. L. Leung *et al.*, Respiratory virus shedding in exhaled breath and efficacy of
face masks. *Nat. Med.* 26, 676–680 (2020).

6. V. Stadnytskyi, C. E. Bax, A. Bax, P. Anfinrud, The airborne lifetime of small speech
droplets and their potential importance in SARS-CoV-2 transmission. *Proc. Natl.
Acad. Sci. U.S.A.*, 10.1073/pnas.2006874117 (2020).

7. R. Zhang *et al.*, Formation of urban fine particulate matter. *Chem. Rev.* 115, 3803–
3855 (2015).

8. R. Tellier, Aerosol transmission of influenza A virus: A review of new studies. *J. R.
Soc. Interface* 6 (suppl. 6), S783–S790 (2009).

9. O. V. Pyankov, S. A. Bodnev, O. G. Pyankova, I. E. Agranovski, Survival of aerosol-
ized coronavirus in the ambient air. *J. Aerosol Sci.* 115, 158–163 (2018).

10. M. Richard, R. A. M. Fouchier, Influenza A virus transmission via respiratory aerosols or droplets as it relates to pandemic potential. *FEMS Microbiol. Rev.* 40, 68–85
(2016).

11. T. P. Weber, N. I. Stilianakis, Inactivation of influenza A viruses in the environment
and modes of transmission: A critical review. *J. Infect.* 57, 361–373 (2008).

12. N. van Doremalen *et al.*, Aerosol and surface stability of SARS-CoV-2 as compared
with SARS-CoV-1. *N. Engl. J. Med.* 382, 1564–1567 (2020).

13. A. W. H. Chin *et al.*, Stability of SARS-CoV-2 in different environmental conditions. *Lancet* 1, E10 (2020).

14. K. A. Rychlik *et al.*, In utero ultrafine particulate matter exposure causes offspring
pulmonary immunosuppression. *Proc. Natl. Acad. Sci. U.S.A.* 116, 3443–3448 (2019).

15. G. Wu *et al.*, Adverse organogenesis and predisposed long-term metabolic syndrome
from prenatal exposure to fine particulate matter. *Proc. Natl. Acad. Sci. U.S.A.* 116,
11590–11595 (2019).

16. X. He *et al.*, Temporal dynamics in viral shedding and transmissibility of COVID-19. *Nat. Med.* 26, 672–675 (2020).

17. D. Lewis, Is the coronavirus airborne? Experts can't agree. *Nature* 580, 175 (2020).

18. Y. Liu *et al.*, Aerodynamic analysis of SARS-CoV-2 in two Wuhan hospitals. *Nature*, 10.1038/s41586-020-2271-3 (2020).

19. L. Ferretti *et al.*, Quantifying SARS-CoV-2 transmission suggests epidemic control with digital contact tracing. *Science* 368, eabb6936 (2020).

20. US Centers for Disease Control and Prevention, Coronavirus Disease 2019 (COVID-19) – Social distancing, quarantine, and isolation. www.cdc.gov/coronavirus/2019-ncov/prevent-getting-sick/social-distancing.html. Accessed 9 May 2020.

21. L. Setti *et al.*, SARS-Cov-2 RNA found on particulate matter of Bergamo in Northern Italy: First preliminary evidence. *Environ. Res.*, 10.1016/j.envres.2020.109754 (2020).0013–9351

22. Z. An *et al.*, Severe haze in northern China: A synergy of anthropogenic emissions and atmospheric processes. *Proc. Natl. Acad. Sci. U.S.A.* 116, 8657–8666 (2019).

23. L. A. Wallace, S. J. Emmerich, C. Howard-Reed, Continuous measurements of air change rates in an occupied house for 1 year: The effect of temperature, wind, fans, and windows. *J. Expo. Anal. Environ. Epidemiol.* 12, 296–306 (2002).

24. Q. Ye, J. F. Fu, J. H. Mao, S. Q. Shang, Haze is a risk factor contributing to the rapid spread of respiratory syncytial virus in children. *Environ. Sci. Pollut. Res. Int.* 23, 20178–20185 (2016).

25. Z. Gong *et al.*, Probable aerosol transmission of severe fever with thrombocytopenia syndrome virus in southeastern China. *Clin. Microbiol. Infect.* 21, 1115–1120 (2015).

26. X. Wu *et al.*, Exposure to air pollution and COVID-19 mortality in the United States. https://projects.iq.harvard.edu/files/covid-pm/files/pm_and_covid_mortality.pdf. Accessed 9 May 2020.

27. S. Guo *et al.*, Elucidating severe urban haze formation in China. *Proc. Natl. Acad. Sci. U.S.A.* 111, 17373–17378 (2014).

28. F. Zhang *et al.*, An unexpected catalyst dominates formation and radiative forcing of regional haze. *Proc. Natl. Acad. Sci. U.S.A.* 117, 3960–3966 (2020).

29. J. Peng *et al.*, Markedly enhanced absorption and direct radiative forcing of black carbon under polluted urban environments. *Proc. Natl. Acad. Sci. U.S.A.* 113, 4266–4271 (2016).

30. J. Howard *et al.*, Face masks against COVID-19: An evidence review. https://doi.org/10.20944/preprints202004.0203.v2 (13 May 2020).

3 Asymptomatic Transmission, the Achilles' Heel of Current Strategies to Control COVID-19

Monica Gandhi, Deborah S. Yokoe, and Diane V. Havlir

Traditional infection-control and public health strategies rely heavily on early detection of disease to contain spread. When COVID-19 burst onto the global scene, public health officials initially deployed interventions that were used to control severe acute respiratory syndrome (SARS) in 2003, including symptom-based case detection and subsequent testing to guide isolation and quarantine. This initial approach was justified by the many similarities between SARS-CoV-1 and SARS-CoV-2, including high genetic relatedness, transmission primarily through respiratory droplets, and the frequency of lower respiratory symptoms (fever, cough, and shortness of breath) with both infections developing a median of 5 days after exposure. However, despite the deployment of similar control interventions, the trajectories of the two epidemics have veered in dramatically different directions. Within 8 months, SARS was controlled after SARS-CoV-1 had infected approximately 8,100 persons in limited geographic areas. Within 5 months, SARS-CoV-2 has infected more than 2.6 million people and continues to spread rapidly around the world.

What explains these differences in transmission and spread? A key factor in the transmissibility of COVID-19 is the high level of SARS-CoV-2 shedding in the upper respiratory tract,[1] even among presymptomatic patients, which distinguishes it from SARS-CoV-1, where replication occurs mainly in the lower respiratory tract.[2] Viral loads with SARS-CoV-1, which are associated with symptom onset, peak a median of 5 days later than viral loads with SARS-CoV-2, which makes symptom-based detection of infection more effective in the case of SARS CoV-1.[3] With influenza, persons with asymptomatic disease generally have lower quantitative viral loads in secretions from the upper respiratory tract than from the lower respiratory tract and a shorter duration of viral shedding than persons with symptoms,[4] which decreases the risk of transmission from paucisymptomatic persons (i.e., those with few symptoms).

Arons et al. now report in the *Journal* an outbreak of COVID-19 in a skilled nursing facility in Washington State where a health care provider who was working while symptomatic tested positive for infection with

SARS-CoV-2 on March 1, 2020.[5] Residents of the facility were then offered two facility-wide point-prevalence screenings for SARS-CoV-2 by real-time reverse-transcriptase polymerase chain reaction (rRT-PCR) of nasopharyngeal swabs on March 13 and March 19–20, along with collection of information on symptoms the residents recalled having had over the preceding 14 days. Symptoms were classified into typical (fever, cough, and shortness of breath), atypical, and none. Among 76 residents in the point-prevalence surveys, 48 (63%) had positive rRT-PCR results, with 27 (56%) essentially asymptomatic, although symptoms subsequently developed in 24 of these residents (within a median of 4 days) and they were reclassified as presymptomatic. Quantitative SARS-CoV-2 viral loads were similarly high in the four symptom groups (residents with typical symptoms, those with atypical symptoms, those who were presymptomatic, and those who remained asymptomatic). It is notable that 17 of 24 specimens (71%) from presymptomatic persons had viable virus by culture 1 to 6 days before the development of symptoms. Finally, the mortality from COVID-19 in this facility was high; of 57 residents who tested positive, 15 (26%) died.

An important finding of this report is that more than half the residents of this skilled nursing facility (27 of 48) who had positive tests were asymptomatic at testing. Moreover, live coronavirus clearly sheds at high concentrations from the nasal cavity even before symptom development. Although the investigators were not able to retrospectively elucidate specific person-to-person transmission events and although symptom ascertainment may be unreliable in a group in which more than half the residents had cognitive impairment, these results indicate that asymptomatic persons are playing a major role in the transmission of SARS-CoV-2. Symptom-based screening alone failed to detect a high proportion of infectious cases and was not enough to control transmission in this setting. The high mortality (>25%) argues that we need to change our current approach for skilled nursing facilities in order to protect vulnerable, enclosed populations until other preventive measures, such as a vaccine or chemoprophylaxis, are available.

A new approach that expands COVID-19 testing to include asymptomatic persons residing or working in skilled nursing facilities needs to be implemented now. Despite "lockdowns" in these facilities, coronavirus outbreaks continue to spread, with 1 in 10 nursing homes in the United States (>1,300 skilled nursing facilities) now reporting cases, with the likelihood of thousands of deaths.[6] Mass testing of the residents in skilled nursing facilities will allow appropriate isolation of infected residents so that they can be cared for and quarantine of exposed residents to minimize the risk of spread. Mass testing in these facilities could also allow cohorting[7] and some resumption of group activities in a nonoutbreak setting. Routine rRT-PCR testing in addition to symptomatic screening of new residents before entry, conservative guidelines for discontinuation of isolation,[7] and periodic retesting of long-term residents, as well as both periodic rRT-PCR screening and surgical masking of all staff, are important concomitant measures.

There are approximately 1.3 million Americans currently residing in nursing homes.[8] Although this recommendation for mass testing in skilled nursing facilities could be initially rolled out in geographic areas with high rates of community COVID-19 transmission, an argument can be made to extend this recommendation to all U.S.-based skilled nursing facilities now because case ascertainment is uneven and incomplete and because of the devastating consequences of outbreaks. Immediately enforceable alternatives to mass testing in skilled nursing facilities are few. The public health director of Los Angeles has recommended that families remove their loved ones from nursing homes,[9] a measure that is not feasible for many families.

Asymptomatic transmission of SARS-CoV-2 is the Achilles' heel of COVID-19 pandemic control through the public health strategies we have currently deployed. Symptom-based screening has utility, but epidemiologic evaluations of COVID-19 outbreaks within skilled nursing facilities such as the one described by Arons et al. strongly demonstrate that our current approaches are inadequate. This recommendation for SARS-CoV-2 testing of asymptomatic persons in skilled nursing facilities should most likely be expanded to other congregate living situations, such as prisons and jails (where outbreaks in the United States, whose incarceration rate is much higher than rates in other countries, are increasing), enclosed mental health facilities, and homeless shelters, and to hospitalized inpatients. Current U.S. testing capability must increase immediately for this strategy to be implemented.

Ultimately, the rapid spread of COVID-19 across the United States and the globe, the clear evidence of SARS-CoV-2 transmission from asymptomatic persons[5], and the eventual need to relax current social distancing practices argue for broadened SARS-CoV-2 testing to include asymptomatic persons in prioritized settings. These factors also support the case for the general public to use face masks[10] when in crowded outdoor or indoor spaces. This unprecedented pandemic calls for unprecedented measures to achieve its ultimate defeat.

References

1. Wölfel R, Corman VM, Guggemos W, et al. Virological assessment of hospitalized patients with COVID-2019. Nature 2020 April 1 (Epub ahead of print).
2. Cheng PK, Wong DA, Tong LK, et al. Viral shedding patterns of coronavirus in patients with probable severe acute respiratory syndrome. Lancet 2004;363:1699–700.
3. To KK-W, Tsang OT-Y, Leung W-S, et al. Temporal profiles of viral load in posterior oropharyngeal saliva samples and serum antibody responses during infection by SARS-CoV-2: an observational cohort study. Lancet Infect Dis 2020 March 23 (Epub ahead of print).
4. Ip DKM, Lau LLH, Leung NHL, et al. Viral shedding and transmission potential of asymptomatic and paucisymptomatic influenza virus infections in the community. Clin Infect Dis 2017;64:736–42.

5. Arons MM, Hatfield KM, Reddy SC, et al. Presymptomatic SARS-CoV-2 infections and transmission in a skilled nursing facility. N Engl J Med. DOI: 10.1056/NEJMoa2008457.

6. Cenziper D, Jacobs J, Mulcahy S. Nearly 1 in 10 nursing homes nationwide report coronavirus cases. Washington Post. April 20, 2020 (www.washingtonpost.com/business/2020/04/20/nearly-one-10-nursing-homes-nationwide-report-coronavirus-outbreaks/).

7. Centers for Disease Control and Prevention. Key strategies to prepare for COVID-19 in long-term care facilities (LTCFs): updated interim guidance. April 15, 2020 (www.cdc.gov/coronavirus/2019-ncov/hcp/long-term-care.html).

8. Centers for Disease Control and Prevention. Nursing home care. March 11, 2016 (www.cdc.gov/nchs/fastats/nursing-home-care.htm).

9. Dolan J, Hamilton M. Consider pulling residents from nursing homes over coronavirus, says county health director. Los Angeles Times. April 7, 2020 (www.latimes.com/california/story/2020-04-07/coronavirus-nursing-homes-residents-remove-la-county).

10. Centers for Disease Control and Prevention. Use of cloth face coverings to help slow the spread of COVID-19. April 3, 2020 (www.cdc.gov/coronavirus/2019-ncov/prevent-getting-sick/cloth-face-cover.html).

Part II

The Origin in China

This section examines the origin of COVID-19 in China. We know from Part I of this book that coronaviruses like SARS and COVID-19 are both zoonotic diseases, which is a term for infectious diseases with an animal-to-human transmission trail. SARS had leaped from bats to masked palm civet cats to humans in Chinese wet markets, while COVID-19 also originated in bats but took a different route in a wet market possibly through pangolins to humans (Han 2020; Lam et al. 2020). Pangolins are anteater-like creatures who are an endangered species commanding high prices. This is because their meat is a desired food delicacy in China and their scales are used for medicinal purposes in the practice of traditional Chinese medicine. If COVID-19 was transmitted from bats to pangolins is not known, but the possibility for this occurring comes from testing the genome sequence of the coronavirus in bats and pangolins, and comparing it to the virus's genome in humans (Andersen et al. 2020; Han 2020; Tu et al. 2020; Zhou et al. 2020). The first reading in this section is from Guan-Zhu Han (2020) on the yet to be determined connection between pangolins and COVID-19.

Although pangolins are an endangered species and their sale is unlawful, they nonetheless were available for purchase in Chinese wet markets. Smuggling, along with lax health and safety regulations, combined with ineffective local government inspections and unenforced legal sanctions, allowed wild animal sales to continue. The transmission of COVID-19 from its source to humans likely took place in the Huanan Seafood Wholesale Market in Wuhan, China, that included a wet market selling wild animals for human consumption. Wuhan is a large city of about 11 million people in central China and capital of Hubei Province. While the wet market in Wuhan is directly connected to the first identified outbreak, the actual origin of the viral transmission to humans is uncertain (Zhang and Holmes 2020). Whether humans who may unknowingly have been infected with the virus brought it there or whether infected bats or pangolins being sold in the market initiated the outbreak at that precise location has not been determined. Of the first 41 patients diagnosed with COVID-19 in Wuhan, 27 of them were linked directly to the Huanan market (Huang et al. 2020). They were mainly food handlers and their family members, as was in the case of

SARS. This likely happened in the wet market that brought the virus into contact with humans in a crowded and relatively unhygienic environment.

The first COVID-19 case (the so-called patient "zero") was allegedly a 55-year-old Chinese man who worked on a farm. He was hospitalized in mid-November 2019 with a previously unknown type of pneumonia. By December 8, there were more patients. No alarm was sounded. However, Dr. Li Wenliang, a 34-year-old ophthalmologist at Wuhan Central Hospital, began noticing some of his eye patients had a viral infection. He thought it was possibly a reoccurrence of SARS and began alerting his medical school classmates through social media (WeChat) about this possibility on December 30, 2019. Another physician, Dr. Ai Fen, the head of the hospital's emergency department likewise shared information about a SARS-type virus with her colleagues by way of social media; the hospital administration reprimanded her for spreading rumors. The Wuhan police arrested Dr. Li and took him and some of his colleagues into custody the first week of January 2020 for "rumor-mongering." Since Dr. Li was the source of the information, the police required him to sign a confession admitting to deceptive practices before they would release him. A month later, on February 7, 2020, he died from the yet-to-be-named coronavirus after catching it from a patient he was treating for glaucoma, becoming one of the heroes of the pandemic.

However, despite the efforts of local government officials to stifle information about a possible epidemic in their city, increasing numbers of people were becoming sick. After the SARS pandemic in 2003, the Chinese government had established a computerized alert system to notify the central government in Beijing immediately of any type of infectious outbreak. No notifications came from Wuhan. Instead, local health officials did not want bad news to reach Beijing about medical problems in their city and required such information to be sent to them first (Myers 2020b). Thus local politics intervened to stop the flow of information. Although the first hospitalized patient was in mid-November, the news did not reach Beijing until December 30, when internal documents were leaked online from an unknown whistleblower source. The documents were those of local officials ordering hospitals to send information about a mysterious pneumonia directly to them and to take precautionary measures to avoid the infection from spreading. Two health officials and the communist party secretaries for Wuhan and Hubei Province later lost their jobs because of the cover-up.

A local lab had partially unraveled the genome sequence of the new virus by December 27. On December 31, the day after Dr. Li signed his confession and the leaked documents were sent to Beijing, the Wuhan Health Commission confirmed 27 cases of an unknown pneumonia in the city's hospitals. They only counted the cases linked to the seafood market and indicated there was no evidence of human-to-human transmission (Wee and McNeil 2020). This information was passed to the World Health

Organization (WHO) the same day who repeated what they were told in their global announcement.

On January 1, 2020, the Huanan Seafood Wholesale Market was ordered closed. On January 2, the government's Wuhan Virology Lab deciphered the full virus genome but did not publicly announce it until January 9. Acknowledgment also came that day that a new coronavirus (SARS-CoV-2) was the culprit and its genome was shared with the WHO on January 12. On January 20, it was determined that the virus could indeed spread from one human to another. In the meantime, infected people were traveling out of Wuhan and Hubei Province, spreading the disease to cities in China and other countries. A travel ban to and from Wuhan was finally issued on January 23, and a lockdown imposed three weeks after the virus was officially reported. Millions of people in other Chinese cities were soon put into lockdown, requiring them to stay home except for essential purposes. The fact that Wuhan was a significant commercial and industrial hub and a center of transportation in central China underscored the significance of this measure. But it was too late. COVID-19 had already been carried to the Middle East, Europe, and the United States.

Initially, it seemed that China had rapidly and aggressively responded to this disease, unlike its much-criticized response to the SARS epidemic in 2003. Some early models forecasted that the infection rate was such that on average one infected individual would infect two others, but that rate was reduced to 1.05 infections per individual in the last two weeks of January 2020 during the Wuhan lockdown (Cyranoski 2020). A report issued by the WHO-China Joint Mission on Coronavirus Disease 2019 (COVID-19) in February 2020 praised the efforts of China in reducing the number of cases in the country through strictly-enforced home isolation, wearing of masks, contact tracing, and travel bans in affected areas. The Report (2020:19) stated that: "This unique and unprecedented public health response in China reversed the escalating cases in both Hubei, where there has been widespread community transmission, and in the importation provinces, where family clusters appear to have driven the outbreak." By October 2020, the COVID-19 pandemic had largely passed through China, leaving it ranked No. 54 in the world with over 85,000 reported cases and 4,634 deaths in a population of over 1.4 billion people.

However, other reports emerged about the police detaining health care workers in Wuhan on January 1 for spreading "rumors" about the virus and the government being slow in sharing information about the symptoms and demographic data on infected individuals. The official Chinese Communist Party newspaper did not mention the epidemic and the government's response until three weeks after the virus had been reported to the WHO (Shih, Rauhala, and Sun 2020). Although China's containment efforts were effective in reducing the spread of the virus, another model found that if China had imposed their containment efforts only a week earlier, the number of COVID-19 infections could have been reduced by 65 percent. The reduction was estimated by the model to be 95 percent if the measures had been in place three weeks earlier (Lai et al. 2020).

The second reading in this section is by Hulian Tu and his colleagues (2020) describing the characteristics of COVID-19, its transmission, clinical features, symptoms in patients, and types of medical intervention. It is included to provide more detailed information on the origin and configuration of COVID-19 in China. The third reading is by Matthew Kavanagh (2020), who explores the question of whether autocratic states like China are able to respond more quickly and efficiently to the outbreak of disease than democratic countries? The reasoning between this question rests on the capability of an authoritarian state with one party-rule like China to order the mobilization of its resources for containing the disease without debate and negotiation, and enforce its dictates with police powers. However, in this organizational arrangement, officials below the central authority have to await instructions before acting. Moreover, as happened in China, information unfavorable to local officials was suppressed by them in order to maintain favor with higher authority, thereby causing a delay in taking preventive measures and allowing the pandemic to become the global calamity that it became.

Once China imposed its containment controls, it was able to report its first day of no new local infections by the middle of March while the virus continued to spread globally. Despite this apparent success, the Chinese government faced a growing political backlash both at home and abroad in how it handled the pandemic. The death of Dr. Li from the coronavirus who had been detained for warning of the threat in early January led to expressions of outrage directed at the government through social media. This movement was countered by the Chinese government's campaign of increased online policing, suppression of critical coverage by the news media, and a major propaganda campaign to promote the government's success in controlling the virus and claims of victory (Wong 2020). Economically, the first quarter of 2020 saw production drop almost 7 percent from the same time last year, the first time that China officially acknowledged a contraction in the economy since it started releasing official economic statistics in 1976 (Bradshear and Goel 2020). Even with the containment of the virus, the negative economic consequences of the pandemic on the global economy posed an obstacle to China's potential for economic growth.

The pandemic also led to growing mistrust and unhappiness with China internationally. The relationship between China and the United States, in particular, became more strained. The United States claimed that China was vastly underreporting its cases of coronavirus. Also, U.S. President Donald Trump frequently referred to COVID-19 as the "China virus" or "China plague" to cast blame on Beijing for the outbreak. The United States briefly pointed to unsubstantiated reports that the virus accidentally escaped from a Wuhan virology lab, while a Chinese official countered with a claim that a U.S. Army delegation spread the virus in a visit to Wuhan in October 2019

(Andersen et al. 2020; Myers 2020a). Then in July 2020, Chinese hackers were caught trying to steal research online from U.S. companies working on a vaccine for COVID-19. In response, the United States closed the Chinese consulate in Houston, Texas, where the spying originated and China reacted by closing the American consulate in Chengdu in Szechwan Province.

This feud went beyond political rhetoric and spying accusations to a significant policy change by the United States when President Trump announced a U.S. withdrawal from the World Health Organization due to what was perceived as the organization's "China-centric" response to the pandemic, especially in light of the United States' $480 million annual contribution to WHO compared to China's $39 million (Rauhala, Demirjian, and Olorunnipa 2020). In WHO's defense, China previously had not allowed WHO in the country to investigate SARS, so there was nothing to be gained by publicly criticizing the Chinese over COVID. WHO had chosen to be supportive of the Chinese government in order to continue to gain and maintain China's cooperation in combating the pandemic. However, repeating China's early claim that the virus was not a human-to-human transmission was an error.

This situation sets the stage for the fourth reading by Raj Verma (2020) on China's diplomatic efforts to change its international image in response to criticism from several countries, especially the United States. The reading maintains that this situation is of utmost importance for China because of potentially adverse global reactions that could affect future trade relations and international politics while calling attention to the country's shortcomings in civil rights, environmental protection, public health, government control of the media, and suppression of internal dissent. Thus, power politics has entered into the debate over responsibility for the pandemic. After initial resistance to international pressure, China agreed to allow the World Health Organization to investigate the origins of the virus in July 2020. Despite this cooperative move, China's support for the investigation has been subject to skepticism as its government has not been very transparent about its own research into the origins of the virus, and has also called on the WHO to investigate other countries as part of its inquiry (Hernández and Qin 2020).

In the meantime, while the world was preoccupied with the virus, China passed a new security law in 2020, removing previously agreed-upon rights for the special administrative region of Hong Kong—a former British colony—in order to arrest and imprison protestors at will and deport them to the Chinese mainland.

China did unravel the COVID-19 genome and made it available to scientists around the world. It also provided data on patients, symptoms, treatments, and quarantine measures, while being eventually successful in containing the virus despite later flare-ups in Beijing and Hong Kong. A major challenge for China after the pandemic is dealing with international resentment when answers are sought concerning the cause of the deaths, the global economic recession, the financial costs and loss of livelihoods, and the lives interrupted by social isolation. China will likely be called upon to account for the origin of the pandemic and the delay in notifying the world until after travelers had already spread the disease globally and especially to take action to prevent future pandemics. The fact that so many forms of influenza such as avian flu and the coronaviruses of SARS and COVID-19 have come out of China in recent decades marks the need for significant reforms in the country's approach to public health.

Critical Thinking Questions

1. What is the transmission trail of COVID-19 in Wuhan, China? What is social about this trail?
2. Why did China's warning system for epidemics fail to quickly alert the central government? Describe what constrained the flow of information about the pandemic.
3. How did China contain the virus?
4. What problems does China face in the future because of the pandemic?

References

Andersen, Kristian G., Andrew Rambaut, W. Ian Lipkin, Edward C. Holmes, and Robert L. Garry. 2020. "The Proximal Origin of SARS-CoV-2." *Nature Medicine* 26:450–55.

Bradshear, Keith and Vindu Goel. 2020. "China's Economy Shrinks 6.8 Percent, Ending Four Decades of Growth." *New York Times* (April 17).

Cyranoski, David. 2020. "What China's Coronavirus Response Can Teach the Rest of the World." *Nature* 579(March 17):479–80.

Gandhi, Monica, Deborah S. Yokoe, and Diane V. Havlir. 2020. "Asymptomatic Transmission, the Achilles' Heel of Current Strategies to Control Covid-19." *New England Journal of Medicine* 382(May 28):2158–60.

Han, Guan-Zhu. 2020. "Pangolins Harbor SARS-CoV-2-Related Coronaviruses." *Trends in Microbiology* 28(7):515–17.

Hernández, Javier C. and Amy Qin. 2020. "China Uses W.H.O. Inquiry to Tout Coronavirus Response." *New York Times* (July 21).

Huang, Chaolin, Yeming Wang, Xingwang Li, Lili Ren et al. 2020. "Clinical Features of Patients Infected with 2019 Novel Coronavirus in Wuhan, China." *Lancet* 395(10223):497–506.

Kavanagh, Matthew. 2020. "Authoritarianism, Outbreaks, and Information Politics." *Lancet Public Health* (March):e135–36.

Lai, Shengjie, Nick W. Ruktanonchai, and Lingchai Zhou. 2020. "Effect of Non-Pharmaceutical Interventions to Contain COVID-19 in China." *Nature*. https://doi.org/10.1038/s41586-020-2293-x.

Lam, Tommy Tsan-Yuk, Marcus Ho-Hin Shum, Hua-Chen Zhu et al. 2020. "Identifying SARS-CoV-2-Related Coronaviruses in Malayan Pangolins." *Nature* 583(July 9):282–85.

Myers, Steven Lee. 2020a. "China Spins Tale That the U.S. Army Started the Coronavirus Epidemic." *New York Times* (March 13).

Myers, Steven Lee. 2020b. "China Created a Fail-Safe System to Track Contagions—It Failed." *New York Times* (March 30).

Rauhala, Emily, Karoun Demirjian, and Toluse Olorunnipa. 2020. "Trump Administration Sends Letter Withdrawing U.S. from World Health Organization over Coronavirus Response: The Notice of Withdrawal is a Dramatic Move that Could Reshape Public Health Diplomacy." *Washington Post* (July 7).

Report of the WHO-China Joint Mission on Coronavirus Disease 2019 (COVID-19). 2020. (February 16–24).

Shih, Gerry, Emily Rauhala, and Lena H. Sun. 2020. "Early Missteps and State Secrecy in China Probably Allowed the Coronavirus to Spread Farther and Faster." *Washington Post* (February 1).

Tu, Huilan, Sheng Tu, Shiqi Gao, Awen Shao, and Jifang Sheng. 2020. "The Epidemiological and Clinical Features of COVID-19 and Lessons From This Global Infectious Public Health Event." *Journal of Infection* 81(1):1–9.

Verma, Raj. 2020. "China's Diplomacy and Changing the COVID-19 Narrative." *International Journal: Canada's Journal of Global Policy Analysis* 75(2):248–58.

Wee, Sui-Lee and Donald G. McNeil. 2020. "China Identifies New Virus Causing Pneumonia-Like Illness." *New York Times* (January 9).

Wong, Chun Han. 2020. "China's Virus Censorship and Propaganda Draw Backlash; The Fast-Spreading Covid-19 Epidemic has Stirred a Flood of Negative Opinion about the Communist Party's Handling of the Crisis." *Wall Street Journal* (February 25).

Zhang, Yong-Zhen and Edward C. Holmes. 2020. "A Genomic Perspective on the Origin and Emergence of SARS-CoV-2." *Cell* 181(2):223–27.

Zhou, Peng, Xing-Lou Yang, Xian-Guang Wang, Ben Hu et al. 2020. "A Pneumonia Outbreak Associated with a New Coronavirus of Probable Bat Origin." *Nature* 579(February 3):270–73.

4 Pangolins Harbor SARS-CoV-2-Related Coronaviruses

Guan-Zhu Han

The outbreak of coronavirus disease 2019 (COVID-19) has been spreading rapidly throughout the globe, resulting in ~0.8 million confirmed infections as of March 31, 2020. On March 11, 2020, the World Health Organization (WHO) declared the COVID-19 outbreak a pandemic. COVID-19 is caused by severe acute respiratory syndrome coronavirus 2 (SARS-CoV-2), a positive-sense single-stranded RNA virus that belongs to the genus *Betacoronavirus* within the family *Coronaviridae* [1,2]. Yet, the origin and evolution of SARS-CoV-2 remains largely unclear. Several recent studies identified SARS-CoV-2-related viruses in Malayan pangolins (*Manis javanica*), providing new insights into the host distribution and evolution of SARS-CoV-2-related viruses [3–7].

Sharing ~80% nucleotide identity, SARS-CoV and SARS-CoV-2 are closely related to each other [1]. SARS-CoV and SARS-CoV-2 have been taxonomically classified into a single viral species, *Severe acute respiratory syndrome-related coronavirus* [8]. A large number of SARS-related coronaviruses (SARSr-CoV) have been isolated from bats. Therefore, it has been widely thought that bats are the natural reservoirs of SARSr-CoV. SARS-CoV-2 is closely related to multiple SARSr-CoVs of bats; for example, a bat CoV, BatCoV RaTG13, detected in *Rhinolophus affinis* from the Yunnan province of China, exhibits very high nucleotide identity (96.2% at the genome level) with SARS-CoV-2. These findings suggest a probable bat origin of SARS-CoV-2 [1,2]. Whereas SARS-CoV and Middle East respiratory syndrome coronavirus (MERS-CoV), two highly contagious CoVs that emerged in humans during the past two decades, might ultimately have bat origins, both of them were introduced into human populations through intermediate hosts [9]. It is possible that SARS-CoV-2 entered human populations through intermediate host(s). However, few SARS-CoV-2-related viruses have been described in mammals other than bats and humans.

Several recent studies reported the identification of SARS-CoV-2-related viruses in Malayan pangolins, native in Southeast Asia, that were smuggled into Southern China [3–7]. Pangolins (or scaly anteaters) are mammals that belong to the order of Pholidota, with one extant family (Manidae) and three genera (*Manis, Phataginus,* and *Smutsia*) [10]. As a source of food and traditional Asian medicines, pangolins are among the most illegally traded mammals in the world [10]. A number of pangolin species have been assessed to be endangered or critically endangered by the International Union for Conservation of Nature (IUCN) Red List of Threatened Species. Two distinct clusters of SARS-CoV-2-related viruses were identified in pangolin samples obtained by anti-smuggling operations in the Guangxi (GX) and Guangdong (GD) provinces of China (Figure 4.1A). Interestingly, the GD pangolin CoVs have a higher amino acid identity (97.4%) with SARS-CoV-2 than does the bat CoV RaTG13 (89.2%) in the receptor-binding domain (RBD) [3–7]. In the remainder of the genome, RaTG13 exhibits a higher sequence identity with SARS-CoV-2 than do the GD pangolin CoVs. This pattern can be explained by either recombination or convergent evolution [3–7]. Phylogenetic analysis based on the synonymous sites of RBD, whose evolution is less likely to be influenced by natural selection, shows that RaTG13 is more closely related to SARS-CoV-2 than are the GD pangolin CoVs (Figure 4.1B), indicating that the high amino acid similarity between the GD pangolin CoVs and SARS-CoV-2 in the RBD might be due to convergent evolution [3].

What is the relationship between the pangolin CoVs and SARS-CoV-2? It has been widely circulated that pangolins potentially serve as the intermediate host of SARS-CoV-2 (www.nature.com/articles/d41586-020-00364-2). SARS-CoV-2 might be of 'probable pangolin origin' [4]. Alternatively, the pangolin CoVs might represent 'trivial' SARS-CoV-2-related viruses that are cryptically circulating in the wild and are not the direct source of SARS-CoV-2. Different scenarios of cross-species transmission will exhibit different phylogenetic patterns (Figure 4.1C). If pangolins act as the intermediate host (spillover to humans once [scenario I] or multiple times [scenario II]), SARS-CoV should fall within the diversity of pangolin CoVs. If SARS-CoV-2-related viruses independently entered into humans and pangolins (scenario III), and pangolin CoVs are not the direct source of SARS-CoV-2, then SARS-CoV-2-related viruses in humans and pangolins should form distinct clusters that nest within the diversity of bat CoVs. Therefore, based on the analysis of the genome regions other than RBD, it can be concluded that these known pangolin CoVs are not the direct source of SARS-CoV-2. Based on the analysis of RBD, we cannot conclude that pangolins are the intermediate host of SARS-CoV-2. It is also possible that the GD pangolin CoVs derived from cross-species transmission from bats (or from other animals) [3]. Clearly, SARS-CoV-2-related viruses are still poorly sampled in mammals (even in bats) to reach a conclusion. The identification of two distinct viral clusters in pangolins indicates that SARS-CoV-2-related viruses might be more widely distributed in wild mammals than expected. Further surveillance of SARS-CoV-2-related viruses in mammals might help to clarify the origin of SARS-CoV-2.

The high similarity between the Guangdong pangolin CoVs and SARS-CoV-2 in the RBD raises concern that these viruses might be readily

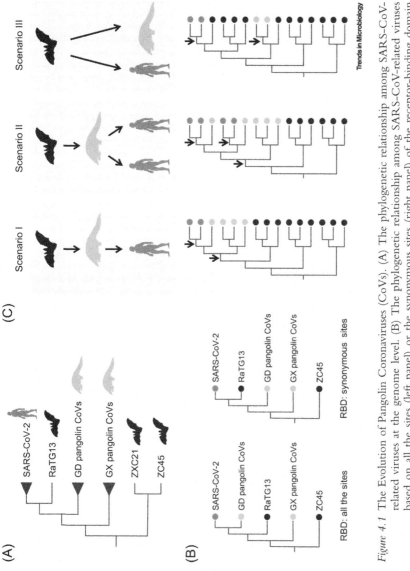

Figure 4.1 The Evolution of Pangolin Coronaviruses (CoVs). (A) The phylogenetic relationship among SARS-CoV-related viruses at the genome level. (B) The phylogenetic relationship among SARS-CoV-related viruses based on all the sites (left panel) or the synonymous sites (right panel) of the receptor-binding domain (RBD). (C) Cross-species transmission scenarios and their expected phylogenetic patterns. Pangolin CoVs might ultimately originate from cross-species transmission from bats. Pangolins serve as the intermediate host, and SARS-CoV-2 arose through spillover from pangolins to humans once (scenario I) or multiple times (scenario II). SARS-CoV and pangolin CoVs originated independently through cross-species transmission from bats (scenario III). Black arrows indicate cross-species transmission events.

transmitted to human populations. More work is needed to explore the pathogenicity and diversity of CoVs in pangolins. Nevertheless, due to their status of being endangered, and the risk of causing future CoV outbreaks, the hunting, handling, and trafficking of pangolins should be strictly prohibited.

Acknowledgments

G.-Z. Han was supported by the National Natural Science Foundation of China (31922001 and 31701091).

References

1. Zhou, P. *et al.* (2020) A pneumonia outbreak associated with a new coronavirus of probable bat origin. *Nature* 579, 270–273
2. Wu, F. *et al.* (2020) A new coronavirus associated with human respiratory disease in China. *Nature* 579, 265–269
3. Lam, T.T. *et al.* (2020) Identifying SARS-CoV-2 related coronaviruses in Malayan pangolins. *Nature*. Published online March 26, 2020. https://doi.org/10.1038/s41586-020-2169-0
4. Zhang, T. *et al.* (2020) Probable pangolin origin of SARS-CoV-2 associated with the COVID-19 outbreak. *Curr. Biol.* 30, 1–6
5. Liu, P. *et al.* (2019) Viral metagenomics revealed Sendai virus and coronavirus infection of Malayan pangolins (*Manis javanica*). *Viruses* 11, 979
6. Wong, M.C. *et al.* (2020) Evidence of recombination in coronaviruses implicating pangolin origins of nCoV-2019. *bioRxiv*. Posted February 13, 2020. https://doi.org/10.1101/2020.02.07.939207
7. Xiao, K. *et al.* (2020) Isolation and characterization of 2019-nCoV-like coronavirus from Malayan pangolins. *bioRxiv*. Posted February 20, 2020. https://doi.org/10.1101/2020.02.17.951335
8. Coronaviridae Study Group of the International Committee on Taxonomy of Viruses (2020) The species Severe acute respiratory syndrome-related coronavirus: classifying 2019-nCoV and naming it SARS-CoV-2. *Nat. Microbiol.* 5, 536–544
9. Forni, D. *et al.* (2017) Molecular evolution of human coronavirus genomes. *Trends Microbiol.* 25, 35–48
10. Gaubert, P. *et al.* (2018) The complete phylogeny of pangolins: scaling up resources for the molecular tracing of the most trafficked mammals on earth. *J. Hered.* 109, 347–359

5 Current Epidemiological and Clinical Features of COVID-19; a Global Perspective From China

Huilan Tu, Sheng Tu, Shiqi Gao, Anwen Shao, and Jifang Sheng

Introduction

In December 2019, a cluster of cases of unexplained viral pneumonia was identified in Wuhan, a metropolitan city in Hubei province, China. Initially, most of the confirmed cases were linked with the Huanan seafood market in Wuhan, where numerous types of live wild animals are sold, including poultry, bats, groundhogs, and snakes. To identify the causative agent of this disease, a large number of tests were conducted, which ruled out several etiological agents that may cause similar symptoms, including the severe acute respiratory syndrome coronavirus (SARS-CoV), Middle East respiratory syndrome coronavirus (MERS-CoV), avian influenza virus, and other common respiratory pathogens. Finally, a new coronavirus, putatively named 2019-nCoV by the World Health Organization (WHO) on January 12, 2020, was identified as the causative pathogen of this outbreak. On January 20, after a visit to Wuhan, Professor Zhong Nanshan, a SARS intervention specialist, confirmed that 2019-nCoV was spreading between people,[1] which led to increased vigilance by the Chinese government and people. At 10:00 a.m. on January 23, Wuhan, the birthplace of the disease, declared a general closure to prevent its further spread. However, Wuhan is a major transportation hub located in the central region of the People's Republic of China with approximately 11 million inhabitants,[2] and the period from the end of December 2019 to February 2020 was the time of the "Spring Festival travel rush." Although the Chinese government made great efforts to control the flow of people, the disease spread rapidly from Wuhan to other cities, as well as other countries, likely through asymptomatic carriers.[3] On January 30, 2020, the WHO declared the outbreak of novel coronavirus a public health emergency of international concern, the sixth public health emergency after H1N1 (2009), polio (2014), Ebola in West Africa (2014), Zika (2016), and Ebola in the Democratic Republic of Congo (2019).[4] The International Committee on Taxonomy of Viruses renamed 2019-nCoV as severe acute respiratory syndrome coronavirus 2 (SARS-CoV-2), and the related pneumonia as coronavirus disease 2019 (COVID-19) on

February 12, 2020.[5] As the disease is highly infectious, "the law of the People's Republic of China on the prevention and treatment of infectious diseases" lists it as a class B infectious disease, and recommends preventive and control measures similar to those against class A infectious diseases. The outbreak is ongoing, and poses a great global challenge. Health workers, governments, and the public need to co-operate globally to prevent its further spread.

Etiological Characteristics and Origin of COVID-19

Coronaviruses were first described by Tyrell and Bynoe in 1966, who isolated the viruses from patients suffering from the common cold.[6] Tyrell and Bynoe called them coronaviruses because they are spherical virions with a core shell and surface projections resembling a solar corona.[7] Coronaviruses are members of the subfamily *Coronavirinae* in the family *Coronaviridae*, order *Nidovirales*. Members of this subfamily were genetically classified into four major genera: *Alphacoronavirus, Betacoronavirus, Gammacoronavirus*, and *Deltacoronavirus*.[8] Alphacoronaviruses and betacoronaviruses infect only mammals and usually cause respiratory illness in humans and gastroenteritis in animals. The gammacoronaviruses and deltacoronaviruses predominantly infect birds, but some can also infect mammals.[9] Six types of coronavirus have been identified in humans (HCoVs), including HCoV-NL63, HCoV-229E, HCoV-OC43, HCoV-HKU1, SARS-CoV, and MERS-CoV. The first two belong to the *Alphacoronavirus* genus and the latter four to the genus *Betacoronavirus*.[10] SARS-CoV and MERS-CoV can cause severe respiratory syndrome in humans, while the other four human coronaviruses induce only mild upper respiratory diseases in immunocompetent hosts.[11,12] Coronaviruses did not attract worldwide attention until the 2003 SARS epidemic, followed by the 2012 MERS outbreak and, most recently, the novel coronavirus pandemic.

SARS-CoV-2 was found to be a positive-sense, single-stranded RNA virus belonging to the *Betacoronavirus* B lineage and is closely related to the SARS-CoV virus.[13] Full-length genome sequences were obtained and indicated that the SARS-CoV-2 genome shares 79.6% sequence identity with that of SARS-CoV.[14] Notably, SARS-CoV-2 infects human lung alveolar epithelial cells through receptor-mediated endocytosis using angiotensin-converting enzyme II (ACE2) as an entry receptor. Attachment to the receptor mediates the subsequent fusion between the viral envelope and host cell membrane, thereby allowing viral entry into the host cell.[15,16]

The origin of the disease has not been determined. As most of the confirmed cases were linked to direct exposure to the Huanan seafood market,[17] it was initially believed that the origin of the virus may have been the seafood market. Based on current sequence databases, all human coronaviruses have animal origins: SARS-CoV and MERS-CoV originated in bats, their natural reservoir, but were transmitted to humans via intermediate host civets and camels, respectively.[18] HCoV-NL63 and HCoV-229E are also considered to have originated in bats, while HCoV-OC43 and HKU1 likely originated in rodents.[11,12] SARS-CoV-2 is closely related to two bat-derived coronavirus strains, bat-SL-CoVZC45 and bat-SL-CoVZXC21[13,19] and is 96% identical at the whole-genome level to bat coronavirus TG13.[7,14] This suggests that SARS-CoV-2 may also have originated in bats, and was then transmitted to humans *via* an intermediate host in the Huanan seafood market. Analysis of the genome of a coronavirus isolated from pangolins indicated that the isolated strains and SARS-CoV-2 are 99% similar. This suggests that pangolins may be potential intermediate hosts for SARS-CoV-2, and the transmission and evolution path of SARS-CoV-2 may be from bat-CoV to pangolins, and then to humans. However, on February 20, 2020, the website of the Xishuangbanna Tropical Botanical Garden of the Chinese Academy of Sciences published an article that suggested that the seafood market may not have been the source of COVID-19, and that SARS-CoV-2 may have been introduced from elsewhere and then spread rapidly in the market. The symptom onset date for the first patient identified was December 1, 2019, and no epidemiological link was found between the patient and later cases.[17] Based on factors such as the incubation period of the virus, the first new coronavirus infection may have appeared in late November 2019 or even earlier.

In the global spread of SARS-CoV-2, several countries have reported numerous cases that cannot be traced to the putative source of the infection. The first confirmed case of COVID-19 in the United States was a patient who had traveled to Wuhan, China, but reported that he had not visited the seafood market or health care facilities, and had not had any contact with sick people during his stay in Wuhan.[20] The source of his SARS-CoV-2 infection is still unknown. In Italy, meanwhile, where the epidemic is getting worse, "patient zero" has yet to be identified.[21] Greater efforts are required to trace the source of the virus, control it, and clarify its intermediate host, which is of vital importance to controlling the transmission of SARS-CoV-2.[22]

Epidemiology

In general, the emergence of an infectious disease comprises three vital elements: infectious source, transmission route, and susceptible population.[23] At present, SARS-CoV-2-infected patients are the main source of infection, producing a large quantity of virus in the upper respiratory tract during a prodrome period.[24] Because of the mild clinical symptoms during the incubation period, patients can remain mobile and carry out routine activities, leading to the spread of infection. Asymptomatic carriers can also be a source of infection.[25] The incubation period of the disease is 1–14 days, usually 3–7 days, and can even reach 24 days, making it difficult to screen for infections. Additionally, the disease is mainly spread by respiratory droplets and contact. Infections among 14 health workers confirmed the disease's high infectivity and raised concerns that some people may be "super spreaders" of the virus.[1] In a relatively closed environment, aerosol transmission can also occur.[26]

Nosocomial transmission is also a severe problem. As of February 12, 2020, a total of 3,019 health workers had been infected, and accounted for 3.83% of the total number of infections.[27] Personal protective equipment (PPE), including fluid-resistant gown, gloves, eye protection, full face shield, and fit-tested N95 respirators, is necessary to maximize the safety of health care workers who need to be in contact with critically ill patients with confirmed or suspected SARS-CoV-2 infection.[28] A recent study found that SARS-CoV-2 can be detected in the tears and conjunctival secretions of new coronavirus pneumonia patients with conjunctivitis,[29] which suggests that ocular infection may be a source of SARS-CoV-2 transmission. The possibility of fecal-oral transmission also needs to be considered, as viral nucleic acids have been found in fecal samples and anal swabs from some COVID-19-infected patients.[30] On February 5, 2020, multiple media outlets also reported that a newborn infant delivered by a woman who had tested positive for SARS-CoV-2 during the epidemic in Wuhan had also tested positive for the virus 30 h following his/her birth.[2] There is currently no evidence to suggest that SARS-CoV-2 can undergo intrauterine or transplacental transmission;[31,32] however, when delivering a neonate from an infected patient or a person suspected of being infected, neonatologists should wear suitable protective equipment. Moreover, the newborns must be isolated as soon as they are suspected of being infected.

Although all populations are susceptible to SARS-CoV-2,[26] particular attention and efforts to protect or reduce transmission should be directed at vulnerable groups such as children, health care providers, pregnant women, and the elderly. As of January 29, 2020, a study had obtained data regarding the clinical symptoms and outcomes for 1,099 COVID-19 patients who had been hospitalized at 552 sites. Their median age was 47 years.[33] SARS-CoV-2 has caused severe illness and death primarily in older people, particularly those with pre-existing conditions such as diabetes and heart disease,[34] possibly due to a weakened immune system that permits a faster progression of viral infection. Although children are as likely to be infected by the coronavirus as adults, they are less likely to experience severe symptoms,[35] which suggests that measures such as school closures may help slow the spread of the virus.

The proportion of pregnant women among the confirmed cases is low; nevertheless, pregnant women are known to be particularly susceptible to respiratory pathogens and severe pneumonia.[31] Furthermore, the occurrence of pneumonia during pregnancy can lead to several adverse obstetric outcomes, such as premature rupture of membranes (PROM) and preterm labor (PTL), intrauterine fetal demise (IUFD), intrauterine growth restriction (IUGR), and neonatal death, and therefore poses great risks to both pregnant women and their unborn children.[36,37] The mortality rate among pregnant women due to respiratory pathogens is substantially higher than that among ordinary people; for example, the 1918 influenza pandemic resulted in a mortality rate of 2.6% for the overall population, but 37% among pregnant women.[38] Therefore, pregnant women infected with SARS-CoV-2 should be cared for in a health care facility with close maternal and fetal monitoring. In this regard, experiences with illnesses associated with other highly pathogenic coronaviruses, such as SARS and MERS, may also be relevant to SARS-CoV-2, including early isolation, aggressive infection control procedures, oxygen therapy, avoidance of fluid overload, empiric antibiotics, and fetal and uterine contraction monitoring.[39]

Transmission Dynamics and Epidemic Status of COVID-19

Understanding the transmissibility of SARS-CoV-2 remains crucial for predicting the course of the epidemic and the likelihood of sustained transmission.[40] The reproduction number, R, is used to reflect the transmissibility of a virus, and represents the average number of new infections generated by each infected person, the initial constant of which is called the basic reproduction number, R_0: the larger the R_0 is, the stronger the transmission potential of the virus.[41] An R-value >1 indicates that the outbreak will be self-sustaining unless effective control measures are implemented, while an R-value <1 indicates that the number of new cases will decrease over time and the outbreak will eventually stop.[42] Compared with the R_0 of H1N1 (1.25)[43] and that of SARS (2.2–3.6),[44] the R_0 of SARS-CoV-2 was estimated as 2.2 (95% CI, 1.4 to 3.9),[2] 3.11 (95% CI, 2.39–4.13),[45] and 2.68 (95% CI, 2.47–2.86)[46] by different groups and is significantly larger than 1, indicating that SARS-CoV-2 has a high transmissibility potential and consequently the ability to cause outbreaks. It may be very difficult to contain or control the spread of this virus without adequate prevention and control measures. The effective reproduction number (R_t) quantifies the number of infections caused by each new case occurring at time t. It is typically lower than that of R_0 owing to the effect of control measures in reducing transmission, and the depletion of susceptible individuals during the epidemic; epidemic decay is guaranteed only where R_t is maintained below 1.[47]

The SEIR model, a classic method used to analyze the epidemic trend of an infectious disease, can reflect the flow of people between four states: susceptible (S), exposed (E), infectious (I), and recovered (R), and has been shown to be predictive for a variety of acute infectious diseases such as Ebola and SARS.[48,49] Based on previous studies and the experience gained from the SARS epidemic, Wang et al. applied this model to estimate the epidemic trend in Wuhan, China. If the prevention and control measures were sufficient in Wuhan, the R_t was assumed to gradually decrease at different phases from a high level of transmission (R_t = 3.1, 2.6, and 1.9) to below 1 (R_t = 0.9 or 0.5), and the estimated number of infections would peak in late February.[42] Judging from the dwindling number of newly diagnosed cases in China (Figure 5.1), the prevention and control measures implemented were indeed effective. However, the global situation remains very serious (Figure 5.2), and rigorous measures should be maintained so as to reduce the R_t to an ideal level and control the infection.

The WHO in Geneva declared the coronavirus outbreak to be a pandemic on March 11, 2020. Up to March 26, 2020, at least 82,078 cases of COVID-19 had been confirmed in China, with 3,298 known deaths, representing a fatality rate of approximately 4%. The outbreak in China seems to be slowing, as evidenced by the reduction in the daily number of newly diagnosed cases (Figures 5.1 and 5.2). The coronavirus outbreak seems to be spreading faster outside China than inside (Figure 5.1B). The WHO reported that more than 462,801 people have been infected worldwide, more than 380,723 of which are outside of China. (WHO; http://2019ncov. chinacdc.cn/2019-ncov/global.html). This does not mean that the outbreak is out of control, and as long as countries take robust action to detect cases early, isolate and care for patients, and track contacts, there is still a chance of containing the virus.

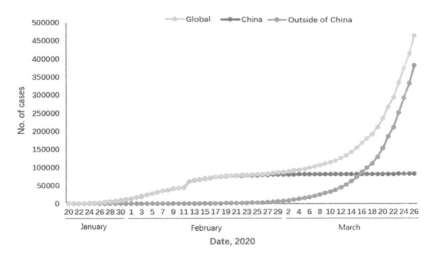

Figure 5.1 New daily cases of laboratory-confirmed coronavirus disease 2019 (COVID-19) as of March 26, 2020. (A) Daily numbers of new cases globally and (B) daily numbers of new cases from China (including the Hong Kong Special Administrative Region [SAR] and Macau SAR) and outside of China.

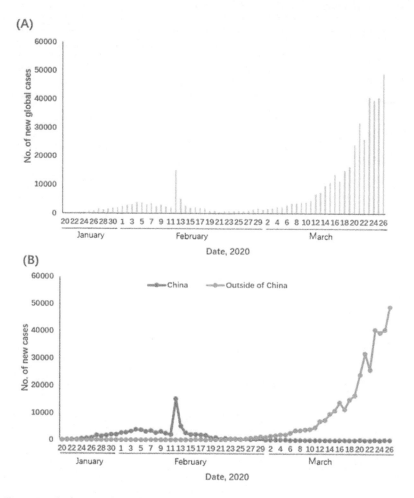

Figure 5.2 Daily cumulative laboratory-confirmed cases of coronavirus disease 2019 (COVID-19) as of March 26, 2020. Daily numbers of global cases and daily numbers of cases from China (including Hong Kong Special Administrative Region [SAR] and Macau SAR)] and outside of China.

Clinical Features and Diagnosis of COVID-19

Recently, Guan et al. reported that the common clinical manifestations of 2019-nCoV infection among 1,099 laboratory-confirmed cases of COVID-19 included fever (88.7%), cough (67.8%), fatigue (38.1%), sputum production (33.7%), shortness of breath (18.7%), sore throat (13.9%), and headache (13.6%).[33] In addition, a few COVID-19 patients also showed gastrointestinal symptoms,[30] i.e., diarrhea (3.8%) and vomiting (5.0%).[33] Although studies have indicated that fever is the dominant symptom (Table 5.1), some

Table 5.1 Demographics, clinical characteristics, and clinical outcomes of patients infected with COVID-19.

	Guan et al.[33] (n = 1099) n (%)	Huang et al.[17] (n = 41) n (%)	Chen et al.[50] (n = 99) n (%)	Wang et al.[51] (n = 138) n (%)
Age, years	47.0 (35.0–58.0)	49.0 (41.0–58.0)	55.5 (13.1)	56.0 (42.0–68.0)
Female sex	459/1096 (41.9)	11/41 (27)	32 (32)	63 (45.7)
Current smoking	137/1085 (12.6)	3 (7)	NA	NA
Any comorbidity	261 (23.7)	13 (32)	50 (51)	64 (46.4)
Diabetes	81 (7.4)	8 (20)	NA	14 (10.1)
Hypertension	165 (15.0)	6 (15)	NA	43 (31.2)
Cardiovascular disease	42 (3.9)	6 (15)	40 (40)	20 (14.5)
COPD	12 (1.1)	1 (2)	NA	4 (2.9)
Malignancy	10 (0.9)	1 (2)	1 (1)	10 (7.2)
Chronic liver disease	23 (2.1)	1 (2)	NA	4 (2.9)
Presentation				
Fever	975 (88.7)	40 (98)	82 (83)	136 (98.6)
Cough	745 (67.8)	31 (76)	81 (82)	82 (59.4)
Fatigue	419 (38.1)	18 (44)	NA	96 (69.6)
Myalgia	164 (14.9)	NA	11 (11)	48 (34.8)
Sputum production	370 (33.7)	11/39 (28)	NA	37 (26.8)
Short of breath	205 (18.7)	22/40 (55)	31 (31)	43 (31.2)
Sore throat	153 (13.9)	NA	5 (5)	24 (17.4)
Headache	150 (13.6)	3/38 (8)	8 (8)	9 (6.5)
Diarrhea	42 (3.8)	1/38 (3)	2 (2)	14 (10.1)
Nausea or Vomiting	55 (5.0)	NA	1 (1)	19 (13.7)
Chills	126 (11.5)	NA	NA	NA
Haemoptysis	10 (0.9)	2/39 (5)	NA	NA
Outcome				
Discharged	55 (5.0)	28 (68)	31 (31)	47 (34.1)
Remained hospitalized	1029 (93.6)	7 (17)	57 (58)	85 (61.6)
Died	15 (1.4)	6 (15)	11 (11)	6 (4.3)

Note: Data are median (IQR), mean (SD), n (%), or n/N (%), where N is the total number of patients with available data. COPD, chronic obstructive pulmonary disease; NA, not available.

severely or critically ill patients may have moderate, low, or even no significant fever.[50,51] Therefore, undue emphasis should not be placed on a patient's body temperature for disease evaluation in clinical treatment and daily screening. Most patients have a good prognosis, while a few are in a critical condition, especially the elderly and those with underlying chronic conditions such as cardiac disease and diabetes.[52] Sepsis is the most frequently observed complication, followed by respiratory failure, acute respiratory distress syndrome (ARDS), heart failure, and septic shock.[53]

The first symptoms of COVID-19 are nonspecific. Differential diagnosis should include the possibility of a wide range of infectious (e.g., adenovirus, influenza, parainfluenza, respiratory syncytial virus [RSV], human metapneumovirus [HmPV]) and noninfectious (e.g., vasculitis, dermatomyositis) common respiratory disorders.[54] For health care workers, timely differential diagnosis of patients is important for reducing cross-infection and controlling the outbreak.

Computed tomography (CT) has an important role to play in the diagnosis and evaluation of COVID-19. Multiple patchy ground glass opacities in bilateral, multifocal lung lesions, with peripheral distribution, are typical chest CT imaging features in COVID-19 patients, whereas pleural effusion, pericardial effusion, cavitation, thoracic lymphadenopathy, and pulmonary emphysema are uncommon imaging findings.[55–57] Studies have shown that CT has a low rate of missed COVID-19 diagnosis (3.9%, 2/51)[58] and the sensitivity of chest CT was greater than that of RT-PCR (98% vs. 71%, respectively, $p < 0.001$),[59] indicating that CT may be useful as a standard method for the diagnosis of COVID-19. However, CT cannot identify specific viruses or distinguish between viruses.[58] Bernheim et al. reported that 20/36 (56%) early-stage patients had a normal CT,[60] which suggests that chest CT is unlikely to be a reliable standalone tool to rule out COVID-19 infection, especially for patients with early symptom onset.

To date, the gold-standard method for the clinical diagnosis of COVID-19 is nucleic acid detection in nasal and throat swab samples or other respiratory tract samples by real-time PCR, which is then further confirmed by next-generation sequencing.[61,62] However, this diagnostic method has several shortcomings, such as a low detection rate and high false-negative rates. Moreover, this method is suitable only for diagnosis, and cannot be used to judge the severity and progression of the disease. Additionally, the supply cannot keep up with the demand, and it takes one day or more to obtain results, which may be detrimental to the timely treatment of patients.[63] The Chinese health authorities have issued the fifth version of the diagnosis and treatment plan for COVID-19.[64] According to the updated criteria, suspected cases with imaging characteristics of pneumonia can be clinically diagnosed as COVID-19 in Hubei province. In this way, patients can receive standardized treatment as soon as possible, so as to further improve the success rate of treatment and contain the spread of the epidemic. Recently, Li et al. developed a rapid and simple point-of-care lateral flow immunoassay that can simultaneously detect IgM and IgG antibodies against SARS-CoV-2 in human blood within 15 min. This rapid test has great potential benefit for the fast screening of SARS-CoV-2 infections to prevent virus transmission and assure the timely treatment of patients.[65]

Intervention Methods

Potential Therapeutic Interventions

At present, there is no specific antiviral treatment recommended for COVID-19, and no vaccine is available. For mildly to moderately ill patients, active symptomatic support remains key for treatment, such as maintaining hydration and nutrition and controlling fever and cough. For patients with severe infection or those with respiratory failure, oxygen inhalation through a mask, high nasal oxygen flow inhalation, non-invasive ventilation, or mechanical ventilation is needed. Extracorporeal membrane oxygenation (ECMO) can be implemented if the other methods do not work.[66] Additionally, hemodynamic support is essential for managing septic shock,[54] and antibiotics and antifungals may also be required. As corticosteroid therapy is commonly used among critically ill MERS patients,[67] short courses of corticosteroids at low-to-moderate doses can be used with caution.[68,69] As anxiety and fear are common among COVID-19 patients, dynamic assessment strategies should be established to monitor their mental health.[70]

Identifying effective antiviral agents to combat the disease is urgently needed. Current guidelines[26] recommend IFN-alpha, lopinavir/ritonavir, ribavirin, chloroquine phosphate, and arbidol as antiviral therapies. IFN-alpha is a broad-spectrum antiviral drug that can inhibit the replication of animal and human coronaviruses,[71,72] while lopinavir is a proteinase inhibitor used to treat HIV infection, with ritonavir being used as a booster.[73,74] In Korea, the viral load of one patient was reduced and clinical symptoms improved with combined administration of lopinavir and ritonavir.[75] However, a randomized, controlled, open-label trial in China found that lopinavir/ritonavir cotreatment did not significantly enhance clinical improvement, reduce mortality, or diminish throat viral RNA detectability in seriously ill COVID-19 patients.[76] The efficacy of lopinavir/ritonavir in treating COVID-19 requires further clinical confirmation. Ribavirin, a synthetic guanosine analog and broad-spectrum inhibitor of RNA and DNA viruses, is frequently used for the treatment of SARS and MERS patients.[77,78] Morgenstern et al.[79] reported that, compared with single treatment, a combination of ribavirin and IFN-beta inhibited SARS-CoV replication when administered at greatly reduced concentrations. However, the use of ribavirin is associated with significant toxicity, including hemolysis and reduced hemoglobin levels,[80] indicating that ribavirin should be used with caution as a treatment for COVID-19. Multicenter clinical trials conducted in China indicated that chloroquine phosphate, widely used to treat malaria and autoimmune diseases,[81,82] may have some efficacy against COVID-19 associated pneumonia, with acceptable safety.[83–85] Arbidol, a Russian-made small indole-derivative molecule, is used for prophylaxis and treatment of influenza and other respiratory viral infections.[86,87] Deng et al.[88] found that arbidol combined with lopinavir/ritonavir might delay the progression of lung lesions and reduce the viral load in COVID-19 patients. Nearly all the mentioned drug options are associated with the treatment of SARS, MERS, or other new influenza viruses and additional randomized, prospective studies are still needed to determine their efficacy against COVID-19.

There are many other antiviral drugs with potential as treatment options against COVID-19. Remdesivir, a nucleotide analog prodrug currently in clinical trials for the treatment of Ebola virus infections,[89] is a promising compound,[90] since preclinical studies have suggested that remdesivir may be effective for both prophylaxis and treatment of HCoV infections.[54,91,92] Elfiky[93] found that sofosbuvir was a potent inhibitor of COVID-19 RNA-dependent RNA polymerase (RdRp). Oseltamivir is a neuraminidase inhibitor indicated for the treatment of influenza.[94,95] Nafamostat can block MERS-CoV infection in vitro[96] and is potentially applicable to the treatment of Ebola virus disease.[97] Favipiravir is a broad-spectrum antiviral that has shown promise for treating influenza[98] and may also be effective against the Ebola virus.[99] Nitazoxanide is both an antiprotozoal agent and a first-in-class broad-spectrum antiviral agent[100] that may be useful for the treatment of MERS infections.[101]

It has recently been suggested that treatment with angiotensin–converting enzyme inhibitors (ACEIs) and angiotensin receptor 1 (AT1R) inhibitors might reduce the pulmonary inflammatory response in COVID-19 patients.[102] Monoclonal antibody therapy[103] and convalescent plasma[104] also have potential as therapeutic interventions to treat COVID-19. Chinese traditional medicines, such as ShuFengJieDu[105,106] and Lianhuaqingwen capsules[107,108] can also aid in the prevention and treatment of infectious respiratory diseases such as influenza A (H1N1). Radix astragali (Huangqi), Radix glycyrrhizae (Gancao), Radix saposhnikoviae (Fangfeng), *Rhizoma Atractylodis Macrocephalae* (Baizhu), *Lonicerae Japonicae Flos* (Jinyinhua), and *Forsythiae Fructus* (Lianqiao) have long been used for the prevention of contagious respiratory viral diseases, indicating that Chinese herbal formulas may also be treatment options for COVID-19.[109,110] In addition, fighting viruses with antibiotics is often overlooked,[111] and drugs such as teicoplanin[112,113] and ivermectin[114–116] may also be useful to treat COVID-19 (Table 5.2).

Nonpharmaceutical Interventions

Currently, the therapeutic strategies employed to deal with COVID-19 are only supportive, and prevention aimed at reducing transmission is another strategy. On January 23, 2020, the local government of Wuhan announced the

Table 5.2 Common and potential treatment options of COVID-19.

Classes	Drugs	Action mode	Target diseases	Reference
Anti-viral	Lopinavir/Ritonavir	Protease inhibitors	HIV/AIDS, SARS, MERS	[73,74]
	Ribavirin	Synthetic guanosine nucleoside	HCV, SARS, MERS	[77,78]
	Arbidol	Broad-spectrum antiviral compound	Influenza virus	[86,87]
	Remdesivir	Nucleotide analogue prodrug	A wide array of RNA virus including Ebola	[54,89,91,92]
	Oseltamivir	Neuraminidase inhibitor	Influenza virus	[94,95]
	Sofosbuvir	Nucleotide Inhibitor	Hepatitis C	[93]
	Nafamostat	Synthetic serine protease inhibitor	MERS, Ebola	[96,97]
	Favipiravir	Nucleoside analog	Ebola, Influenza A(H1N1)	[98,99]
	Nitazoxanide	Antiprotozoal agent	A wide range of viruses including human/animal coronaviruses	[100,101]
Anti-malarial	Chloroquine phosphate	9-aminoquinolin	Malaria, Autoimmune disease	[81,82]
Anti-biotic	Teicoplanin	Glycopeptide antibiotic	Gram-positive infections	[112,113]
	Ivermectin	Broad-spectrum anti-parasitic compound	Chikungunya virus and other Alphaviruses, Parasitic infection	[114,–116]
Herbal treatments	Chinese traditional medicine like ShuFengJieDu Capsules, Lianhuaqngwen Capsule, Huangqi, Gancao, Fangfeng, Baizhu, Jinyinhua, and Lianqiao.		Upper respiratory tract infection including Influenza virus	[105–108,110]

suspension of public transport services, and closed airports, railway stations, and highways in the city. Since then, many other cities have also begun to regulate traffic.[117] Transportation quarantine has been comprehensively strengthened in passenger stations and other public places, and temperature tests have been carried out to screen for potential cases of COVID-19. In addition, strict monitoring measures have been put in place in various regions for returnees, especially those returning from Hubei province or with suspected exposure to the infection. The Chinese government has also employed numerous other coercive measures to limit population mobility, such as canceling public gatherings, closing schools, encouraging remote work, and extending the Chinese Spring Festival holidays.[23] The Chinese government attached great importance to the COVID-19 outbreak and invested a large amount of manpower and funds for the purchase of medical equipment, drugs, and protective equipment, and fully implement medical treatment.[118] Rapidly sharing scientific information is an effective means of reducing public panic about COVID-19.[119] However, the internet also has the potential for the dissemination of misinformation,[120] and governments should be responsible for providing accurate information and clarifying 'fake news' to help the public to deal with this new infection.

Routine, long-term implementation of some of the measures to interrupt or reduce the spread of SARS-CoV-2 might be difficult. However, many simple and low-cost interventions, such as handwashing,[121,122] may reduce the transmission of epidemic-causing respiratory viruses. Wearing masks as a public health intervention may also help break the transmission link with apparently healthy infectious sources.[123–125] At present, for the public, the most direct and effective way to prevent the spread of the disease is to take protective measures, including improving personal hygiene, wearing a medical mask, having enough rest, maintaining ventilation, and avoiding crowds.

Discussion

Coronaviruses have been associated with several outbreaks of infectious disease in humans, including SARS in 2002–2003 and MERS in 2012. According to the WHO, a total of 8,098 people worldwide became sick with SARS during the 2003 outbreak, 774 of whom died. After the SARS outbreak, MERS became the second coronavirus to cause a serious global public health crisis. From 2012 to 2018, the WHO recorded 2,220 laboratory-confirmed cases, resulting in at least 790 deaths.[126] According to the current statistics, the number of COVID-19 infections and deaths far exceeds that of SARS and MERS and is still increasing. The reservoir host of the 2003 SARS virus was thought to be the Asian civet (*Paguma larvata*). The focal point of host-to-human transmission was thought to be the live animal market in Guangdong province in China, much like the ongoing COVID-19 outbreak.[127] The COVID-19 outbreak is another reminder of the ability of viral spill-over from animals to cause severe disease in humans. While it is unclear whether the Huanan seafood market is the source of the current outbreak, a total ban on the illegal wildlife trade is imminent.

The epidemic situation in China has improved. As this is a sudden and new infectious disease, many limitations, such as the lack of administrative capacity, insufficient financial support, low professional quality of some personnel, and inadequate equipment, as well as other inadequacies of the national disease control system, have seriously affected the effective control of COVID-19.[128] To modernize the disease control system in the future, it is necessary to establish sound public health laws and regulations, and form a disease control system in line with the national conditions, so that it can play a timely and effective role in any future infectious disease outbreak.[129]

The SARS-CoV-2 epidemic continues. In the last few months, substantial progress has been made in pathogen monitoring, identifying sources, basic etiology, and clinical treatment. The Chinese government has taken a series of timely and effective measures to contain the spread of the epidemic in China. However, the global situation is very serious, and numerous questions remain unanswered. It will take the combined efforts of all the countries in the world for the epidemic to ultimately subside. However, the coronaviruses identified to date might be only the tip of the iceberg, and other novel and severe zoonotic events may yet occur. Therefore, close monitoring and vigilance remain a top priority for health workers and health authorities. We are not only dealing with the current crisis, but also learning from this experience, so as to establish an effective emergency response system to prevent similar crises in the future.

Acknowledgments

This work was funded by the National Natural Science Foundation of China (81701144 and 81670567), and Zhejiang Provincial Natural Science Foundation of China (No. LED20H190003).

References

1. Li X, et al. Potential of large "first generation" human-to-human transmission of 2019-nCoV. *J Med Virol* 2020;92(4):448–54.
2. Li Q, et al. Early transmission dynamics in Wuhan, China, of novel coronavirus-infected pneumonia. *N Engl J Med* 2020. doi:10.1056/NEJMoa2001316.
3. Wang C, et al. A novel coronavirus outbreak of global health concern. *Lancet (London, England)* 2020;395(10223):470–3.
4. Lai C-C, et al. Severe acute respiratory syndrome coronavirus 2 (SARS-CoV-2) and coronavirus disease-2019 (COVID-19): the epidemic and the challenges. *Int J Antimicrob Agents* 2020:105924.
5. Gorbalenya, A.E., et al. Severe acute respiratory syndrome-related coronavirus: the species and its viruses – a statement of the Coronavirus Study Group. *Nat Microbiol* 2020. doi:10.1101/2020.02.07.937862
6. Tyrrell DA, Bynoe ML. Cultivation of viruses from a high proportion of patients with colds. *Lancet (London, England)* 1966;1(7428):76–7.
7. Velavan TP, Meyer CG. The COVID-19 epidemic. *Trop Med Int Health* 2020;25(3):278–80.

8. Cui J, Li F, Shi ZL. Origin and evolution of pathogenic coronaviruses. *Nat Rev Microbiol* 2019;17(3):181–92.
9. Woo PC, et al. Discovery of seven novel mammalian and avian coronaviruses in the genus deltacoronavirus supports bat coronaviruses as the gene source of alphacoronavirus and betacoronavirus and avian coronaviruses as the gene source of gammacoronavirus and deltacoronavirus. *J Virol* 2012;86(7):3995–4008.
10. Tang Q, et al. Inferring the hosts of coronavirus using dual statistical models based on nucleotide composition. *Sci Rep* 2015;26(4):243–50.
11. Su S, et al. Epidemiology, genetic recombination, and pathogenesis of coronaviruses. *Trends Microbiol* 2016;24(6):490–502.
12. Forni D, et al. Molecular evolution of human coronavirus genomes. *Trends Microbiol* 2017;25(1):35–48.
13. Lu R, et al. Genomic characterisation and epidemiology of 2019 novel coronavirus: implications for virus origins and receptor binding. *Lancet (London, England)* 2020;395(10224):565–74.
14. Zhou P, et al. A pneumonia outbreak associated with a new coronavirus of probable bat origin. *Nature* 2020. doi:10.1038/s41586-020-2012-7.
15. Zu ZY, et al. Coronavirus Disease 2019 (COVID-19): a perspective from China. *Radiology* 2020:200490.
16. Wan Y, et al. Receptor recognition by novel coronavirus from Wuhan: an analysis based on decade-long structural studies of SARS. *J Virol* 2020. doi:10.1128/JVI.00127-20.
17. Huang C, et al. Clinical features of patients infected with 2019 novel coronavirus in Wuhan, China. *Lancet (London, England)* 2020;395(10223):497–506.
18. Al-Hazmi A. Challenges presented by MERS corona virus, and SARS corona virus to global health. *Saudi journal of biological sciences* 2016;23(4):507–11.
19. Wu F, et al. A new coronavirus associated with human respiratory disease in China. *Nature* 2020. doi:10.1038/s41586-020-2008-3.
20. Holshue ML, et al. First case of 2019 Novel Coronavirus in the United States. *N Engl J Med* 2020;382(10):929–36.
21. Carinci F. Covid-19: preparedness, decentralisation, and the hunt for patient zero. *BMJ* 2020;368. doi:10.1136/bmj.m799.
22. Cheng ZJ, Shan J. 2019 Novel coronavirus: where we are and what we know. *Infection* 2020. doi:10.1007/s15010-020-01401-y.
23. Yang Y, Shang W, Rao X. Facing the COVID-19 outbreak: what should we know and what could we do? *J Med Virol* 2020. doi:10.1002/jmv.25720.
24. Zou L, et al. SARS-CoV-2 viral load in upper respiratory specimens of infected patients. *N Engl J Med* 2020. doi:10.1056/NEJMc2001737.
25. Rothe C, et al. Transmission of 2019-nCoV infection from an asymptomatic contact in Germany. *N Engl J Med* 2020;382(10):970–1.
26. Medicine, G.O.o.N.H.C.O.o.S.A.o.T.C., The diagnosis and treatment of novel coronavirus (2019-nCoV) infected pneumonia (Trial Version 6). 2020: p. 1–5.
27. Wang Y, et al. Unique epidemiological and clinical features of the emerging 2019 novel coronavirus pneumonia (COVID-19) implicate special control measures. *J Med Virol* 2020. doi:10.1002/jmv.25748.
28. Wax RS, Christian MD. Practical recommendations for critical care and anesthesiology teams caring for novel coronavirus (2019-nCoV) patients. *Can J Anaesthesia = Journal canadien d'anesthesie* 2020. doi:10.1007/s12630-020-01591-x.
29. Xia J, et al. Evaluation of coronavirus in tears and conjunctival secretions of patients with SARS-CoV-2 infection. *J Med Virol* 2020. doi:10.1002/jmv.25725.

30. Gao QY, Chen YX, Fang JY. 2019 novel coronavirus infection and gastrointestinal tract. *J Digest Dis* 2020. doi:10.1111/1751-2980.12851.
31. Chen H, et al. Clinical characteristics and intrauterine vertical transmission potential of COVID-19 infection in nine pregnant women: a retrospective review of medical records. *Lancet (London, England)* 2020;395(10226):809–15.
32. Schwartz DA. An analysis of 38 pregnant women with COVID-19, their newborn infants, and maternal-fetal transmission of SARS-CoV-2: maternal coronavirus infections and pregnancy outcomes. *Arch Pathol Lab Med* 2020. Epub ahead of print.
33. Guan W-J, et al. Clinical characteristics of coronavirus disease 2019 in China. *N Engl J Med* 2020. doi:10.1056/NEJMoa2002032.
34. Chen C, et al. Analysis of myocardial injury in patients with COVID-19 and association between concomitant cardiovascular diseases and severity of COVID-19. *Zhonghua xin xue guan bing za zhi* 2020;48:E008.
35. Bi, Q., et al., Epidemiology and transmission of COVID-19 in Shenzhen China: analysis of 391 cases and 1,286 of their close contacts. 2020. doi:10.1101/2020.03.03.20028423.
36. Schwartz DA, Graham AL. Potential maternal and infant outcomes from (Wuhan) coronavirus 2019-nCoV infecting pregnant women: lessons from SARS, MERS, and other human coronavirus infections. *Viruses* 2020;12(2):E194.
37. Madinger NE, Greenspoon JS, Ellrodt AG. Pneumonia during pregnancy: has modern technology improved maternal and fetal outcome? *Am J Obstet Gynecol* 1989;161(3):657–62.
38. Gottfredsson M. The Spanish flu in Iceland 1918. Lessons in medicine and history. *Laeknabladid* 2008;94(11):737–45.
39. Rasmussen SA, et al. Coronavirus Disease 2019 (COVID-19) and pregnancy: what obstetricians need to know. *Am J Obstet Gynecol* 2020. doi:10.1016/j.ajog.2020.02.017.
40. Lipsitch M, Swerdlow DL, Finelli L. Defining the epidemiology of Covid-19 – Studies needed. *N Engl J Med* 2020. doi:10.1056/NEJMp2002125.
41. Li X, et al. Transmission dynamics and evolutionary history of 2019-nCoV. *J Med Virol* 2020. doi:10.1002/jmv.25701.
42. Wang H, et al. Phase-adjusted estimation of the number of Coronavirus Disease 2019 cases in Wuhan. *China. Cell Discov* 2020;6:10–10.
43. Roberts MG, Nishiura H. Early estimation of the reproduction number in the presence of imported cases: pandemic influenza H1N1-2009 in New Zealand. *PLoS One* 2011;6(5):e17835.
44. Lipsitch M, et al. Transmission dynamics and control of severe acute respiratory syndrome. *Science (New York, N.Y.)* 2003;300(5627):1966–70.
45. Read, J.M., et al., Novel coronavirus 2019-nCoV: early estimation of epidemiological parameters and epidemic predictions. 2020. doi:10.1101/2020.01.23.20018549.
46. Wu JT, Leung K, Leung GM. Nowcasting and forecasting the potential domestic and international spread of the 2019-nCoV outbreak originating in Wuhan, China: a modelling study. *Lancet (London, England)* 2020;395(10225):689–97.
47. Riley S, et al. Transmission dynamics of the etiological agent of SARS in Hong Kong: impact of public health interventions. *Science (New York, N.Y.)* 2003;300(5627):1961–6.
48. Chowell G, et al. The basic reproductive number of Ebola and the effects of public health measures: the cases of Congo and Uganda. *J Theor Biol* 2004;229(1):119–26.
49. Fang H, Chen J, Hu J. Modelling the SARS epidemic by a lattice-based Monte-Carlo simulation. In: *Proceedings of the Annual International Conference of the IEEE*

Engineering in Medicine and Biology Society; 2005. p. 7470–3. IEEE Engineering in Medicine and Biology Society.

50. Chen N, et al. Epidemiological and clinical characteristics of 99 cases of 2019 novel coronavirus pneumonia in Wuhan, China: a descriptive study. *Lancet* 2020;395(10223):507–13.
51. Wang D, et al. Clinical Characteristics of 138 Hospitalized Patients with 2019 Novel Coronavirus-Infected Pneumonia in Wuhan, China. *JAMA* 2020.
52. Li B, et al. Prevalence and impact of cardiovascular metabolic diseases on COVID-19 in China. *Clin Res Cardiol* 2020. Epub ahead of print.
53. Zhou F, et al. Clinical course and risk factors for mortality of adult inpatients with COVID-19 in Wuhan, China: a retrospective cohort study. *Lancet* 2020.
54. Cascella M, et al. *Features, evaluation and treatment coronavirus (COVID-19)*. Stat-Pearls Publishing Copyright © 2020, StatPearls Publishing LLC.: Treasure Island (FL); 2020.
55. Xu X, et al. Imaging and clinical features of patients with 2019 novel coronavirus SARS-CoV-2. *Eur J Nucl Med Mol Imaging* 2020. Epub ahead of print.
56. Wang Y, et al. Temporal changes of CT findings in 90 patients with COVID-19 pneumonia: a longitudinal study. *Radiology* 2020:200843.
57. Zhou S, et al. CT features of Coronavirus Disease 2019 (COVID-19) pneumonia in 62 patients in Wuhan, China. *AJR Am J Roentgenol* 2020:1–8.
58. Han R, et al. Early clinical and CT manifestations of Coronavirus Disease 2019 (COVID-19) pneumonia. *AJR Am J Roentgenol* 2020:1–6.
59. Li Y, Xia L. Coronavirus Disease 2019 (COVID-19): role of chest CT in diagnosis and management. *AJR Am J Roentgenol* 2020:1–7.
60. Fang Y, et al. Sensitivity of chest CT for COVID-19: comparison to RT-PCR. *Radiology* 2020:200432.
61. Bernheim A, et al. Chest CT findings in Coronavirus Disease-19 (COVID-19): relationship to duration of infection. *Radiology* 2020:200463.
62. Wang Y, et al. Combination of RT-qPCR testing and clinical features for diagnosis of COVID-19 facilitates management of SARS-CoV-2 outbreak. *J Med Virol* 2020. doi:10.1002/jmv.25721.
63. Corman VM, et al. Detection of 2019 novel coronavirus (2019-nCoV) by real-time RT-PCR. *Euro surveillance: bulletin Europeen sur les maladies transmissibles = European communicable disease bulletin* 2020;25(3):2000045.
64. Dai W-C, et al. CT imaging and differential diagnosis of COVID-19. *Canadian Association of Radiologists journal = Journal l'Association canadienne des radiologistes* 2020:846537120913033.
65. Medicine, G.O.o.N.H.C.O.o.S.A.o.T.C., The diagnosis and treatment of novel coronavirus (2019-nCoV) infected pneumonia (Trial Version 5). 2020.52(02): p. 96+95.
66. Li Z, et al. Development and clinical application of a rapid IgM-IgG combined antibody test for SARS-CoV-2 infection diagnosis. *J Med Virol* 2020. doi:10.1002/jmv.25727.
67. She J, et al. 2019 novel coronavirus of pneumonia in Wuhan, China: emerging attack and management strategies. *Clin Transl Med* 2020;9(1):19.
68. Arabi YM, et al. Corticosteroid therapy for critically ill patients with Middle East Respiratory Syndrome. *Am J Respir Crit Care Med* 2018;197(6):757–67.
69. Shang L, et al. On the use of corticosteroids for 2019-nCoV pneumonia. *Lancet* 2020;395(10225):683–4.
70. Zhou W, et al. Potential benefits of precise corticosteroids therapy for severe 2019-nCoV pneumonia. *Signal Transduct Target Ther* 2020;5:18.

71. Xu K, et al. [Management of corona virus disease-19 (COVID-19): the Zhejiang experience]. *Zhejiang Da Xue Fue Bao Yi Xue Ban* 2020;49(1).

72. Pei J, et al. Chicken interferon type I inhibits infectious bronchitis virus replication and associated respiratory illness. *J Interferon Cytokine Res* 2001;21(12):1071–7.

73. Turner RB, et al. Prevention of experimental coronavirus colds with intranasal alpha-2b interferon. *J Infect Dis* 1986;154(3):443–7.

74. Yao TT, et al. A systematic review of lopinavir therapy for SARS coronavirus and MERS coronavirus: a possible reference for coronavirus disease-19 treatment option. *J Med Virol* 2020.

75. Cvetkovic RS, Goa KL. Lopinavir/ritonavir: a review of its use in the management of HIV infection. *Drugs* 2003;63(8):769–802.

76. Lim J, et al. Case of the index patient who caused tertiary transmission of COVID-19 infection in Korea: the application of Lopinavir/Ritonavir for the treatment of COVID-19 infected pneumonia monitored by quantitative RT-PCR. *J Korean Med Sci* 2020;35(6):e79.

77. Cao B, et al. A Trial of Lopinavir-Ritonavir in adults hospitalized with severe Covid-19. *N Engl J Med* 2020.

78. Koren G, et al. Ribavirin in the treatment of SARS: a new trick for an old drug? *CMAJ* 2003;168(10):1289–92.

79. Arabi YM, et al. Ribavirin and interferon therapy for critically ill patients with Middle East Respiratory Syndrome: a multicenter observational study. *Clin Infect Dis* 2019.

80. Morgenstern B, et al. Ribavirin and interferon-beta synergistically inhibit SARS-associated coronavirus replication in animal and human cell lines. *Biochem Biophys Res Commun* 2005;326(4):905–8.

81. Booth CM, et al. Clinical features and short-term outcomes of 144 patients with SARS in the greater Toronto area. *JAMA* 2003;289(21):2801–9.

82. Golden EB, et al. Quinoline-based antimalarial drugs: a novel class of autophagy inhibitors. *Neurosurg Focus* 2015;38(3):E12.

83. Savarino A, et al. Effects of chloroquine on viral infections: an old drug against today's diseases? *Lancet Infect Dis* 2003;3(11):722–7.

84. Gao J, Tian Z, Yang X. Breakthrough: chloroquine phosphate has shown apparent efficacy in treatment of COVID-19 associated pneumonia in clinical studies. *Biosci Trends* 2020;14(1):72–3.

85. Touret F, de Lamballerie X. of chloroquine and COVID-19. *Antiviral Res* 2020;177:104762.

86. Devaux CA, et al. New insights on the antiviral effects of chloroquine against coronavirus: what to expect for COVID-19? *Int J Antimicrob Agents* 2020:105938.

87. Blaising J, Polyak SJ, Pécheur EI. Arbidol as a broad-spectrum antiviral: an update. *Antiviral Res* 2014;107:84–94.

88. Kadam RU, Wilson IA. Structural basis of influenza virus fusion inhibition by the antiviral drug Arbidol. *Proc Natl Acad Sci U S A* 2017;114(2):206–14.

89. Deng L, et al. Arbidol combined with LPV/r versus LPV/r alone against Corona Virus Disease 2019: a retrospective cohort study. *J Infect* 2020. pii: S0163-4453(20)30113-4.

90. Tchesnokov EP, et al. Mechanism of inhibition of Ebola Virus RNA-dependent RNA polymerase by Remdesivir. *Viruses* 2019;11(4).

91. Martinez MA. Compounds with therapeutic potential against novel respiratory 2019 coronavirus. *Antimicrob Agents Chemother* 2020. pii: AAC.00399-20.

92. Wang M, et al. Remdesivir and chloroquine effectively inhibit the recently emerged novel coronavirus (2019-nCoV) in vitro. *Cell Res* 2020;30(3):269–71.

93. Khan S, et al. The emergence of a novel coronavirus (SARS-CoV-2), their biology and therapeutic options. *J Clin Microbiol* 2020. pii: JCM.00187-20.

94. Elfiky AA. Anti-HCV, nucleotide inhibitors, repurposing against COVID-19. *Life Sci* 2020;248:117477.

95. McQuade B, Blair M. Influenza treatment with oseltamivir outside of labeled recommendations. *Am J Health Syst Pharm* 2015;72(2):112–16.

96. Jefferson T, et al. Oseltamivir for influenza in adults and children: systematic review of clinical study reports and summary of regulatory comments. *BMJ* 2014;348:g2545.

97. Yamamoto M, et al. Identification of Nafamostat as a potent inhibitor of Middle East Respiratory Syndrome coronavirus S protein-mediated membrane fusion using the split-protein-based cell-cell fusion assay. *Antimicrob Agents Chemother* 2016;60(11):6532–9.

98. Nishimura H, Yamaya M. A synthetic Serine Protease inhibitor, Nafamostat Mesilate, is a drug potentially applicable to the treatment of Ebola Virus disease. *Tohoku J Exp Med* 2015;237(1):45–50.

99. Goldhill DH, et al. The mechanism of resistance to favipiravir in influenza. *Proc Natl Acad Sci U S A* 2018;115(45):11613–18.

100. Guedj J, et al. Antiviral efficacy of favipiravir against Ebola virus: a translational study in cynomolgus macaques. *PLoS Med* 2018;15(3):e1002535.

101. Rossignol JF. Nitazoxanide: a first-in-class broad-spectrum antiviral agent. *Antiviral Res* 2014;110:94–103.

102. Rossignol JF. Nitazoxanide, a new drug candidate for the treatment of Middle East respiratory syndrome coronavirus. *J Infect Public Health* 2016;9(3):227–30.

103. Sun ML, et al. [Inhibitors of RAS might be a good choice for the therapy of COVID-19 pneumonia]. *Zhonghua Jie He He Hu Xi Za Zhi* 2020;43:E014.

104. Shanmugaraj B, et al. Perspectives on monoclonal antibody therapy as potential therapeutic intervention for Coronavirus Disease-19 (COVID-19). *Asian Pac J Allergy Immunol* 2020.

105. Cunningham AC, Goh HP, Koh D. Treatment of COVID-19: old tricks for new challenges. *Crit Care* 2020;24(1):91.

106. Li Y, et al. Anti-inflammatory effects of Shufengjiedu capsule for upper respiratory infection via the ERK pathway. *Biomed Pharmacother* 2017;94:758–66.

107. Ji S, et al. Unique synergistic antiviral effects of Shufeng Jiedu Capsule and oseltamivir in influenza A viral-induced acute exacerbation of chronic obstructive pulmonary disease. *Biomed Pharmacother* 2020;121:109652.

108. Ding Y, et al. The Chinese prescription lianhuaqingwen capsule exerts anti-influenza activity through the inhibition of viral propagation and impacts immune function. *BMC Complement Altern Med* 2017;17(1):130.

109. Duan ZP, et al. Natural herbal medicine Lianhuaqingwen capsule anti-influenza A (H1N1) trial: a randomized, double blind, positive controlled clinical trial. *Chin Med J (Engl)* 2011;124(18):2925–33.

110. Luo H, et al. Can Chinese medicine be used for prevention of Corona virus disease 2019 (COVID-19)? A review of historical classics, research evidence and current prevention programs. *Chin J Integr Med* 2020;26(4):243–50.

111. Lu H. Drug treatment options for the 2019-new coronavirus (2019-nCoV). *Biosci Trends* 2020;14(1):69–71.

112. Colson P, Raoult D. Fighting viruses with antibiotics: an overlooked path. *Int J Antimicrob Agents* 2016;48(4):349–52.

113. Shea KW, Cunha BA. Teicoplanin. *Med Clin North Am* 1995;79(4):833–44.

114. Baron SA, et al. Teicoplanin: an alternative drug for the treatment of coronavirus COVID-19? *Int J Antimicrob Agents* 2020:105944.

115. Varghese FS, et al. Discovery of berberine, abamectin and ivermectin as antivirals against chikungunya and other alphaviruses. *Antiviral Res* 2016;126:117–24.

116. Laing R, Gillan V, Devaney E. Ivermectin – Old drug. *New Tricks? Trends Parasitol* 2017;33(6):463–72.

117. Lee YJ, Lee C. Ivermectin inhibits porcine reproductive and respiratory syndrome virus in cultured porcine alveolar macrophages. *Arch Virol* 2016;161(2):257–68.

118. Lau H, et al. The positive impact of lockdown in Wuhan on containing the COVID-19 outbreak in China. *J Travel Med* 2020. pii: taaa037, Epub ahead of print.

119. Wang W, Tang J, Wei F. Updated understanding of the outbreak of 2019 novel coronavirus (2019-nCoV) in Wuhan, China. *J Med Virol* 2020;92(4):441–7.

120. Song P, Karako T. COVID-19: real-time dissemination of scientific information to fight a public health emergency of international concern. *Biosci Trends* 2020. doi:10.5582/bst.2020.01056.

121. The L. COVID-19: fighting panic with information. *Lancet (London, England)* 2020;395(10224):537–537.

122. Rabie T, Curtis V. Handwashing and risk of respiratory infections: a quantitative systematic review. *Trop Med Int Health* 2006;11(3):258–67.

123. Mbakaya BC, Lee PH, Lee RLT. Hand hygiene intervention strategies to reduce diarrhoea and respiratory infections among schoolchildren in developing countries: a systematic review. *Int J Environ Res Public Health* 2017;14(4):371.

124. Cowling BJ, et al. Facemasks and hand hygiene to prevent influenza transmission in households: a cluster randomized trial. *Ann Intern Med* 2009;151(7):437–46.

125. MacIntyre CR, Chughtai AA. Facemasks for the prevention of infection in health-care and community settings. *BMJ* 2015;350 h694-h694.

126. Leung CC, Lam TH, Cheng KK. Mass masking in the COVID-19 epidemic: people need guidance. *Lancet (London, England)* 2020. doi:10.1016/S0140-6736(20)30520-1.

127. Al-Omari A, et al. MERS coronavirus outbreak: implications for emerging viral infections. *Diagn Microbiol Infect Dis* 2019;93(3):265–85.

128. Peeri NC, et al. The SARS, MERS and novel coronavirus (COVID-19) epidemics, the newest and biggest global health threats: what lessons have we learned? *Int J Epidemiol* 2020:dyaa033.

129. Wang X, Zhang X, He J. Challenges to the system of reserve medical supplies for public health emergencies: reflections on the outbreak of the severe acute respiratory syndrome coronavirus 2 (SARS-CoV-2) epidemic in China. *Biosci Trends* 2020;14(1):3–8.

6   Authoritarianism, Outbreaks, and Information Politics

Matthew M. Kavanagh

Are autocratic states such as China better equipped than their more democratic counterparts to respond to disease outbreaks? On Dec. 31, 2019, China alerted WHO to an outbreak of pneumonia of unknown cause in the city of Wuhan in Hubei province. The epidemic quickly spread, with cases of a novel coronavirus (2019-nCoV) confirmed throughout China and elsewhere in Asia, Europe, North America, and Australia. The Chinese Government's forceful response has drawn praise from global health officials. Scholars and health leaders have long debated whether democracy improves, hinders, or is immaterial for public health.[1-3] Does this signal an authoritarian advantage in tackling outbreaks?

On the surface, the power of authoritarianism is on display in China's response to 2019-nCoV. The Huanan seafood market suspected as the outbreak source was closed and decontaminated within a day of the announcement. Within 3 days of confirmed human-to-human transmission, with cases rising and the world's largest mass travel event underway for the lunar new year Spring Festival, the Chinese Government imposed an unprecedented *cordon sanitaire*. Movement of more than 50 million people across Hubei province was rapidly restricted, curtailing transportation inside cities and outbound transportation by air, train, and bus.[4] Authorities halted Spring Festival celebrations in Beijing and restricted movement into other major cities. Two 1,000-bed hospitals were built within days. These moves reflect a level of control only available to authoritarian governments. WHO officials have congratulated China for setting "a new standard for outbreak response."[5]

Yet, time is key to controlling outbreaks; getting good information and acting on it rapidly can halt outbreaks before they need emergency measures. The early history of the 2019-nCoV outbreak raises questions about whether this situation is an example of beneficial autocracy.

For Amartya Sen, authoritarian states face serious challenges in information and accountability.[6] Governments in closed political systems, without open media and opposition parties, struggle to receive accurate information in a timely manner and to convey urgent information to the public. Governments can be the victims of their own propaganda, because the country's political institutions provide incentives to local officials to avoid sharing bad news with their central bosses and await instructions before acting.

Information politics in China undermined a rapid response to the 2019-nCoV outbreak. Health-care workers suspected an outbreak in early December 2019,[7] but information with which the public might have taken preventive measures was suppressed, and communication channels that might have alerted senior officials to the growing threat were shut down.[8] Police detained a clinician and seven other people posting reports on 2019-nCoV, threatening punishment for spreading so-called rumors. Social media was censored; a preliminary analysis of Weibo and WeChat published on China's biggest online platform[9] showed outbreak discussions were nearly non-existent through much of January 2020, until the Chinese Government changed its official stance on Jan. 20, 2020.

Through much of January 2020, the Wuhan Municipal Health Commission reported no evidence of human-to-human transmission, no infection among health workers, that severe cases of disease caused by 2019-nCoV infection were confined to those with underlying conditions and older people, and that the Huanan seafood market was the source.[11] Reports in *The Lancet*[7] and *New England Journal of Medicine*,[12] however, show that half of patients admitted to intensive-care units were aged 25–49 years, and two-thirds had no underlying illnesses. Human-to-human transmission and health-worker infection were evident before the Chinese Government made an announcement.[12] This information either did not make it to authorities or the public was misinformed. The mayor of Wuhan has said publicly that not only was information not revealed in a timely manner but also they did not use information effectively.[10] By the time quarantine went into effect on Jan. 23, 2020, 5 million people had left the city of Wuhan for holiday travel.[10] Outbreaks were subsequently reported throughout China.

Without open media and an opposition to check on bureaucratic hierarchy, knowledge from the front lines of the 2019-nCoV outbreak did not reach Beijing. Weeks into the outbreak, leaders were forced to publicly threaten that officials withholding information "will be nailed on the pillar of shame for eternity."[4]

Is there an authoritarian advantage in disease response? It seems that authoritarian information politics inhibited a rapid response to the 2019-nCoV outbreak in China, which could have limited the crisis. It is not yet clear if the extraordinary cordons and influx of resources enabled by autocratic rule will prove a successful public health strategy. Yet, in building capacity to prevent, detect, and respond to outbreaks, democratic openness and competitive politics seem more asset than inadequacy.

References

1. Ruger JP. Democracy and health. *QJM* 2005; 98: 299–304.
2. Gerring J, Thacker SC, Alfaro R. Democracy and human development. *J Polit* 2012; 74: 1–17.

3. Bollyky TJ, Templin T, Cohen M, Schoder D, Dieleman JL, Wigley S. The relationships between democratic experience, adult health, and cause-specific mortality in 170 countries between 1980 and 2016: an observational analysis. *Lancet* 2019; 393: 1628–40.

4. Qin A, Wang V. Wuhan, center of coronavirus outbreak, is being cut off by Chinese authorities. *New York Times.* Jan 24, 2020. www.nytimes.com/2020/01/22/world/asia/china-coronavirus-travel.html (accessed Feb 10, 2020).

5. WHO. WHO Emergencies Coronavirus Emergency Committee Second Meeting. Jan 30, 2020. www.who.int/docs/default-source/ coronaviruse/transcripts/ihr-emergency-committee-for-pneumonia-due-to-the-novel-coronavirus-2019-ncov-press-briefing-transcript-30012020. pdf?sfvrsn=c9463ac1_2 (accessed Feb 10, 2020).

6. Sen A. Development as freedom. Oxford: Oxford University Press, 1999.

7. Huang C, Wang Y, Li X, et al. Clinical features of patients infected with 2019 novel coronavirus in Wuhan, China. *Lancet* 2020; published online Jan 24. https://doi.org/10.1016/S0140-6736(20)30183-5.

8. Yuan L. China silences critics over deadly virus outbreak. *New York Times.* Jan 25, 2020. www.nytimes.com/2020/01/22/health/virus-corona. html (accessed Feb 11, 2020).

9. SINA. The mystery of the Wuhan epidemic: evidence from reptiles and text analysis. Jan 27, 2020. https://cj.sina.com.cn/articles/view/1961718870/74 ed745601900 pcsq?autocallup=no (accessed Feb 11, 2020).

10. Zhenhua L. Wuhan Mayor offers to resign over coronavirus response. *Caixin* 2020; published online Jan 28. www.caixinglobal.com/2020-01-28/wuhan-mayor-offers-resignation-over-coronavirus-response-101508899.html (accessed Feb 10, 2020).

11. Wuhan Municipal Health Commission. Questions and answers on pneumonia epidemic and new coronavirus infection. [In Chinese.] Jan 14, 2020. http://wjw.wuhan.gov.cn/front/web/ showDetail/2020011509040 (accessed Feb 11, 2020).

12. Li Q, Guan X, Wu P, et al. Early transmission dynamics in Wuhan, China, of novel coronavirus-infected pneumonia. *N Engl J Med* 2020; published online Jan 29. https://doi.org/10.1056/NEJMoa2001316.

7 China's Diplomacy and Changing the COVID-19 Narrative

Raj Verma

Introduction

On 11 March 2020, COVID-19 (a disease caused by the SARS-CoV-2 virus or novel coronavirus) was declared a pandemic by the World Health Organization (WHO). Although the exact source of SARS-CoV-2 has not been identified, reports suggest that it spread from a so-called wet market, or live animal market, in Wuhan, Hubei Province, China.[1] As of 22 April 2020, SARS-COV2 has infected more than 2.5 million people and killed more than 180,000. The United States has the highest death toll and has more infected people than China. Italy and Spain have also reported more deaths than China.[2] COVID-19 has devastated the global economy, and, according to the International Monetary Fund, the global economy is undergoing the worst economic downturn since the global depression in the 1930s, with a majority of the countries forecast to experience economic recession.

This chapter analyses why China wants to change the COVID-19 narrative. It explores both domestic and external factors to explicate the phenomenon. It also discusses the various measures undertaken by China to change the narrative. The chapter proceeds as follows. The second section discusses why China has been blamed for the global spread of COVID-19. This is followed by a discussion of the measures adopted by China to change the COVID-19 narrative. The final section discusses the rationale for changing the narrative. The conclusion summarizes the argument.

Is China to Blame?

Globally, it is a common belief that the Chinese government is to blame for the spread of COVID-19. China has been associated with the origin of the pandemic. The Chinese government has been criticized for poor regulation of animal markets. In 2007, infectious disease experts argued that "the presence of a large reservoir of SARS-CoV-2-like viruses in horseshoe bats, together with the culture of eating exotic mammals in southern China, is a time bomb. The possibility of the re-emergence of SARS and other novel viruses from animals or laboratories and therefore the need for preparedness should not be ignored."[3] In March 2019, Chinese experts warned that it is "highly likely that future SARS- or MERS-like coronavirus outbreaks will originate from bats, and there is an increased probability that this will occur in China."[4] It seems these warnings were well ignored.

China has been chastised by various countries, especially the United States, for suppressing information and not taking necessary measures that could have helped in controlling the spread of and/or eradicating the disease in the earlier stages. First, local officials in Wuhan silenced whistle blowers. Eight doctors from Wuhan Central Hospital, including Li Wenliang (an ophthalmologist), were given "education" and "criticism" and warned by the Wuhan police against passing along information about the virus. Second, local Wuhan officials thwarted the first two teams sent by China's National Health Commission from obtaining evidence that COVID-19 could spread through human infection. Third, the Wuhan municipal health commission (WHC) prevented expert groups sent by the national and Hubei provincial health commissions from having an open conversation with doctors in the infectious disease wards and emergency care. This prevented experts from gathering valuable insights on the virus, such as the number of health-care workers infected with the virus. Fourth, the WHC used its own restrictive criteria and communicated these to hospital officials. On 11 January 2020, the WHC announced that there were zero new cases. Such announcements were made on a daily basis, which led to both a false sense of security among the people and the medical staff, and a steep rise in infections in medical personnel.[5]

In a report published by South China Morning Post on 13 March 2020, Yang Gonghuan, former Deputy Director of China's Centre for Disease Control and Prevention (China CDC) says that after the SARS outbreak in 2002–2003, China spent 730 million renminbi to build an early reporting and warning system for the US Centers for Disease Control (CDC). However, according to Yang and leaked documents from the Wuhan central hospital, the early warning system was not activated in December 2019 when the outbreak occurred. Yang asserts that COVID-19 could have been prevented if the system had been operational.[6]

China informed the WHO on 31 December 2019 but kept its citizens in the dark despite other countries' reporting of infections. Although the first symptom of infection from SARS-CoV-2 was evident in Wuhan on 1 December 2019, it was only on 23 January 2020 that China acted decisively. This is despite the fact that, by 7 January 2020, China's top leadership, including President Xi, had been fully informed about the virus outbreak.

By 23 January 2020, approximately 5 million people had already left Wuhan. China did not ban international flights and, although checks were conducted on outbound passengers for symptoms, these were inadequate because it takes between five days to two weeks for the symptoms to emerge in the infected person. A travel ban would have prevented the global spread of the disease. On the contrary, Beijing severely criticized countries that imposed a travel ban on people coming from China. According to a study conducted by the University of Southampton in the United Kingdom, if China had acted three weeks earlier, infectious cases could have been reduced by 95 percent.

On 19 March 2020, U.S. President Donald Trump blamed China for the virus outbreak. Trump said, "The world is paying a very big price for what they did . . . . It could have been stopped right where it came from, China."[7] He stated that Washington would have been able to act faster if Beijing had shared the information regarding SARS-CoV-2 with the United States. Trump has repeatedly referred to SARS-CoV-2 as the "Chinese virus."[8] Some U.S. officials have also used the terms "Wuhan virus," "China virus," and "Kung-Flu," which have racist connotations. SARS-CoV-2 has led to xenophobia and racist attacks not only against Chinese citizens but also against those who appear to be Chinese.

China's Attempts at Changing the COVID Narrative

President Xi in his speech on 3 February 2020 (featured on state television and published on 8 February 2020 in the Communist Party of China's [CPC's] bimonthly *Qiushi* and also other official mouthpieces) indicated his desire to win international support and understanding through diplomacy and propaganda.[9] Xi also issued a directive to China's state media to publish reports that put China's fight against COVID-19 in a positive light. China's propaganda apparatus has been working tirelessly to change the COVID-19 narrative.

In an initial phase of this propaganda apparatus, the Chinese government and some parts of China's social media have launched a collaborative campaign questioning the origins of SARS-CoV-2 after a Chinese government official, in the first week of March 2020, asked media not to report that the virus originated in China. This is despite the fact that the origin of the virus was never in dispute, even in the Chinese state media and Ministry for Foreign Affairs (MOFA).[10] The Xinhua News *Agency, Global Times, China Daily, People's Daily*, and China Global Television Network, along with local and provincial media outlets, have published reports and editorials questioning the origin and cause of the virus. They have denied that the virus originated in China and stated that it originated in the United States. In a press conference on 27 February 2020, Zhong Nanshan, a scientist leading the Chinese government's response to COVID-19, raised the eyebrows of the global community when he stated that SARS-CoV-2 may not have originated in China.[11] An email sent by the Chinese embassy in Australia for foreign journalists stated, "journalists are politicizing the coronavirus by suggesting it originated in China."[12] On 9 March 2020, China's MOFA commented on Twitter that "China's endeavor to combating the epidemic has bought time for int'l preparedness."[13]

In fact, China has turned the tables on the United States and has become much more offensive in externalizing the blame. In an astonishing volte-face, Chinese diplomats, as well as the spokesperson for MOFA have engaged in an outright campaign of denial and misinformation. In one such move, the government authorized a campaign to blame the United States military for bringing the virus into China during the Military World Games held in Wuhan in October 2019.

Continuing this disinformation campaign, China's diplomatic corps has conducted more than 400 interviews and written more than 300 articles on SARS- CoV-2.[14] On 22 March 2020, Lijian Zhao, the spokesperson and deputy director of the information department at MOFA, commented on Twitter that the "US CDC admitted some COVID19 patients were misdiagnosed as flu during 2019 flu season. 34 million infected and 20,000 died. If COVID19 began last September, & US has been lack of testing ability, how many would have been infected? US should find out when patient zero appeared."[15] Furthermore, Hua Chunying, director of the information department at MOFA, wrote on Twitter that 36 million U.S. citizens were infected by flu and 22,000 died. More importantly, she also stated (out of context) that the U.S. CDC admitted that some of the cases were COVID-19.[16] Later, China cited (out of context) Giuseppe Remuzzi, director of the Mario Negri Institute for Pharmacological Research in Milan, to claim that SARS CoV-2 originated in Lombardy, Italy, in October 2019.[17] China also expelled 13 journalists from U.S. media outlets, such as the *Wall Street Journal*, the *New York Times*, and the *Washington Post*, as demands grew for greater transparency in combating COVID-19.[18]

However, none of the media outlets, Chinese officials, or netizens have provided an explanation to substantiate their hypotheses. A spanner in the works was thrown by China's ambassador to the United States, Cui Tiankai. In an interview on 22 March 2020, Ambassador Cui reaffirmed his statement made on 9 February 2020 that SARS-CoV-2 was not developed in a United States military laboratory. Scientists have also categorically stated that the virus has natural origins, and epidemiologists have confirmed that the virus originated from China, further undermining the claims made by Chinese officials and media.[19]

In a second initiative to place China in a positive light, President Xi has declared victory over SARS-CoV-2. Reports indicate that no new infections are being reported in China, and the country is highlighting this as its achievement. On the contrary, Chinese sources are reporting imported cases of COVID-19.[20] China has also zealously highlighted the struggles faced by the United States and European countries, with Beijing and Chinese citizens criticizing the shortcomings and inefficiencies of Western governments, especially the United States, in tackling COVID-19. To this end, China quoted the director general of the WHO, who, on 13 March 2020, stated that Europe was now the global epicenter of COVID-19. China also reported that there were fewer cases during the peak than were being reported outside China.

In a third effort to place the country in a positive light, China has provided medical assistance and vital health equipment, and has been willing to share its expertise with various countries in tackling the pandemic. China announced that it will provide aid to 82 countries, the WHO, and the African Union. The country has also sent medical aid, such as ventilators and other intensive care unit (ICU) facilities, masks, gloves and testing kits, medicines, and portable colour ultrasound equipment. The government sent additional medical experts and offered training to countries across the globe. Chinese media and MOFA officials have left no stone unturned to cultivate in these countries gratitude towards China. In addition to offering medical aid across the world, China also donated US$20 million to the WHO and provided a low interest loan of US$500 million to be paid over 10 years to Sri Lanka to combat COVID-19.[21]

In addition to direct aid from the Chinese government, Chinese philanthropic foundations and companies have joined in giving aid. The Alibaba Foundation and the Jack Ma Foundation have both pledged to donate medical equipment (1,000 medical-use face shields and protective suits, 100,000 masks, and 20,000 testing kits) to all 54 countries in Africa. The two foundations have already provided medical assistance to France, Spain, Italy, Belgium, Ukraine, Iran, Iraq, South Korea, and Japan, and the Jack Ma Foundation also announced a donation of 1,000,000 masks and 500,000 testing kits to the United States. The Jack Ma Foundation also published a handbook to help countries fight COVID-19. Huawei has also provided testing kits and masks to Italy, Ireland, Spain, Poland, the Czech Republic, and Holland. Furthermore, Oppo, Xiaomi, and other Chinese smartphone companies have also sent thousands of masks to European countries.

Why Changing the COVID-19 Narrative Is Important for China

There are three reasons why China is trying to change the narrative regarding COVID-19. The first is China's quest for great power status. Under President Xi, China wants to be recognized as a great power (some experts say a superpower) and has launched the ambitious trillion-dollar Belt and Road Initiative and multilateral financial institutions, such as the Asian Infrastructure Investment Bank and the Silk Road Fund. The country has become a key proponent of globalization, provided financial assistance and loans, and built infrastructure in more than 100 countries. It is also trying to change the rules of the game, have a bigger voice in decision-making in global institutions, and become a rule maker rather than a rule taker.

The stakes are very high for China. The Chinese leadership is afraid that the virus outbreak may force the world to focus on China's less developed domestic conditions, environmental degradation, intrusive and malfunctioning government, and poor public health-care system. These issues might change global perceptions regarding China. China's leadership is trying to shift the blame for its initial botched response to COVID-19, which highlights the shortcomings of its political system—structural flaws and the government's incompetence. China is also concerned that it might be blamed for the ensuing global recession, which would sound a death knell for China's reputation. Such an outcome has the potential to shift manufacturing and trade away from China, which will adversely affect its economy and its aspirations for great/superpower status.

The Chinese government's tactic of shifting blame during a crisis is not new. There are numerous instances in which China has used nationalism to not only shift the blame but also to galvanize the Chinese public in times of crisis. During the Cold War, Chinese propaganda targeted the United States as an imperial power. The recent targeting of the United States can be traced to the geopolitical struggle between the two countries in the Asia-Pacific. For instance, the Chinese government drummed up nationalism in the United States–China trade war, maintaining that the United States, especially President Donald Trump, is responsible for it. In another example of Chinese propaganda, an article published in the *People's Daily* labelled the United States as the "Enemy of the world."[22] China claims that the United States wants to curtail China's rise because it envisages a rising and economically and militarily strong China as a threat to its hegemony. However, as much as the Chinese government blames the United States for its struggles, it never informed its citizens regarding its own violation of World Trade Organization rules, such as providing subsidies and tax rebates to enterprises geared towards exports, or the practice of dumping and manipulating its currency, among others.

China's provision of aid to countries helps to portray China as a Good Samaritan, a responsible and reliable partner, and to change the narrative on COVID-19. China is using COVID-19 to portray itself as an essential global power. It is a manufacturing powerhouse and the largest producer of medical equipment such as masks, gloves, ventilators, and ICU facilities. It has the capability and the capacity to provide global public goods, especially when the developed West, led by the United States, has failed to do so. China is concerned about its global image and standing in world affairs. Consequently, the country is using COVID-19 to frame its global assistance concerning the pandemic to push President Xi's rhetoric of a "community of common destiny," part of the country's Belt and Road Initiative narrative.

Additionally, China is reciprocating aid because it received substantial aid from international organizations and 80 countries, including the European Union (EU), in the initial stages of the virus outbreak. Pakistan, Japan, Iran, Egypt, Cambodia, Brunei, Belarus and international organizations, such as the United Nations International Children's Emergency Fund donated disinfectants, gloves, protective suits, and face masks to China. The United States pledged to spend US$100 million to help China and other countries to combat SARS-CoV-2 and sent 17.8 tons of medical equipment to China. The private sector in the United States also donated hundreds of millions of dollars to China. The EU sent more than 50 tons of medical supplies to China and also allocated e10 million for research to combat SARS-CoV-2. The Japanese government and private sector have also sent medical supplies and made monetary contributions to China. Hence, the Chinese government and Chinese enterprises have provided medical assistance and personal protective equipment to numerous countries (already discussed). China's actions are based on a quote from the Book of Songs: "You throw a peach to me, I give you a white jade for friendship." The quote signifies the country's traditional virtue of repaying kindness with greater goodwill.

The need to maintain the CPC's regime legitimacy also plays a role in the Chinese government's efforts to change the COVID-19 narrative. President Xi's legitimacy is built on technocratic competence. The outbreak has the potential to seriously dent his personal legacy. Chinese citizens have criticized not only the local and provincial governments in Wuhan and Hubei, but also the central government led by President Xi for their initial mishandling of the virus outbreak. Xi's credibility as a populist leader has been diminished by his absence from the frontlines in the battle against COVID-19. The death of Dr. Li Wenliang (who has been declared a national hero), led to an outpouring of national grief, anger, mistrust, and criticism of the CPC and President Xi, even from executives, academics, and prominent officials. People were incensed with the government's disingenuity about Dr. Li's death and the extent to which the government was willing to exert control.

Dr. Li's death became the top trending topic on Chinese social media with an estimated 1.5 billion views. Since then, it has become an issue that has both galvanized the public and prompted further mishandling by government figures. There were calls on social media platforms in China for more freedom of speech, demands for the Wuhan government to apologize, and calls for a law to protect whistle-blowers (all the hashtags were censored quickly). On the eve of President Xi's visit to Wuhan, on 7 March 2020, Wang Zhonglin—Wuhan's top leader—announced that he planned to offer "'gratitude education' for residents of the city, who should 'thank the General Secretary, and thank the Chinese Communist Party.'"[23] Wang's statement led to intense anger across Chinese social media. Because of the wave of recriminations and criticisms, Wang's remarks were deleted from the Wuhan government's WeChat account and the CPC affiliated newspaper *Changjiang Daily*, where the article was published. Wang's remarks came a day after a video emerged in which Wuhan residents in high-rise buildings yelled, "Fake! Fake! Everything is fake!"[24] at Vice Premier Sun Chunlan, who was touring the area. It is likely that the CPC's botched response in the initial stages of COVID-19 may have impacted its support among the urban middle class.

Criticism has come not only from China's citizens but those within the CPC as well. According to a report published by Radio Free Asia, President

Xi is under tremendous pressure from within the CPC for his handling of SARS-CoV-2. The report states that an open letter has been circulating on WeChat since the second week of March 2020 calling for an emergency expanded meeting of the politburo to discuss "Xi's issues" and to decide whether he should step down from his posts. It has been difficult to trace the origins of the letter. Citing Wu Qian, former professor at Tsinghua University, the report says the letter emerged after the disappearance of Ren Zhiqiang, a social media star and property tycoon who criticized the government's response to COVID-19. Citing Wu, it also states that there is growing divergence between Xi and second generation "princelings" in the CPC who are disappointed and discontent with Xi because of Ren Zhiqiang's disappearance.[25]

The brewing discontent has prompted the party-state to leave no stone unturned to disassociate COVID-19 from Wuhan and China. If China's reputation is affected, it will lead to a decrease in foreign investments. China may no longer be a part of the global/regional supply chains, which will, in turn, severely impact economic growth and the CPC's regime legitimacy. This, in addition to a global economic meltdown, will negatively impact China's exports and reduce economic growth. Finally, COVID-19 may also lend support to anti-globalization voices (paradoxically, China under President Xi has become the new champion of globalization in an attempt to boost the Belt and Road Initiative China's economy, and its status in the world).

Thus, China has declared no new cases in mainland China. The declaration complements the narrative of China winning the war against COVID-19, downplaying its role in spreading the virus, illustrating the efficacy of its system, comparing its success vis-à-vis the West, especially the United States, and telling the domestic audience that China is the world's saviour. This illustrates China's victory in the "people's war" over SARS-CoV-2, led by Commander-in-Chief, President Xi. It also helps elevate Xi's position as both a global leader and a model for leaders and people across the globe to emulate, and it strengthens his domestic political legitimacy in the eyes of the Chinese people.

Conclusion

The COVID-19 pandemic has underlined the worst facets of the Chinese command and control system of governance since President Xi assumed power. Thus, the party-state is leaving no stone unturned to disassociate COVID-19 from Wuhan and China. The campaign to change the COVID-19 narrative is an attempt to shore up support for the regime, especially President Xi, who, according to Chinese official sources, has been spearheading the fight against COVID-19. The Chinese government declaration of victory over COVID-19 aims to illustrate Xi's leadership abilities, the superiority of China's political and economic system, and the heroic efforts of the Chinese people led by the CPC.

Finally, the pandemic has led to an increase in anti-China and anti-Chinese sentiment. Citizens living in China, those overseas, and those who appear to be Chinese have been subject to racism and violent attacks. As the situation worsens, it will blow up and, unfortunately, may lead to further attacks and xenophobia. Another unintended consequence is the increase in xenophobia and racism in China against foreigners who are perceived as spreading SARS-CoV-2.

Notes

1. The United States has launched an investigation to ascertain if SARS-CoV-2 emerged or was released from a laboratory close to the wet market in Wuhan.
2. The European Union, the United States, the United Kingdom, Germany, Australia, and other countries have demanded greater transparency from China regarding the death toll and number of infections. They also want China to play by the rules and share its expertise in fighting COVID-19.
3. Shahid Hamid, "China is avoiding blame by trolling the world," *The Atlantic*, 19 March 2020, www.theatlantic.com/ideas/archive/2020/03/china-trolling-world-and-avoiding-blame/ 608332/ (accessed 1 April 2020).
4. Ibid.
5. Dali L. Yang, "Wuhan officials tried to cover up COVID-19—and sent it careening outward," *The Washington Post*, 10 March 2020, www.washingtonpost.com/politics/2020/03/10/wuhan-officials-tried-cover-up-covid-19-sent-it-careening-outward/ (accessed 1 April 2020).
6. Guo Rui, "Coronavirus: Why did China's multimillion-dollar early warning system fail?" *South China Morning Post*, 13 March 2020, www.scmp.com/news/china/society/article/3075027/ coronavirus-why-did-chinas-multimillion-dollar-early-warning (accessed 2 April 2020).
7. Dan Mangan, "Trump blames China for coronavirus pandemic: 'The world is paying a very big price for what they did,'" *CNBC*, 19 March 2020, www.cnbc.com/2020/03/19/coronavirus-outbreak-trump-blames-china-for-virus-again.html (accessed 2 April 2020).
8. There is a broad consensus that President Donald Trump is trying to shift the blame on to China for his failure to combat COVID-19 adequately.
9. Josephine Ma and Mimi Lau, "Xi Jinping 'told China's top echelon' to tackle coronavirus outbreak in early days," *South China Morning Post*, 15 February 2020, www.scmp.com/news/china/ politics/article/3050815/xi-jinping-put-chinas-top-echelon-notice-early-days-coronavirus (accessed 2 April 2020).
10. Huileng Tan, "Beijing objects to term 'Wuhan coronavirus,' and says it may not have originated in China," *CNBC*, 10 March 2020, www.cnbc.com/2020/03/10/china-objects-to-term-wuhan-coronavirus-used-by-mike-pompeo.html (accessed 2 April 2020); Peter Hasson, "Media rhetoric on 'Wuhan virus' echoes Chinese propaganda," *The Daily Signal*, 20 March 2020, www.daily signal.com/2020/03/20/media-rhetoric-on-wuhan-virus-echoes-chinese-propaganda/ (accessed 2 April 2020).
11. Lily Kuo, "'American coronavirus': China pushes propaganda casting doubt on virus origin," *The Guardian*, 13 March 2020, www.theguardian.com/world/2020/

mar/12/conspiracy-theory-th at-coronavirus-originated-in-us-gaining-traction-in-china (accessed 2 April 2020).

12. Bethany Allen-Ebrahimian, "Beijing's coronavirus propaganda blitz goes global," *Axios*, 11 March 2020, www.axios.com/beijings-coronavirus-propaganda-blitz-goes-global-f2bc610c-e83f-4890-9ff8-f49521ad6a14.html (accessed 3 April 2020).

13. Allen-Ebrahimian, "Beijing's coronavirus propaganda."

14. Wang Yi, "Resolutely Defeating the COVID-19 Outbreak and Promoting the Building of a Community with a Shared Future for Mankind," MOFA, Peoples Republic of China, 2 March 2020, www.fmprc.gov.cn/mfa_eng/wjb_663304/wjbz_663308/2461_663310/t1751673.shtml (accessed 3 April 2020).

15. Lijian Zhao, official twitter account, 22 March 2020, https://twitter.com/zlj517/status/124172363 5964039168 (accessed 2 April 2020).

16. Hua Chunying, official twitter account, 20 March 2020, https://twitter.com/SpokespersonCHN (accessed 2 April 2020). China and the United States called a truce and promised to cooperate in combating COVID-19 after a telephone conversation between President Xi and President Trump on 27 March 2020. However, President Trump has continued to blame China to cover up his lack of leadership and incompetence in combating COVID-19.

17. Matt Ho, "Italian professor repeats warning coronavirus may have spread outside China last year," *South China Morning Post*, 24 March 2020, www.scmp.com/news/china/science/article/ 3076792/italian-professor-repeats-warning-coronavirus-may-have-spread (accessed 2 April 2020).

18. Cissy Zhou, "China expels American journalists from 3 US newspapers: The New York Times, Wall Street Journal and Washington Post," *South China Morning Post*, 18 March 2020, www.scmp.com/news/china/diplomacy/article/3075647/china-revokes-press-credentials-american- journalists-3-us (accessed 1 April 2020).

19. Kuo, 'American coronavirus'; Eliza Barclay, "The conspiracy theories about the origins of the coronavirus, debunked," *Vox*, 12 March 2020, www.vox.com/2020/3/4/21156607/how-did-the-coronavirus-get-started-china-wuhan-lab (accessed 2 April 2020); Tan, Beijing objects to.

20. Doubts have been raised regarding Beijing's claims of no new cases being reported from the mainland. This is partly due to long-standing concerns regarding veracity of data from China. Media reports from Japan, China, and Hong Kong indicate that the dip in new cases is because of reduction in testing. Additionally, there is a blind spot in China's calculation because it does not take into account asymptomatic cases (a person might be carrying SARS-CoV-2 but exhibits no symptoms). The *South China Morning Post* reported that it saw classified Chinese government data at the end of February 2020, which showed 43,000 asymptomatic cases. On 22 April 2020, *the Hindustan Times* reported a dozen cases in China of people who had recovered from COVID-19 but were now asymptomatic and could infect others.

21. "Mask diplomacy: China tries to rewrite coronavirus narrative," *The Straits Times*, 20 March 2020, www.straitstimes.com/asia/east-asia/mask-diplomacy-china-tries-to-rewrite-coronavirus-nar rative (accessed 2 April 2020).

22. "China ratchets up anti-US rhetoric with old war films and travel alerts," *CNN*, 6 June 2019, https://lite.cnn.com/en/article/h_8fbf9f842752713d2d298740db41a d2b (accessed 3 April 2020).

23. Qian Gang, "The politics of gratitude," *China Media Project*, 23 March 2020, http:// chinamediap roject.org/2020/03/23/the-politics-of-gratitude/ (accessed 2 April 2020).

24. David Bandurski, "Thank you, no thank you," *China Media Project*, 7 March 2020, https://ch inamediaproject.org/2020/03/07/thank-you-no-thank-you/ (accessed 2 April 2020).

25. "China's president feeling the pressure from dissent in own party," *Radio Free Asia*, 23 March 2020, www.rfa.org/english/news/china/coronavirus-xijinping-03232020141057.html (accessed 4 April 2020).

Part III

Europe

The pandemic next flared up in Europe. As the first reading in this section by Gianfranco Spiteri and his colleagues (2020) shows, the initial cases in the WHO European Region came from two clusters of infection that appeared in France (Haute-Savoie) and Germany (Bavaria). Of the initial 38 confirmed cases studied, it was found 14 had been infected in China and the remainder in Europe. This reading examines the ages, gender, infection site, hospitalization, and symptoms of this first group of European infectives.

Spain

Spain confirmed its first COVID-19 case on January 31, 2020, when a tourist from Germany tested positive in the Canary Islands and was hospitalized. Subsequent new cases involved infected people visiting Spain from France and Italy. COVID-19 soon spread to all Spanish provinces. Instead of a single patient "zero" in Spain, there were multiple introductions of the virus into the country. As infection rates soared, particularly in Barcelona and Madrid, hospitals became overcrowded, with beds and equipment in short supply. The Spanish government declared a "State of Alarm" on March 13 and the country went into lockdown on March 15, with police and army units enforcing the quarantine until it was relaxed in stages as cases diminished. Fines were levied for violations. Altogether, there were some 1.1 million cases in Spain and 35,000 deaths by October 2020. The poor, the elderly, the homeless, and those working in low-paid but essential jobs were disproportionately infected by the virus (Burgen and Jones 2020). Some 65 percent of deaths were persons age 80 or older.

Italy

Countries elsewhere began having severe problems as well, especially Italy in Europe and Iran in the Middle East. Italy, Iran, and China are all linked in the COVID-19 pandemic as travel connections to these three countries were responsible for almost two-thirds of the first reported cases in 99 other affected countries (Dawood et al. 2020). Also Italy, as in China, was slow to start isolating affected areas and restricting movement. Specific cities and regions were locked down and even outdoor activities like walking and jogging from home were banned. Yet the virus jumped to other locales before lockdowns occurred. The worst areas of sickness were in northern Italy. The first known patient, a 38-year-old man in the Lombardy region in the north, had not been to China and was thought to have contracted the virus from another European (Horowitz, Bubota, and Povoledo 2020). Consequently, he is not considered patient "zero" and likely the virus had been active in the region prior to his infection. It is not clear exactly how or when the virus got to Italy, but it apparently was undetected for a long time which contributed to the severity of the outbreak once it was noticeable. The first known patient, however, was a "super spreader." When feeling ill with severe symptoms, he went to a hospital in the town of Codogno in Lombardy on February 18 but refused admission and went home before returning a second time, infecting several people at the hospital and others he interacted with while conducting an active social life, attending dinners, and playing on a soccer team when contagious. The spread of the disease was so quick that in the next 24 hours some 36 additional patients were admitted to the hospital, none of whom had any direct contact with the first patient (Horowitz et al. 2020).

Italy became the next epicenter of the catastrophe in Europe. Italy had over 485,000 confirmed cases by October 2020; over 37,000 died. One reason Italy had such a high mortality rate was because of a large, disproportionate elderly population, with almost a quarter of all Italians age 65 and over. Italy has the oldest population in Europe and second-oldest in the world after Japan (Horowitz 2020). As is now known, advanced age is a major risk factor for high mortality from COVID-19 and this is particularly the case when combined with age-related comorbid health conditions. However, the situation in Italy improved as lockdown procedures were followed by a steady decline in new cases and fatalities. By June, restrictions were eased and Italy became the first European country to fully open its international borders and terminate the 14-day quarantine requirement for visitors.

Germany

COVID-19 was first detected in Germany in late January 2020 with an outbreak in Bavaria. This case was traced to a resident of China who had been in contact with his family in Wuhan and was visiting Germany for a business meeting (Böhmer et al. 2020). By mid-March, Germany had imposed lockdown measures including the closing of schools and non-essential businesses. This action was significant, but Germany was not as strict on individual movement as the measures imposed in China, or even other European countries such as Italy and Spain (Müller et al. 2020). Shortly before the lockdown, German Chancellor Angela Merkel was blunt with the German people about the impact of the coronavirus in saying that two-thirds of the population could be infected, and the country's objective should be to slow down the spread of the virus and not overburden the hospitals (Bennhold and Eddy 2020).

Germany's lockdown efforts proved to be successful. The number of new infections in Germany consistently decreased from the beginning of April through mid-May (Müller et al. 2020). What distinguished the German situation during the early part of the pandemic was its low death rates from the virus. By April, Germany's rate was only 1.2 percent compared to 11 percent in Italy, 9 percent in Spain, and 8 percent in the United Kingdom. When October came, Germany had about 414,500 confirmed cases but a still relatively low 10,000 deaths. Germany's quick action on lockdowns and early and widespread testing that included younger people with mild symptoms were credited for Germany's better results (Stafford 2020).

Germany's response to the pandemic has been considered successful, especially in comparison to its European peers. However, Germany has also encountered some significant political obstacles. Protest movements critical of the government's restrictions began to emerge in April. Although Germany's far right political party, Alternative for Germany, was associated with this movement, protesters also included anti-vaccination groups and citizens concerned about job loss (Bennhold 2020). As tensions grew, evidenced by a protest of 15,000 people in Berlin at the beginning of August, Germany experienced an increase in cases, demonstrating the challenge of virus control. Of interest is that a large-scale social protest against vaccination made an initial major public appearance which suggests that some segments of a population will object to taking an anti-viral vaccine when available and their attitudes will have be addressed in future public health campaigns.

United Kingdom

COVID-19 reached the United Kingdom in late January 2020 and spread thereafter infecting even the British Prime Minister Boris Johnson who was hospitalized and recovered. How the virus reached Britain is not known, but London's Heathrow Airport had three direct daily round-trip flights to Wuhan, China, as well as travel back and forth between COVID-19 hot spots in Italy, Germany, Spain, and other sites. On March 26, the government issued stay-at-home orders, banning non-essential travel and closing businesses, schools, pubs, restaurants, indoor sports facilities, and places of worship. There was criticism that the shut-down had come too late and should have been initiated sooner. Parliament passed the Coronavirus Act 2020 giving the government emergency powers for the first time since World War II to control the pandemic and authorizing the police to enforce the measures. The lockdown was lifted on May 10, 2020. However, by the summer of 2020, Britain went on to experience the greatest economic recession of any country in Europe because of work stoppages during the pandemic.

In the meantime, the UK had the highest mortality from COVID-19 of any country in Europe with some 44,600 deaths by October 2020. There were over 831,000 confirmed cases at that time. More than 90 percent of deaths were people with comorbid conditions and over 60 years of age (Williamson et al. 2020). As seen in the second reading by Krithi Ravi (2020), black, Asian, and other ethnic minorities had a greater risk of death from the virus than British whites. Whereas age is the strongest predictor of mortality for COVID-19, ethnic minorities tend to be a considerably younger population in the UK since many are migrants with few people of older ages in their ranks. Only 5 percent of ethnic minorities are age 65 and over in the UK compared to 18 percent of whites, yet among the older population some 35 percent of the most severe COVID-19 cases were minorities. This is the outcome even though significantly more whites tend to be older with comorbid conditions. Consequently, Ravi (2020:1) makes the significant observation "that research into ethnic disparities in COVID-19 mortality must consider social as well as biological factors."

The Williamson et al. (2020) study using data from the records of millions of adult deaths in England, including those from COVID-19, likewise shows blacks and South Asians at higher risk of dying from the virus than those of white ethnicity, but this result was only partially attributed to greater comorbidities. There was also a strong association between deprivation and risk of infection. Given racial/ethnic inequalities in employment, housing, education, and access to quality health care, along with a preponderance of jobs in the service sector making it more difficult to work at home, deprivation emerges as a critical factor in the greater exposure of racial/ethnic minorities to the virus. What this signifies is that age and underlying illnesses are not the whole story about how the pandemic affects people everywhere, not just in Europe.

Sweden

Finally, there is the example of Sweden taking a completely different approach than other countries to the virus, even those in Scandinavia. Sweden chose not to have a significant lockdown upon the arrival of COVID-19. It did close its secondary schools and colleges, but allowed its elementary schools, bars, and restaurants to remain open. Although Sweden's approach faced criticism that it was not taking the threat of the virus seriously enough, Sweden's approach was rooted in its history of individual responsibility rather than risk acceptance or downplaying its significance (Nygren and Olofsson 2020). The government still relied on expert advice, but its approach was based on its guidance as serving as recommendations rather than mandates to its citizens. In addition to individual responsibility, a culture based on a high level of trust and an institutional arrangement in which government agencies, and local and regional governments are fairly autonomous in providing health care made a soft lockdown response an appropriate fit (Pierre 2020).

The early results of the Swedish response to the coronavirus pandemic, however, were not promising. While Sweden did not experience the intensity of outbreaks in Italy, Spain, and Britain, it experienced a death rate 30 percent higher than usual for the spring, which was much higher than that of Denmark, Norway, and Finland at the time (Leatherby and McCann 2020). By October 2020, Sweden had over 111,000 cases of the virus and 5,933 deaths. About half of Sweden's deaths were in nursing homes. Denmark, in contrast, had 697 deaths, Finland 353, and Norway 279. Consequently, Sweden's mortality from COVID-19 was exceptionally high for Scandinavia. The soft lockdown also did not produce an economic benefit as its economy was expected to contract by 4.5 percent in 2020, which was comparable to a 3.9 percent expected contraction in Norway, which imposed a much stricter lockdown and experienced a much lower death rate in the first few weeks of the pandemic (Goodman 2020). One suggestion for Sweden's negative results has been that its planners did not have the knowledge that the virus could be spread asymptomatically and its testing system was still developing (Pierre 2020).

Despite the criticism and some unfavorable results, it is still very possible that Sweden's response may be viewed more positively over time. Although Sweden's death rates were relatively high, the spread of the coronavirus was not as swift as in some other countries in the world. With the virus showing no signs of abatement the heading into 2021, strict lockdowns may not be politically, economically, or socially viable in the long-term, especially for liberal democracies facing protests and failing economies. A softer approach may seem to be more attractive to some countries, as testing capacity and the development of therapeutics continue to improve. The unique Swedish response to the COVID-19 pandemic is discussed in greater detail in the third reading by Jon Pierre (2020).

Herd Immunity

The fourth and final reading in this section is on a European approach to "herd immunity" as a strategy in coping with the pandemic by Fredrich Jung and his colleagues (2020). Herd immunity is the idea that while the aged and people with preexisting conditions are protected, up to 60–70 percent of the rest of the population can be safely infected over time with only mild symptoms building up a general "herd" immunity to the virus through the body's natural production of antibodies. The probability of success for this strategy is discussed in the reading.

Russia

Of course, the ultimate remedy is to develop a vaccine providing immunity to the virus. And in August 2020, Russia announced that the Gamaleya Institute had developed such a vaccine. Russia ranked fourth in the world at that time in total cases (almost 900,000) with approximately 5,000 deaths. By October, Russia still ranked fourth in the world with nearly 1.5 million confirmed cases and over 25,525 reported deaths. The vaccine (Sputnik V) was not expected to be widely available until the end of the year. It had been tested in a non-random clinical trial involving 76 volunteers, all of whom developed an immune response and reported no serious side effects. The vaccine was touted as being 100 percent effective. These results were published in *Lancet* on September 4, but the data and no further information were released.

The WHO noted, however, that the Gamaleya institute had yet to conduct Phase III (efficacy) tests on thousands of volunteers in highly controlled trials, which is the only method of ensuring a safe and effective vaccine. Pre-clinical testing involves testing vaccines on animals, followed by Phase I (safety tests) that consists of testing for safety and dosage on a few people and Phase II (expanded tests) in which testing is performed on hundreds of people, including children and the aged, before moving on to Phase III. Just how well the Russian vaccine works on a large population remains unknown as this book goes to press. As the WHO pointed out, it is not who is first that counts, but which vaccine is proven to be the most effective. In the meantime, researchers in the United States, England, China, and now Russia are conducting Phase III trials.

With cases rising in Russia in the fall of 2020, employers in Moscow were required to have 30 percent of their employees work remotely because of the coronavirus situation in the city, while workers over the age of 65 years and those with chronic diseases were likewise required to work remotely. Medical institutions, defense agencies, and other government organizations were exempt.

Critical Thinking Questions

1. Which population groups in Europe are most affected by the pandemic?
2. Why did Italy become an epicenter of the pandemic in Europe?
3. Why did Germany fare relatively well during the pandemic compared to other European countries?
4. The UK had the highest mortality rate in Europe. Why?
5. What was unique about Sweden's response? Was it successful? Explain your answer.
6. Explain "herd immunity." Do you think it would work?

References

Bennhold, Katrin. 2020. "Germany's Coronavirus Protests: Anti-Vaxxers, Anticapitalists, Neo-Nazis." *New York Times* (May 18).

Bennhold, Katrin and Melissa Eddy. 2020. "Merkel Gives Germans a Hard Truth About the Coronavirus." *New York Times* (March 11).

Böhmer, Merle M., Udo Buchholz, Victor M. Corman et al. 2020. "Investigation of a COVID-19 Outbreak in Germany resulting from a Single Travel-associated Primary Case: a Case Series." *Lancet Infectious Diseases* 20(8):920–28.

Burgen, Stephen and Sam Jones. 2020. "Poor and Vulnerable Hardest Hit by Pandemic in Spain." *The Guardian* (April 1).

Dawood, Fatimah S., Philip Ricks, Gibril J. Njie, Michael Daugherty et al. 2020. "Observations of the Global Epidemiology of COVID-19 from the Prepandemic Period using Web-based Surveillance: A Cross-sectional Analysis." *Lancet Infectious Diseases* (July 29). https://doi.org/10.1016/S1473-3099(20)30581-8

Goodman, Peter S. 2020. "Sweden Stayed Open to Spare Its Economy. It Didn't Succeed." *New York Times* (July 8).

Horowitz, Jason. 2020. "Italy's Elderly Suffer Toll as Coronavirus Spreads." *New York Times* (March 4).

Horowitz, Jason, Emma Bubota, and Elisabetta Povoledo. 2020. "Italy, Pandemic's New Epicenter, Has Lessons for the World." *New York Times* (March 21).

Leatherby, Lauren and Allison McCann. 2020. "As Neighbors Closed, Sweden Stayed Open. A Deadly Month Shows How Risky That Was." *New York Times* (May 17).

Müller, Olaf, Guangyu Lu, Albrecht Jahn, and Oliver Razum. 2020. "COVID-19 Control: Can Germany Learn from China?" *International Journal of Health and Policy Management* (May 27). https://doi.org/10.34172/ijhpm.2020.78

Nygren, Katarina Giritli and Anna Olofsson. 2020. "Managing the Covid-19 Pandemic Through Individual Responsibility: The Consequences of a World Risk Society and Enhanced Ethopolitics." *Journal of Risk Research*. https://doi.org/10.1080/13669877.2020.1756382

Pierre, Jon. 2020. "Nudges against Pandemics: Sweden's COVID-19 Containment Strategy in Perspective." *Policy and Society* 39(3):478–93.

Ravi, Krithi. 2020. "Ethnic Disparities in COVID-19 Mortality: Are Comorbidities to Blame?" *Lancet* (June 19).

Spiteri, Gianfranco, James Fielding, Michaela Diercke, Christine Campese et al. 2020. "First Cases of Coronavirus Disease 2019 (COVID-19) in the WHO European Region, 24 January to 21 February 2020." *Eurosurveillance* (March 5).

Stafford, Ned. 2020. "Covid-19: Why Germany's Case Fatality Rate Seems So low." *BMJ* (April 7). https://doi.org/10.1136/bmj.m1395.

Williamson, Elizabeth J., Alex J. Walker, Krishnan Bhaskaran et al. 2020. "OpenSafely: Factors Associated with COVID-19 Death in 17 Million Patients." *Nature* https://doi.org/10.1038/s41586-020-2521-4.

8 First Cases of Coronavirus Disease 2019 (COVID-19) in the WHO European Region, 24 January to 21 February 2020

Gianfranco Spiteri, James Fielding, Michaela Diercke, Christine Campese, Vincent Enouf, Alexandre Gaymard, Antonino Bella, Paola Sognamiglio, Maria José Sierra Moros, Antonio Nicolau Riutort, Yulia V. Demina, Romain Mahieu, Markku Broas, Malin Bengnér, Silke Buda, Julia Schilling, Laurent Filleul, Agnès Lepoutre, Christine Saura, Alexandra Mailles, Daniel Levy-Bruhl, Bruno Coignard, Sibylle Bernard-Stoecklin, Sylvie Behillil, Sylvie van der Werf, Martine Valette, Bruno Lina, Flavia Riccardo, Emanuele Nicastri, Inmaculada Casas, Amparo Larrauri, Magdalena Salom Castell, Francisco Pozo, Rinat A. Maksyutov, Charlotte Martin, Marc Van Ranst, Nathalie Bossuyt, Lotta Siira, Jussi Sane, Karin Tegmark-Wisell, Maria Palmérus, Eeva K. Broberg, Julien Beauté, Pernille Jorgensen, Nick Bundle, Dmitriy Pereyaslov, Cornelia Adlhoch, Jukka Pukkila, Richard Pebody, Sonja Olsen, and Bruno Christian Ciancio

A cluster of pneumonia of unknown origin was identified in Wuhan, China, in December 2019 [1]. On 12 January 2020, Chinese authorities shared the sequence of a novel coronavirus termed severe acute respiratory syndrome coronavirus 2 (SARS-CoV-2) isolated from some clustered cases [2]. Since then, the disease caused by SARS-CoV-2 has been named coronavirus disease 2019 (COVID-19). As at 21 February 2020, the virus had spread rapidly mostly within China but also to 28 other countries, including in the World Health Organization (WHO) European Region [3–5].

Here we describe the epidemiology of the first cases of COVID-19 in this region, excluding cases reported in the United Kingdom (UK), as at 21 February 2020. The study includes a comparison between cases detected among travellers from China and cases whose infection was acquired due to subsequent local transmission.

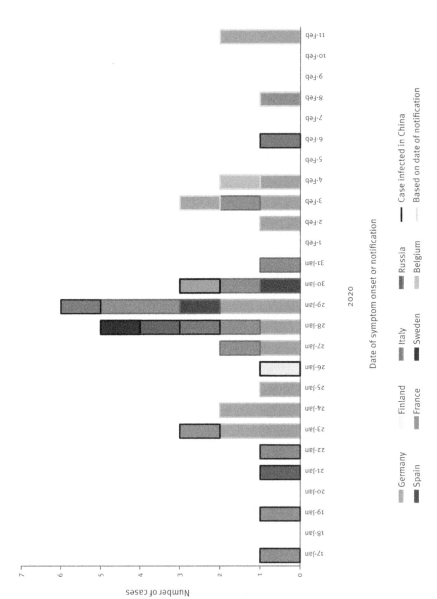

Figure 8.1 Epidemic curve of reported COVID-19 cases by date of symptom onset, or date of notification, WHO European Region, as of 21 February 2020 (n = 38)[a,b].

Surveillance in the WHO European Region

On 27 January 2020, the European Centre for Disease Prevention and Control (ECDC) and the WHO Regional Office for Europe asked countries to complete a WHO standard COVID-19 case report form for all confirmed

Table 8.1 Characteristics of confirmed COVID-19 cases, WHO European Region, as at 21 February 2020 (n = 38).[a]

Characteristics	Number of cases overall	Number of cases infected in Europe	Number of cases infected in China	p value[b]
Age range in years				
0–17	4	3	0	0.08
18–49	24	13	9	
50–64	7	5	2	
≥ 65	3	0	3	
Sex				
Male	25	14	8	0.6
Female	13	7	6	
Hospitalised				
Yes	35	21	14	ND
No	2	ND	ND	
Unknown	1	ND	ND	
Symptoms[c] (31 cases with available information)				
Asymptomatic	2	ND	ND	ND
Fever	20	ND	ND	
Cough	14	ND	ND	
Weakness	8	ND	ND	
Headaches	6	ND	ND	
Sore throat	2	ND	ND	
Rhinorrhoea	2	ND	ND	
Shortness of breath	2	ND	ND	
Mean days from onset to hospitalisation (29 cases)	3.7	4.6	2.5	ND
Mean days from onset to first positive laboratory test (16 cases)	5.1	6.5	5.2	ND

Notes: COVID-19: coronavirus disease 2019; ND: not determined or known; WHO: World Health Organization.

a The table does not include nine cases reported in the United Kingdom.

b Chi-squared test for difference in distributions between cases infected in Europe and those infected in China.

c A single case could have more than one symptom. Only symptoms reported by two or more cases shown.

and probable cases according to WHO criteria [6–8]. The overall aim of surveillance at this time was to support the global strategy of containment of COVID-19 with rapid identification and follow-up of cases linked to affected countries in order to minimise onward transmission. The surveillance objectives were to: describe the key epidemiological and clinical characteristics of COVID-19 cases detected in Europe; inform country preparedness; and improve further case detection and management. Data collected included demographics, history of recent travel to affected areas, close contact with a probable or confirmed COVID-19 case, underlying conditions, signs and symptoms of disease at onset, type of specimens from which the virus was detected, and clinical outcome. The WHO case definition was adopted for surveillance: a confirmed case was a person with laboratory confirmation of SARS-CoV-2 infection (ECDC recommended two separate SARS-CoV-2 RT-PCR tests), irrespective of clinical signs and symptoms, whereas a probable case was a suspect case for whom testing for SARS-CoV-2 was inconclusive or positive using a pan-coronavirus assay [8]. By 31 January 2020, 47 laboratories in 31 countries, including 38 laboratories in 24 European Union and European Economic Area (EU/EEA) countries, had diagnostic capability for SARS-CoV-2 available (close to 60% of countries in the WHO European Region), with cross-border shipment arrangements in place for many of those lacking domestic testing capacity. The remaining six EU/EEA countries were expected to have diagnostic testing available by mid-February [9].

Epidemiology of First Cases in the European Region

As at 09:00 on 21 February 2020, 47 confirmed cases of COVID-19 were reported in the WHO European Region and one of these cases had died [4]. Data on 38 of these cases (i.e. all except the nine reported in the UK) are included in this analysis.

The first three cases detected were reported in France on 24 January 2020 and had onset of symptoms on 17, 19 and 23 January respectively [10]. The first death was reported on 15 February in France. As at 21 February, nine countries had reported cases (Figure 8.1): Belgium (1), Finland (1), France (12), Germany (16), Italy (3), Russia (2), Spain (2), Sweden (1) and the UK (9 – not included further).

The place of infection (assessed at national level based on an incubation period presumed to be up to 14 days [11], travel history and contact with probable or confirmed cases as per the case definition) was reported for 35 cases (missing for three cases), of whom 14 were infected in China (Hubei province: 10 cases; Shandong province: one case; province not reported for three cases). The remaining 21 cases were infected in Europe. Of these, 14 were linked to a cluster in Bavaria, Germany, and seven to a cluster in Haute-Savoie, France [12,13]. Cases from the Bavarian cluster were reported from Germany and Spain, whereas cases from the Haute-Savoie cluster were reported from France and Spain. Cases linked to the Haute-Savoie cluster were also detected in the UK, including the index case of this cluster, who was infected in Singapore before travelling to France [14]. The index case for the cluster in Bavaria was reported to be infected in China [15].

The median age of the 38 cases was 42 years (range: 2–81 years) and 25 were male (Table 8.1). The proportion of male cases was higher among cases acquired in Europe (14 males of 21 cases) compared with those acquired in China (8 males of 14 cases) although the difference was not statistically significant (chi-squared test: p = 0.6). There was no difference in median age by sex (males: 45 years; females: 38 years, k-sample median test, p = 1.0) or by whether infection was acquired in Europe or not (acquired in Europe: 47 years; acquired in China: 38 years, p = 0.2).

All but two cases were hospitalised (35 of 37 where information on hospitalisation was reported), although it is likely that most were hospitalised to isolate the person rather than because of severe disease. The time from onset of symptoms to hospitalisation (and isolation) ranged between 0 and 10 days with a mean of 3.7 days (reported for 29 cases). The mean number of days to hospitalisation was 2.5 days for cases imported from China, but 4.6 days for those infected in Europe. This was mostly a result of delays in identifying the index cases of the two clusters in France and Germany. In the German cluster, for example, the first three cases detected locally were hospitalised in a mean of 5.7 days, whereas the following six took only a mean of 2 days to be hospitalised.

Symptoms at the point of diagnosis were reported for 31 cases. Two cases were asymptomatic and remained so until tested negative. The asymptomatic cases were tested as part of screening following repatriation and during contact tracing respectively. Of the remaining 29, 20 reported fever, 14 reported cough and eight reported weakness. Additional symptoms reported included headaches (6 cases), sore throat (2), rhinorrhoea (2), shortness of breath (2), myalgia (1), diarrhoea (1) and nausea (1). Fever was reported as the sole symptom for nine cases. In 16 of 29 symptomatic cases, the symptoms at diagnosis were consistent with the case definition for acute respiratory infection [16], although it is possible that cases presented additional symptoms after diagnosis and these were not reported.

Data on pre-existing conditions were reported for seven cases; five had no pre-existing conditions while one was reported to be obese and one had pre-existing cardiac disease. No data on clinical signs e.g. dyspnea etc. were reported for any of the 38 cases.

All hospitalised cases had a benign clinical evolution except four, two reported in Italy and two reported in France, all of whom developed viral pneumonia. All three cases who were aged 65 years or over were admitted to intensive care and required respiratory support and one French case died. The case who died was hospitalised for 21 days and required intensive care and mechanical ventilation for 19 days. The duration of hospitalisation was reported for 16 cases with a median of 13 days (range: 8–23 days). As at 21 February 2020, four cases were still hospitalised.

Laboratory Diagnosis

All cases were confirmed according to specific assays targeting at least two separate genes (envelope (E) gene as a screening test and RNA-dependent RNA polymerase (RdRp) gene or nucleoprotein (N) gene for confirmation) [8,17]. The specimen types tested were reported for 27 cases: 15 had positive nasopharyngeal swabs, nine had positive throat swabs, three cases had positive sputum, two had a positive nasal swab, one case had a positive nasopharyngeal aspirate and one a positive endotracheal aspirate.

Discussion

As at 09:00 on 21 February, few COVID-19 cases had been detected in Europe compared with Asia. However the situation is rapidly developing, with a large outbreak recently identified in northern Italy, with transmission in several municipalities and at least two deaths [18]. As at 5 March 2020, there are 4,250 cases including 113 deaths reported among 38 countries in the WHO European region [19].

In our analysis of early cases, we observed transmission in two broad contexts: sporadic cases among travellers from China (14 cases) and cases who acquired infection due to subsequent local transmission in Europe (21 cases). Our analysis shows that the time from symptom onset to hospitalisation/case isolation was about 3 days longer for locally acquired cases than for imported cases. People returning from affected areas are likely to have a low threshold to seek care and be tested when symptomatic, however delays in identifying the index cases of the two clusters in France and Germany meant that locally acquired cases took longer to be detected and isolated. Once the exposure is determined and contacts identified and quarantined (171 contacts in France and 200 in Germany for the clusters in Haute-Savoie and Bavaria, respectively), further cases are likely to be rapidly detected and isolated when they develop symptoms [15,20]. In the German cluster, for example, the first three cases detected locally were hospitalised in a mean of 5.7 days, whereas the following six were hospitalised after a mean of 2 days. Locally acquired cases require significant resources for contact tracing and quarantine, and countries should be prepared to allocate considerable public health resources during the containment phase, should local clusters emerge in their population. In addition, prompt sharing of information on cases and contacts through international notification systems such as the International Health Regulations (IHR) mechanism and the European Commission's European Early Warning and Response System is essential to contain international spread of infection.

All of the imported cases had a history of travel to China. This was consistent with the epidemiological situation in Asia, and supported the recommendation for testing of suspected cases with travel history to China and potentially other areas of presumed ongoing community transmission.

The situation has evolved rapidly since then, however, and the number of countries reporting COVID-19 transmission increased rapidly, notably with a large outbreak in northern Italy with 3,089 cases reported as at 5 March [18,19]. Testing of suspected cases based on geographical risk of importation needs to be complemented with additional approaches to ensure early detection of local circulation of COVID-19, including through testing of severe acute respiratory infections in hospitals irrespectively of travel history as recommended in the WHO case definition updated on 27 February 2020 [21].

The clinical presentation observed in the cases in Europe is that of an acute respiratory infection. However, of the 31 cases with information on symptoms, 20 cases presented with fever and nine cases presented only with fever and no other symptoms. These findings, which are consistent with other published case series, have prompted ECDC to include fever among several clinical signs or symptoms indicative for the suspected case definition.

Three cases were aged 65 years or over. All required admission to intensive care and were tourists (imported cases). These findings could reflect the average older age of the tourist population compared with the local contacts exposed to infection in Europe and do not allow us to draw any conclusion on the proportion of severe cases that we could expect in the general population of Europe. Despite this, the finding of older individuals being at higher risk of a severe clinical course is consistent with the evidence from Chinese case series published so far although the majority of infections in China have been mild [22,23].

This preliminary analysis is based on the first reported cases of COVID-19 cases in the WHO European Region. Given the small sample size, and limited completeness for some variables, all the results presented should be interpreted with caution.

With increasing numbers of cases in Europe, data from surveillance and investigations in the region can build on the evidence from countries in Asia experiencing more widespread transmission particularly on disease spectrum and the proportion of infections with severe outcome [22]. Understanding the infection-severity is critical to help plan for the impact on the healthcare system and the wider population. Serological studies are vital to understand the proportion of cases who are asymptomatic. Hospital-based surveillance could help estimate the incidence of severe cases and identify risk factors for severity and death. Established hospital surveillance systems that are in place for influenza and other diseases in Europe may be expanded for this purpose. In addition, a number of countries in Europe are adapting and, in some cases, already using existing sentinel primary care based surveillance systems for influenza to detect community transmission of SARS-CoV-2. This approach will be used globally to help identify evidence of widespread community transmission and, should the virus spread and containment no longer be deemed feasible, to monitor intensity of disease transmission, trends and its geographical spread.

Additional research is needed to complement surveillance data to build knowledge on the infectious period, modes of transmission, basic and effective reproduction numbers, and effectiveness of prevention and case management options also in settings outside of China. Such special studies are being conducted globally, including a cohort study on citizens repatriated from China to Europe, with the aim to extrapolate disease incidence and risk factors for infection in areas with community transmission. Countries together with ECDC and WHO should use all opportunities to address these questions in a coordinated fashion at the European and global level.

References

1. Wuhan City Health Committee (WCHC). Wuhan Municipal Health and Health Commission's briefing on the current pneumonia epidemic situation in our city 2019. [Accessed 14 Jan 2020]. Available from: http://wjw.wuhan.gov.cn/front/web/showDetail/2019123108989

2. European Centre for Disease Prevention and Control (ECDC). Rapid risk assessment: Outbreak of acute respiratory syndrome associated with a novel coronavirus, Wuhan, China; first update – 22 January 2020. Stockholm: ECDC; 2020. Available from: www.ecdc.europa.eu/en/publications-data/risk-assessment-outbreak-acute-respiratory-syndrome-associated-novel-coronavirus

3. European Centre for Disease Prevention and Control (ECDC). Outbreak of acute respiratory syndrome associated with a novel coronavirus, China: first local transmission in the EU/EEA – third update. 31 January 2020. Stockholm: ECDC; 2020. Available from: www.ecdc.europa.eu/en/publications-data/risk-assessment-outbreak-acute-respiratory-syndrome-associated-novel-1

4. European Centre for Disease Prevention and Control (ECDC). Geographical distribution of 2019-nCov cases globally 2020 – 02 February 2020. Stockholm: ECDC. [Accessed 12 Feb 2020]. Available from: www.ecdc.europa.eu/en/geographical-distribution-2019-ncov-cases

5. World Health Organization Regional Office for Europe. (WHO/Europe). Countries 2020. Copenhagen: WHO/Europe. [Accessed 12 Feb 2020]. Available from: www.euro.who.int/en/countries

6. European Centre for Disease Prevention and Control (ECDC). 2019 novel coronavirus (nCoV) disease data Reporting Protocol Version 1, 27 Jan 2020.

7. World Health Organization (WHO). Coronavirus disease (COVID-19) technical guidance: Surveillance and case definitions. Geneva: WHO; 2020. Available from: www.who.int/emergencies/diseases/novel-coronavirus-2019/technical-guidance/surveillance-and-case-definitions

8. European Centre for Disease Prevention and Control (ECDC). European surveillance for human infection with novel coronavirus (2019-nCoV) 2020. Stockholm: ECDC. [Accessed 30 Jan 2020]. Available from: www.ecdc.europa.eu/en/european-surveillance-human-infection-novel-coronavirus-2019-ncov

9. Reusken CBEM, Broberg EK, Haagmans B, Meijer A, Corman VM, Papa A, et al. On Behalf of Evd-LabNet and Erli-Net. Laboratory readiness and response for novel coronavirus (2019-nCoV) in expert laboratories in 30 EU/EEA countries, January 2020. Euro Surveill. 2020;25(6):2000082. https://doi.org/10.2807/1560-7917.ES.2020.25.6.2000082 PMID: 32046815

10. Bernard Stoecklin S, Rolland P, Silue Y, Mailles A, Campese C, Simondon A, et al. Investigation Team. First cases of coronavirus disease 2019 (COVID-19) in France: surveillance, investigations and control measures, January 2020. Euro Surveill. 2020;25(6):2000094. https://doi.org/10.2807/1560-7917.ES.2020.25.6.2000094 PMID: 32070465

11. Backer JA, Klinkenberg D, Wallinga J. Incubation period of 2019 novel corona-virus (2019-nCoV) infections among travellers from Wuhan, China, 20–28 January 2020. Euro Surveill. 2020;25(5):2000062. https://doi.org/10.2807/1560-7917. ES.2020.25.5.2000062 PMID: 32046819

12. Bayerische Gesundheitsministerium. Lungenentzündungen durch ein neuartiges Coronavirus. [Pneumonia caused by a new type of coronavirus]. Munich: Bayer-ische Gesundheitsministerium; 2020. German. [Accessed 12 Feb 2020]. Available from: www.stmgp.bayern.de/vorsorge/infektionsschutz/infektionsmonitor-bayern/

13. Santé publique France. Epidémie de coronavirus (2019-nCov) au départ de Wuhan, Chine. [Coronavirus epidemic (2019-nCov) originating from Wuhan, China]. Paris: Santé publique France; 2020. French. [Accessed 12 Feb 2020]. Available from: www.santepubliquefrance. fr/maladies-et-traumatismes/maladies-et-infections-respiratoires/infection-a-coronavirus/articles/epidemie-de-coronavirus-2019-ncov-au-depart-de-wuhan-chine

14. Department of Health and Social Care. Chief Medical Officer for England announces 4 further coronavirus cases. London: Department of Health and Social Care; 2020. [Accessed 22 Feb 2020]. Available from: www.gov.uk/government/news/chief-medical-officer-for-england-announces-four-further-coronavirus-cases

15. Santé publique France. COVID-19: situation des cas groupés dans les Alpes, France. [COVID-19: Situation on cluster of cases in the Alps, France]. Paris: Santé publique France; 2020. French. Available from: www. santepubliquefrance.fr/maladies-et-traumatismes/maladieset-infections-respiratoires/infection-a-coronavirus/articles/covid-19-situation-des-cas-groupes-dans-les-alpes-france

16. European Commission. Commission Implementing Decision (EU) 2018/945 of 22 June 2018 on the communicable diseases and related special health issues to be covered by epidemiological surveillance as well as relevant case definitions. 2018;(2119):1–74. Available from: https://eur-lex.europa.eu/legal-content/EN/TXT/PDF/?uri=CELEX:32018D0945&from=en

17. Corman V, Bleicker T, Brünink S, Drosten C, Landt O, Koopmans M, et al. Diag-nostic detection of Wuhan coronavirus 2019 by real-time RT-PCR – Protocol and preliminary evaluation as of Jan 13, 2020. [Accessed 17 Jan 2020]. Geneva: WHO; Jan 2020. Available from: www.who.int/docs/default-source/coronaviruse/wuhan-virus-assay-v1991527e5122341d99287a1b17c111902.pdf?sfvrsn=d381fc88_2

18. European Centre for Disease Prevention and Control (ECDC). Outbreak of novel coronavirus disease 2019 (COVID19): situation in Italy – 23 February 2020. Stock-holm: ECDC; 2020. Available from: www.ecdc.europa.eu/en/publications-data/outbreak-novel-coronavirus-disease-2019-covid-19-situation-italy

19. World Health Organization Regional Office for Europe (WHO/Europe). COVID-19 situation in the WHO European Region. Copenhagen: WHO/Europe. [Accessed 5 Mar 2020]. Available from: https://who.maps.arcgis.com/apps/opsdashboard/index.html#/ead3c6475654481ca51c248d52ab9c61

20. Lebensmittelsicherheit BLfGu, Robert Koch Institute. Beschreibung des bisherigen Ausbruchsgeschehens mit dem neuartigen Coronavirus SARS-CoV-2 in Deutsch-land (Stand: 12. Februar 2020). [Description of the novel coronavirus SARS-CoV-2

outbreak in Germany (as at 12 February 2020)]. German. Epidemiologisches Bulletin. 2020;7:3–4.

21. World Health Organization (WHO). Global Surveillance for COVID-19 disease caused by human infection with novel coronavirus (COVID-19). Geneva: WHO; 2020. [Accessed 4 Mar 2020]. Available from: www.who.int/docs/defaultsource/coronaviruse/20200121-global-surveillance-for-2019-ncov.pdf?sfvrsn=9d82f528_4&download=true

22. The Novel Coronavirus Pneumonia Emergency Response Epidemiology Team. The epidemiological characteristics of an outbreak of 2019 Novel Coronavirus diseases (COVID-19)—China, 2020. China: Chinese Center for Disease Control and Prevention; 2020. [Accessed 18 Feb 2020]. Available from: http://weekly.chinacdc.cn/en/article/id/e53946e2-c6c4-41e9-9a9b-fea8db1a8f51

23. The Novel Coronavirus Pneumonia Emergency Response Epidemiology T. The epidemiological characteristics of an outbreak of 2019 Novel Coronavirus diseases (COVID-19)—China, 2020. China CDC Weekly. 2020;2(8):113–22.

9 Ethnic Disparities in COVID-19 Mortality

Are Comorbidities to Blame?

Krithi Ravi

On June 2, 2020, Public Health England (PHE) reported on the disparities in the risk and outcomes of COVID-19. After adjusting for sex, age, deprivation, and region, people from a Black, Asian, and Minority Ethnic (BAME) background had a higher risk of death from COVID-19 than White British people. This analysis did not adjust for comorbidities, and the PHE report highlighted this to be an important limitation as comorbidities were postulated to be "more commonly seen in some BAME groups."[1]

PHE[1] refers to a study from the COVID-19 Clinical Information Network (CO-CIN), led by Harrison and colleagues,[2] of the difference in survival from COVID-19 associated with membership of an ethnic group. In this study,[2] once comorbidities were accounted for, there was no difference in COVID-19 mortality between ethnic groups. This initially appears to support PHE's conclusion that differences in the distribution of comorbidities may account for the increased COVID-19 mortality of BAME patients.

However, in CO-CIN's analysis[2] of more than 14,000 patients with COVID-19 admitted to UK hospitals, BAME patients were more likely to have diabetes, but less likely to have other comorbidities such as chronic cardiac, pulmonary, kidney, and neurological disease, malignancy, and dementia. In the multivariate analysis of risk factors for COVID-19 mortality, the adjusted hazard ratio for diabetes (1·11) was less than that for chronic cardiac (1·20), pulmonary (1·24), and kidney disease (1·28), and dementia (1·40), and equal to the adjusted hazard ratio for malignancy (1·11).

Furthermore, age was by far the largest contributor to risk of death, with an adjusted hazard ratio of 9·09 for patients aged 70–79 years and 11·72 for those aged 80 years and older, compared with people younger than 50 years. 60·7% of White patients admitted to hospital with COVID-19 were aged 70 years and older, compared with 30·7% of Black, 29·2% of Asian, and 35·2% of Minority Ethnic patients.

As patients from a White ethnic background were more likely to be older and have comorbidities associated with a higher risk of dying from COVID-19, it is very concerning that the case fatality at 30 days after hospital admission for COVID-19 appears to be the same in Black and White patients.[2] The lack of association between ethnicity and COVID-19 mortality after adjustment for comorbidities is not reassuring. This suggests that research into ethnic disparities in COVID-19 mortality must consider social as well as biological factors.

References

1. Public Health England. Disparities in the risk and outcomes of COVID-19. June 2, 2020. https://assets.publishing.service.gov.uk/government/uploads/system/uploads/attachment_data/file/889861/disparities_ review.pdf (accessed June 2, 2020).
2. Harrison E, Docherty A, Semple C. Investigating associations between ethnicity and outcome from COVID-19. April 24, 2020. https://assets.publishing.service.gov.uk/government/uploads/system/uploads/attachment_data/file/886433/s0238-co-cin-report-ethnicity-outcomes-250420-sage29.pdf (accessed June 2, 2020).

10 Nudges Against Pandemics

Sweden's COVID-19 Containment Strategy in Perspective

Jon Pierre

Introduction

Without a doubt, 2020 and presumably several years onwards will go down in history as the years of the COVID-19 pandemic. Beyond the unimaginable human loss and economic devastation that the pandemic is wreaking, we are already beginning to see early signs of what will be a massive research effort aiming at explaining cross-national variations in government responses to the COVID-19 pandemic (for an early assessment, see Toshkov, Yesilkagit, & Carroll, 2020). As the situation is still very much evolving – most experts caution that we have not yet (this being written in June 2020) witnessed more than the early phases of the pandemic – any assessment of governments' strategies to contain the pandemic will be very tentative. What we can say something more definitive about, however, is the strategic choices made by governments, the stringency with which the strategy was rolled out and government performance more broadly during the early, critical stages of the pandemic.

We are currently witnessing an extensive variation across different countries in terms of the strategy they have chosen to respond to the pandemic. Some countries (for instance France and Germany) have chosen a rather forcefully implemented lockdown, allowing society to open up slowly and incrementally when the epidemiological evidence suggests it to be appropriate. A few other countries (for instance, the early containment strategy of the UK) countries have opted for a more varied response, allowing the population to move about while maintaining social distancing and avoiding crowds. The pandemic has had a major, if not devastating, impact on the economy, and governments' measures to alleviate these problems include unprecedented levels of public support to private businesses. However, governments differ significantly in terms of the support they offer to private businesses and the industry (Toshkov et al., 2020).

One of the more contentious debates during the COVID-19 pandemic has revolved around Sweden's strategy to curtail the spread of the virus. During the week of 13 May 2020, Sweden had the highest COVID-related per capita deaths in the world, according to the Financial Times' Coronavirus tracker.

On 25 May, Sweden passed the 4,000 deaths milestone. As Sweden had relied on a different strategy to contain the pandemic, it was only logical to many observers to attribute this poor performance to Sweden's strategic choices.

Yet, there is significant disagreement about the virtues or perils associated with Sweden's COVID strategy. Some have described the Swedish response as dangerously liberal, with only a few constraints on people's movements. Most recently (April 2020), others like Michael Ryan, executive director of the WHO Health Emergencies Program, have made a very different assessment. Ryan argues that while Sweden's strategic objective has been very similar to that of most other countries, i.e. a fairly advanced lockdown and social distancing, the country has relied on other, less coercive means to reach that goal. In late April 2020 Ryan even went so far as to suggest that Sweden may well be a model for other countries in the management of future pandemics.

The debate on whether a less restrictive regime would be more efficient than a strict lockdown has also been intense among experts, politicians and laymen in Sweden. The medical-epidemiologist community remains deeply divided on this issue, as shown by highly critical op-eds authored by more than 20 professors or senior physicians who have questioned the containment strategy designed by the PHA (see for instance *Dagens* Nyheter, 2020a, b).

In addition, as the death toll has steadily increased, advocates of a liberal strategy have emphasized that this is less because the strategy is flawed but more because key elements of the strategy such as protecting the elderly in nursing homes and elsewhere were not properly implemented by local authorities. As we will elaborate later in this chapter, many of these issues hark back to the institutional relationships among the institutions in the Swedish public health and healthcare system and the elderly care sector.

Given that a key objective in fighting a pandemic at a societal level is to alter social behavior in order to minimize interpersonal contact and thereby reduce the spread of communicable disease, any response strategy must depart from pre-existing social norms and behaviors, broadly defined, and those norms vary considerably across countries and even regions. There is a similar variation in the perception of government and its role as a regulator. Thus, while changing social behavior in some countries requires coercive enforcement measures and regulations in other countries changing population behaviors can be accomplished with much more subtle signaling from the government. In both these aspects of containment – the strategic objectives and the selection of instruments to alter social behavior – Sweden has stood out from the majority of countries. The Swedish containment strategy was not centered around a complete lockdown but rather included more selective measures such as minimizing people's visits to areas where a high density of people could be expected. Perhaps most importantly, government and agencies preferred to issue recommendations and advice on the appropriate social behavior instead of coercive regulations. It is this aspect of the Swedish approach that has perhaps triggered most international curiosity.

While the chapter studies policy design and implementation during a major societal crisis, it also raises a series of questions of continuing significance, such as the problems of vertical policy coordination and problems related to decentralized governance (Adam, Hurka, Knill, Peters, & Steinebach, 2019). A large number of issues in contemporary policy-making target regions and cities – not least highly complex and salient issues like climate change adaptation and mitigation – as the main actor in the implementation of public policy. Also, when most countries have built an extensive system of independent executive agencies, a complex principal-agent problem has emerged between departments as the key strategic actor and agencies as the operative structures. Thus, although the chapter draws on empirical observations from an extreme case of public policy, the findings speak to more continuous issues as well.

This chapter will give an overview of the Swedish strategy to contain the COVID-19 pandemic. First, however, we will briefly describe the institutional arrangements in Sweden which define the roles of the Cabinet, the agencies, the regions and local authorities which are the key public actors responsible for the implementation of the strategy. After outlining and assessing the Swedish pandemic strategy we will assess the strategy in terms of its internal logic and outcomes.

Nudges, Nudges Everywhere: The Institutional Arrangements of the Swedish Public Health System

It is often argued that institutional arrangements and the choices they represent enable the government to employ some policy instruments to implement public policy while at the same time preventing it from using others (see, for instance, Rockman & Weaver, 1993). For instance, extensive decentralization allows local institutions to deliver services that have the discretion to respond to local needs and demands at the same time as it prevents redistribution across regions.

Furthermore, institutions operate in a landscape of social norms. Institutions and social norms are closely related. Institutions are essential in reproducing social norms and defining a 'logic of appropriateness', i.e. a set of social norms and expectations on individual social behavior (March & Olsen, 1989). The degree to which institutions can shape social behavior depends to a large extent on the level of institutional trust in society. In political cultures where trust is low (see Hartley and Jarvis, this issue), institutions often have to resort to govern society by coercive measures, whereas if the trust is high institutions can rely on more subtle instruments such as advice or recommendation or even nudges to bring about the desired social behavior (see Einfeld, 2019).

In the present analysis, this perspective on institutional design, trust and social behavior makes very much sense (Trägårdh, 2020). Sweden has for the last two centuries – i.e. long before the executive agencies that emerged as part of the New Public Management reform campaign in the 1980s and 1990s – had a system with highly autonomous agencies (*myndigheter*). Indeed, one could argue that the point of gravity in the central government system is not the Central Government Office (CGO; *regeringskansliet*) with a total staff of about 4,600 but rather at the agency level, where 341 agencies with a total staff of some 226,000 are the locus of expertise, resources and manpower.

How does this arrangement work in practice? How does the fairly small core executive institution ensure that the more sizeable and constitutionally autonomous agencies do not become self-referential organizational structures pursuing their own agenda while operating beyond political control? The answer, in short, is that the government certainly has some formal levers in relationship to the agencies: it appoints the Directors General; controls the budget; and can, if necessary, simply terminate them at any time. In terms of the daily operations of agencies, the most common type of 'steers' (Page & Jenkins, 2005) that government departments give their agencies is conveyed through informal contacts. Several studies substantiate both the significance and the durability of networks between departmental and agency-level staff (for an overview, see Jacobsson & Sundström, 2015).

Thus, although agencies certainly report to their parent department which provides them with an annual budget appropriation and instructions, they do enjoy considerable autonomy vis-à-vis the department, by virtue of their constitutional mandate, their expertise and other organizational resources. The political leadership relies largely on informal contacts and 'steers' coupled with a strong sense of loyalty towards the government of the day among the civil servants (Niemann, 2013).

Turning now to the regional government, the key significance of this tier of government in the present analysis is that the 21 regions are in charge of the healthcare system. The central government provides strong economic support to the regions and conducts oversight of the medical services they deliver but in terms of formal jurisdiction, central government lacks authority in relationship to the regions. The National Board of Health and Welfare (NBHW; *socialstyrelsen*) and the Public Health Agency (PHA; *folkhälsomyndigheten*) offer advice and information and may allocate targeted funding.

The NBHW makes a distinction between 'soft' coordination, which is the daily, routine exchange of information and 'hard' coordination which can include the transfer of costs or resources among regions or align regions with central government services such as units in the national defense.

Local government in Sweden (290 municipalities) delivers the bulk of welfare services, primary education and care of the elderly. This latter service has become a key area of attention during the pandemic, as 90% of the COVID-19 fatalities have occurred among people aged 70 years or older. Again, local governments in Sweden enjoy extensive autonomy in relation to the central government, which essentially prevents national healthcare agencies like the NBHW and the PHA from enforcing rules concerning personal protection equipment or the separation of infected people from non-infected people.

This is the institutional context within which the strategy to contain the COVID-19 pandemic evolved. With autonomous agencies, regions and local authorities, central government policy-making institutions find themselves managing and coordinating a highly decentralized system. Furthermore, agencies in the healthcare sector have no remit over the regions delivering healthcare; their only means of guiding the region is to provide information and to maintain informal networks. Thus, the coordination of the public institutional system is to a large extent achieved through informal mechanisms, bargaining, information and networking. This is not to suggest that the system lacks coordination, but it does suggest that in times of crisis the system may be slow in responding.[1]

Another important observation is that the institutional arrangement is conducive to allowing expertise to influence policy and administrative action. Given that much of the expertise is found in the agencies and to a lesser extent in government departments, it becomes difficult for departments not to invite or consult with experts in the agencies. In the case of the government's response to COVID-19, the Prime Minister as well as other Cabinet members stated early on in the process that they would take advice from the experts and the agencies. And indeed they have; in the daily press briefings from mid-March onwards senior public servants representing the PHA and the NBHW are the main speakers compared to Cabinet ministers.

A final concluding observation relates to the soft coordinating mechanisms in the government system. While they might appear too subtle and vulnerable to provide guidance, particularly in crisis situations, they draw to a large extent on interorganizational networks of specialized public officials. Sweden is a high-trust society, both in terms of interpersonal and institutional trust. This high level of trust facilitates informal yet efficient coordination with very low transaction costs. A big question here was to what extent this model of governance and coordination would also work during a crisis like the COVID-19 pandemic.

The Swedish COVID-19 Containment Strategy

Let us now review the finer details of the Swedish strategy to combat COVID-19. We will first assess the strategy at the institutional level, i.e. institutional roles and patterns of coordination among agencies, regions and local governments. We will then turn to the strategy implemented to adapt social behavior.

The overall goals of the COVID-19 strategy, according to state epidemiologist Lars Tegnell at the PHA, are to protect the elderly and to ensure that the healthcare system is not overloaded with patients. The elderly have a weaker immune system and may also have diabetes, cardiovascular issues or other health problems which make them further susceptible to contract the virus.

Ensuring that the hospitals do not receive more patients than they can handle – the 'flattening of the curve' – is achieved by efforts to restrict large gatherings of people, urging people to maintain social distancing and staying home if they experience any symptoms or if their work allows them to work remotely. Thus, herd immunity is not a strategic goal in and of itself but is more seen as a secondary outcome of the strategy.

We will first go through the main points of the response at the institutional level, i.e. to clarify the role of different institutions. We then turn to the strategic level to see which objectives and instruments have been implemented to address the pandemic.

The Institutional Level

Already at an early stage of the crisis, it was clear that the core executive, i.e. the Prime Minister and other Cabinet ministers and their staff, would not be operationally involved in the crisis management. Instead, agencies like the PHA and the NBHW were to take the lead by virtue of their expertise on pandemics.

Key points:

- Cabinet ministers take the back seat while urging citizens to follow the experts' advice. Daily press briefings are conducted, occasionally with Cabinet ministers but mostly with experts from the PHA, the NBHW and the Civil Contingencies Agency (CCR; *myndigheten för säkerhet och beredskap*).
- The NBHW combines 'soft' and 'hard' coordination.
- The CCR oversees and supports coordination among agencies.
- NBHW and PHA oversee the healthcare system managed by regional governments.
- NBHW oversee nursing homes and other elderly care facilities managed by local authorities.
- Regions are in charge of healthcare.
- Local authorities are in charge of elderly care.

The emphasis on coordination stems in part from the decentralized nature of the institutional system discussed earlier, requiring more coordination efforts than systems with a clear command-line structure of government. Coordination was achieved by relying on soft and informal instruments of guiding agencies' reliance on expertise and informal channels of coordination both among agencies and also between agency level (central government), regions and local authorities. In addition to this 'soft' coordination, the NBHW also used 'hard' coordination with more institutional leverage when coordinating across sectoral boundaries, e.g. to use defense equipment to transfer patients from overloaded regions to less-affected regions.

Compared to many other countries, this model of crisis management differs in terms of the more subtle role of Cabinet ministers. In most countries, a high visibility of the Prime Minister or President is expected to provide leadership and to send a message to the public that the crisis is handled at the top level of government. In Sweden, however, it was clearly announced that the government would follow the advice of the PHA. This should not be seen as an abdication of the political leadership – although there has certainly been criticism raised against what has been seen as a conspicuous absence of political leaders during the pandemic. Crisis management scholars tend to argue that the best strategy to manage crises is not to alter institutional roles and hierarchies but to the extent possible let institutions act, and interact, in familiar roles and relationships (Boin, Hart, Stern, & Sundelius, 2006). Also, while most other countries can declare a state of emergency to centralize authority and make additional resources available, in Sweden that option can only be used when Sweden is in a state of war.

The Strategic and Societal Level

Let us now look at the concrete measures emphasized by the strategy. Epidemiologists and other experts have repeatedly emphasized in the media that all measures should be evidence-based and aligned with science.

   Key points:

* Protect the elderly and fragile;
* Contain the spread of the virus in order to avoid overloading hospitals with patients; 'flatten the curve';
* Restaurants, shops and factories to remain open;
* Restaurants and bars will be inspected by experts from authorities to ensure that patrons are seated with the proper social distance between the tables;
* No complete lockdown but urging people with symptoms to stay home;
* All those who can work from home are recommended to do so;
* Primary schools and daycare centers remain open; high schools and universities provide teaching online;
* Maintain social distancing. Meetings with more than 50 people are not allowed;
* Exercise individual responsibility and sound judgement about self-protection.

In March 2020, the PHA rolled out its strategy with characteristic aplomb. Again, the subtle and non-coercive nature of the measures is striking. There has however been some development over time in this respect. For instance, when inspectors found that restaurants and pubs were too crowded to ensure social distancing, inspections were stepped up and several establishments were forced to close temporarily. Also, early on in the crisis, the recommendation was for people with symptoms to stay home from work.

Later, that recommendation was revised so that unless you have to go to work you should work from home, and obviously not go to work if you have any symptoms.

Overall, the strategies have features of what Damon Barrett (2020) calls a 'harm reduction strategy'; the objective is to protect the healthcare system from overloading while at the same time protecting the most vulnerable and susceptible groups in society from the virus. It should also be noted that primary school and day-care centers have remained open; indeed, Sweden was the only European country which chose not to close down schools (Toshkov et al., 2020).

Equally important as what is in the strategy are the rules and recommendations that are *not* included. Perhaps most importantly, travel restrictions were introduced at a late stage. For instance, direct flights from Iran and northern Italy were admitted even after the corona outbreak in these locales had become known to Swedish authorities. Passengers arriving from those stations were not screened when disembarking the flights, let alone quarantined. We do not know what explains this tardy response in the face of clear evidence of the growing pandemic.

Another item missing in the list of measures is testing. Testing still remains underdeveloped in Sweden although the PHA has conducted several testing campaigns on samples of the population. These tests measure the amount of antibodies in the human blood, i.e. they do not measure whether a person is carrying the Coronavirus but rather if they have contracted the virus and since recovered. As we will argue in more detail later, by not quickly putting a system for testing in place the public health authorities lacked important data on the spread of the virus.

Testing for antibodies is important for a number of reasons, not least to see whether a sufficient percentage of the population has been infected in order to have achieved herd immunity. While herd immunity is not a goal in itself but rather a 'by-product' of the containment strategy, the level of contagion in society is critical to ascertain whether herd immunity has been established. Some, like state epidemiologist Anders Tegnell, suggest that herd immunity will be established when circa 60% of the population have contracted the virus while others, like mathematics professor Tom Britton, suggest that 40% will suffice to achieve herd immunity. In late May, preliminary studies show that only some 6–7% of the population has contracted the virus, suggesting it will take more time to achieve herd immunity than would be the case with a more regular flu virus (Dagens Nyheter, 2020b). Contagion has also proven to 'cluster' regionally and locally, so that some areas have been badly hit by the Coronavirus while other regions have had much lower number of cases.

In terms of how government and agencies employed coercive instruments to induce appropriate social behavior, the government did step up the distinctiveness of its recommendations in March and April 2020 as the scope of the pandemic became clearer. The government has repeatedly emphasized that tougher measures will be introduced unless social distancing is practiced, for instance closing restaurants and bars that do not ensure social distancing or patrons who are not seated.

The government has also introduced a series of support 'packages' giving massive economic support to industry and small businesses and also to local and regional governments. The government has also supported the furloughing of employees by covering the bulk of the employees' salary while furloughed. In addition, the central government committed itself to compensate the subnational government in full for the additional costs incurred by the pandemic.

Assessing the Swedish COVID-19 Strategy

Together with the UK until March 2020, Sweden is the only country to not lock down society in order to reduce the spread of the virus. Instead, as we have seen, Sweden chose a more open strategy, allowing free movement, stressing personal responsibility and to focus its efforts on protecting the old and fragile.

As an outlier, Sweden has rightly attracted international attention where some praise and others dismiss the path chosen by the Swedish public health authorities. Some have focused on the appropriateness of the strategy; others on the degree to which strategic actions and priorities were actually delivered; while yet others have sought to measure the actual outcomes and to compare those data with data from similar countries. Comparisons are often likely to draw on fairly simple measures, particularly when time is of the essence.

Another complexity relating to the success of different containment strategies relates to time. At the time of writing (June 2020), it appears clear that it is still too early to assess the efficiency of the Swedish approach to the COVID-19 pandemic, let alone draw any definite comparative conclusions (but see Toshkov et al., 2020).

For these reasons, evaluating the Swedish COVID-19 strategy and teasing out conclusions that can aid institutional learning may appear easy at first but soon becomes rather complicated. There are a number of variables that make any international comparison difficult. With that said, however, the fact remains that Sweden has recorded a much higher number of deaths than countries with which Sweden is often compared. By mid-May 2020, for example, Norway and Denmark report COVID 19-related fatalities on average in single digits while Sweden records circa 70 deaths daily. And, as mentioned, Sweden had the highest COVID-19 related deaths per capita in May 2020.

As of 3 June 2020, Denmark and Norway reported death tolls per million of 100 and 44, respectively, to be compared to Sweden's 450 deaths per million (Worldometer, June 4). Sweden thus reports more than four times the Danish COVID-19 death numbers; more than 10 times the Norwegian number; and about eight times the Finnish number of 58.

The combination of a liberal containment strategy and an exceptionally high death toll pattern begs questions of causality and why the Swedish public health authorities recommended this strategy. The main factor underlying this choice of containment strategy was not to protect the economy. Sweden is a trade-dependent economy and the global recession meant that overseas demand for Swedish products has plummeted, as has the import of components for the manufacturing industry. Instead, it appears as if the liberal strategy emphasizing personal responsibility was believed to be best suited for the Swedish culture and social behavior.

The public health authorities emphasized that its recommendations were strictly evidence-based. Evidence, by definition, draws on past experiences and hence easily leads to analogy thinking. Institutions facing a crisis sometimes tend to, consciously or subconsciously, think in terms of analogies in order to quickly come up with a plan for managing the crisis (see Boin et al., 2006). However, while the heuristic value of the analogy strategy hinges on an analysis that the present crisis is in fact of a similar nature as a crisis handled in a previous time, that analysis is rarely conducted properly. There is a possibility that the architects of the COVID-19 containment strategy saw this pandemic as similar to the H1N1 or the SARS pandemic in terms of the speed of dissemination of the virus and devised the current strategy accordingly. Key strategic decisions and recommendations might have been made with at least some reference to past pandemics without a thorough investigation of whether the new Coronavirus behaved similarly to previous such viruses or influenza viruses. We will return to this issue later.

Was the Swedish pandemic strategy appropriately designed? Has it been successful? It is, to reiterate a point made earlier, in some ways premature to assess the appropriateness of Sweden's COVID-19 strategy. The PHA argues that countries that chose to lock down their societies, like for instance neighboring Denmark, Norway and Finland, will experience an increasing death toll once they open up their lockdown and that their death toll will even out in the longer run. Elaborating this view, former state epidemiologist and current advisor to PHA and the WHO Johan Giesecke (2020) argues that 'our most important task is not to stop spread (*sic*), which is all but futile, but to concentrate on giving the unfortunate victims optimal care'. Fatalism aside, the perspective that more or less the entire population will contract the virus at some stage sustains the idea that in addition to protecting the healthcare system and the elderly, herd immunity is an important by-product of the containment strategy.

This leads us to an assessment of the theory underpinning Sweden's strategic choices. By late May, the percentage of the population that had contracted the Coronavirus remains around 10% or less. Given that the Coronavirus has been found to be highly contagious, this was an unexpectedly low percentage. The limited spread of a highly contagious virus, or more correctly, the strong regional variations in the spread, is a major puzzle in and of itself. State epidemiologist Tegnell has pointed out in numerous press briefings that the Coronavirus does not behave like most similar viruses. Contracting the virus can affect different individuals to vastly varying degrees, ranging from few or unnoticeable symptoms to death. That means that people can carry the virus and transmit it without their knowledge.

Also, the outbreaks of COVID-19 have been distinctly localized. Epidemiologists still do not know what explains these two patterns. Even so, both of these factors were inconsistent with the theory that underpinned the Swedish containment strategy. Thus, if we assume that there was some degree of analogy thinking that sustained the COVID-19 containment strategy, herd immunity, 'flattening the curve', and protecting old and weak people, which would have been key components of such a strategy, were less efficient than expected.

Advocates of the Swedish containment strategy suggest that the Swedish death toll will decline in late 2020, when herd immunity has been achieved (Giesecke, 2020). They also suggest that we are likely to see mortality rates spike in previously locked down countries once they begin to roll out an 'exit strategy'. Thus, former Swedish state epidemiologist Johan Giesecke (2020) argues that the final assessment of which strategy proved better cannot be done until probably sometime in 2021.

While many aspects of the design of the strategy make sense, the execution of the strategy raises several questions. Perhaps most importantly, a key objective in the PHA strategy has been to ensure that the elderly, in nursing homes and elsewhere, are protected from the virus. This objective, which state epidemiologist Anders Tegnell describes as 'our biggest problem area', has clearly not been achieved (Orange, 2020).

While it was clear early on that older people (70+ years of age) and/or people suffering from diabetes, hypertension or respiratory diseases are particularly susceptible to COVID-19, measures to protect this cohort were few and late to be implemented. The PHA apparently grew frustrated by what it perceived as a lack of training and equipment among nursing home staff, but as nursing homes operated under the auspices of local authorities, the PHA lacked any formal levers to correct those problems. The control span grew even further as several local authorities had contracted out parts of the elderly care to private service providers.

There is much to suggest that the main cause for the very poor performance of nursing homes and other elements of elderly care is related to the institutional arrangements in Sweden discussed earlier. The constitutional division of authority between the state, on the one hand, and regional and local government on the other also meant that the PHA and the NBHW – the two key agencies in the public healthcare sector – were poorly informed about the status of the stockpile for PPEs and other essential equipment at other tiers of government. For instance, when information about the lack of PPE in nursing homes reached the PHA, there was noticeable frustration with the performance of local authorities. It seems clear that while the multi-level institutional arrangement in healthcare and elderly care works fairly well under normal circumstances, it suffers from structural coordination problems which surface in times of crisis when the time elapsed from decision to execution is critical to a successful outcome.

Inspired by New Public Management 'just-in-time models', cities and regions had reduced stockpiles, often to a bare minimum. When local and regional authorities began exploring the market for personal protective equipment (PPE) they soon realized that many of the products they needed were in huge global, and domestic, demand. The shortage of PPEs left staff, and thereby senior people, in nursing homes unprotected.[2] Also, high levels of staff turnover, often with very limited training and occasionally with only a very basic proficiency in the Swedish language, exacerbated the problems in the nursing homes. Thus, one of the key strategic goals and preconditions for a successful implementation of the Swedish COVID-19 strategy – protecting the elderly – failed to a large extent (see Orange, 2020).

Another key aspect of the strategy was that people not showing any symptoms of contracting the Coronavirus could move about in society and go to work, while observing social distancing; 'stay at home if you have any symptoms'. However, it soon became apparent that asymptomatic people could not just carry but also transmit the virus. This was a nothing short of a game changer and a serious blow to the limited mitigation strategy. If anyone in any social context could transmit the virus to other people, containing this highly contagious virus became virtually impossible.

Together, these two significant flaws in the Swedish COVID-19 pandemic strategy – overestimating the capacity of nursing homes to protect the elderly and underestimating the risk of asymptomatic people transmitting the virus – have caused significant problems to the containment of the virus. In addition, Sweden, like many other countries, shares the problem of facilitating mass testing. It could be argued is that the Swedish containment strategy allowing people to move about more freely in society created a bigger need for extensive testing compared to a more restrictive and mitigated strategy. The failure to quickly put a testing regime in place – something which comparable countries like Denmark and several other countries had achieved – meant that public health authorities lacked critical information that could have informed strategic choices.

As we have argued throughout this chapter, the Swedish culture has for a very long period of time has been defined by its collectivity, homogeneity and consensualism (Arter, 2006; Elder, Thomas, & Arter, 1988; see also relevant chapters in Pierre, 2015). This culture has been conducive to subtle but efficient social and institutional signaling. Thus, despite the fragmented nature of the Swedish institutional system, coordination among central government institutions, or between central and subnational governments, has for the most part been conducted to a large extent through informal means but has nonetheless been efficient. Similarly, state institutions have been able to shape social behavior by using subtle instruments.

The containment of the COVID-19 pandemic so far suggests that this model of conducting coordination, particularly in times of crisis, has become less efficient and reliable. Within the public sector, coordination among agencies, regions and local authorities seems to work reasonably well during normal circumstances but less so in times of crises. 'Soft coordination', i.e. coordination among autonomous institutions, takes time. While such processes ensure that all actors are on board a joint project, it is not a model of management that is geared to manage crises where speed and compliance are of the essence.

In terms of ensuring social compliance to government and official recommendations, there are now indications – e.g. recent studies by the Swedish Civil Contingency Agency, MSB – that the public is becoming less responsive to government recommendations or advice. It is difficult to explain why this is happening, particularly as institutional trust overall remains high in Sweden.

Towards Comparative Analysis

One important purpose of this chapter is to lay the groundwork for a broader comparative assessment of national strategies to contain and manage the COVID-19 pandemic. The analytical focus is on the role of expertise, particularly the confidence experts had in their assessments of the pandemic.

In Sweden, the message from senior Cabinet ministers very early in the pandemic was they would take advice from the experts, i.e. the PHA and NBHW staff, on key issues, not least whether to lock down or continue to allow movement while maintaining social distancing. While we have no first-hand information on how confident the epidemiologists in the PHA were in their analysis and the strategic recommendations that followed from that assessment, the consistency of their recommendations suggests that the degree of confidence was high. There also appears to have been a high level of confidence in the healthcare system to handle the pandemic, provided that the mitigation could 'flatten the curve', i.e. keep the number of COVID-19 patients sufficiently low in order for the system to sustain the flow of patients.

The apparent inaction, compared to most other countries, was however less an indication of a slow or weak response but more of a deliberate evidence-based strategy.[3] The PHA epidemiologists were concerned that a complete lockdown would not be sustainable in the longer run but that it could lead to increased societal psychological issues, depression and increased domestic violence. Furthermore, the epidemiologists apparently did not see any reason to question the capacity of local authorities to manage nursing homes appropriately in terms of protecting the elderly and the staff; nor did they appear to be worried about the stockpile of PPE managed by the regions.

In sum, from what we have heard from the PHA experts, it seems clear that the response was not slow or poor. The response followed a playbook based on previous experiences of handling pandemics, protecting social groups that were susceptible to the virus and also ensuring that the healthcare system could accommodate the growing number of patients.

In hindsight, it appears as if there are two broad sets of issues where the early analysis may have been incomplete or flawed. One issue relates to the Coronavirus, particularly how contagious it is. We have already mentioned that although not a goal in itself, herd immunity has been seen as a by-product of the limited mitigation strategy. The Coronavirus has proven to behave differently than previous flu viruses and achieving herd immunity has turned out to be much more long term than was previously thought to be the case. Also, as previously mentioned, the initial strategy was based on the assumption that only people displaying symptoms of COVID-19 were carriers and transmitters of the virus. This assumption was soon falsified, urging a change of some elements of the mitigation strategy.

The other issue relates to the HPA assumptions about the preparedness and capacity of subnational governments to tackle the pandemic. These assumptions have proven to be much too optimistic. While the healthcare system has performed well, elderly care has been a major problem, with a very large number of senior people in nursing homes, but also members of staff, contracting the virus.

These two circumstances – the unexpected features of the Coronavirus compared to previous virus-based pandemics and the poor performance of primarily local authorities – were serious blows to the containment strategy rolled out by the PHA and NBHW. There was confidence in the measures that made up the strategy but perhaps more confidence than a closer inspection would have warranted. Annika Linde, the state epidemiologist between 2005 and 2013 and highly critical of the management of the COVID-19 pandemic, argues that in hindsight a one-month lockdown in Sweden early on when the pandemic first hit would have bought politicians and experts valuable time to assess the situation and to carefully design a strategy, a game plan, to tackle the crisis (*Dagens* Nyheter, 2020c). Instead, she suggests, we ended up in a blame game and failed to stop the inflow of travelers from COVID-19 hotspots in Italy and Iran. The lockdown time could also have been used to gather information on the virus to see whether any analogy with previous similar pandemics was relevant. Again, it is anybody's delight to conduct analyses with all the facts on the table, but even so there is much to suggest that a month of lockdown might have provided the PHA experts with additional and extremely valuable data on the nature of the Coronavirus.

An important takeaway from the Swedish case is that the complex and negotiated relationships between the national public health authorities, the autonomous regions and the also autonomous local authorities are not a perfect institutional system for addressing crises such as pandemics. The system performs well in fair weather, allowing for the inclusion of actors and stakeholders across society, but less so in more challenging situations when strict command lines are required to ensure swift and concerted action.

Concluding Discussion

As we have stated several times in this chapter, the phenomenon under study is still very much evolving. This makes more definitive assessment of the containment strategies adopted by different countries very difficult. This would arguably be particularly important for an assessment of the Swedish containment strategy, as it did not include an early lockdown but rather allowed for a mitigated spread of the virus in the country. This strategy could generate higher death numbers in the early stages but the curve would soon flatten. Meanwhile, countries that opted for a complete lockdown would report fewer deaths in the early stages of the pandemic but higher numbers when they opened up the lockdown. So far, neither of these developments have taken place; Sweden still reports high death numbers while Scandinavian neighbors are now gradually opening up and maintaining their record of very moderate fatalities.

The Swedish case of addressing a pandemic stands out internationally, in terms of its liberal views on constraining social movements and interactions; the instruments used to implement the strategy, and also in terms of the death toll. The big question to investigate once the pandemic is brought under control is to what extent these three factors are causally related in any way. It is certainly tempting to assign causality among the limited mitigation and the number of Corona cases but only a very careful analysis can establish whether that theory is true.

The state epidemiologist Anders Tegnell acknowledged in an interview with Radio Sweden on 2 June that 'if we were to encounter the same disease, with the knowledge we have today, we would probably have to implement a strategy about halfway between what Sweden did and what the rest of the world did'.[4] Thus, the containment strategy was designed very early and was presumably designed drawing on evidence from influenza pandemics and other previous virus pandemics such as H1N1. With more extensive knowledge about the specific behavior of the Coronavirus, Tegnell said, the strategy would have included strategically selected sectors of society that would have been locked down for some period of time. That sequence of actions echoes what Tegnell's predecessor as state epidemiologist, Annika Linde, advocated; that the public health authorities should have imposed a lockdown at a very early stage of the pandemic to gather knowledge about the behavior of this particular virus, and only then outline a containment strategy that would have responded more efficiently to the pandemic.

Arguably, the potential for cross-national learning in the case of pandemic containment strategies is fairly limited. Given that the overarching objective of such a strategy is to alter social behavior, strategies must depart from the pre-existing patterns of behavior and the inclination among citizens to follow government guidelines. In some cultures, such guidelines have to be enforced with severe sanctions for those who ignore the guidelines whereas in other cultures the government can rely on using more subtle means. Sweden would fall into the latter category of countries.

The final analysis of Sweden's strategy to contain the COVID-19 cannot be conducted until late 2021, at best. It is still anybody's guess when societies hit by the pandemic will be able to return to normal. The question of what can be learned from this crisis can be answered first when in-depth analyses, as well as comparative studies, have been completed.

Notes

1. As an example, the present author interviewed an official at the Public Health Agency in March 2020 for a research project on the Swedish program to address antimicrobial resistance. When asked about what the biggest challenges in this work were, the official responded that the agency's lack of jurisdiction over the regions was a major challenge. When later asked what might explain the success in addressing antimicrobial resistance, however, the official stated the collaborations with the regions and local authorities had been a key factor. It appears as if the 'strength of weak ties' is believed to be a better coordinating arrangement than formal command lines (Granovetter, 1973).
2. The lack of facemasks and other personal protective equipment became a problem to the Work Environment Authority (WEA, *arbetsmiljöverket*) requiring such equipment to be used in this type of situation. After consulting with the employer, the Swedish Association of Local Authorities and Regions, however, the WEA changed its ruling from a requirement to a recommendation, triggering massive criticism.
3. If anything, the strategy was almost *too* evidence based; only measures which were support by hard empirical evidence were considered while more precautionary measures that were not equally supported by hard evidence were not implemented.
4. Present author's translation. Tegnell later modified this statement, saying that there is always 'room for improvement' (*'förbättringspotential'*) in any containment strategy.

References

Adam, C., Hurka, S., Knill, C., Peters, B. G., & Steinebach, Y. (2019). Introducing vertical policy coordination to comparative policy analysis: The missing link between policy production and implementation. *Journal of Comparative Policy Analysis*, 25, 499–517.

Arter, D. (2006). *Democracy in Scandinavia: Consensual, majoritarian, or mixed?* Manchester: Manchester University Press.

Barrett, D. (2020). Sweden's Covid harm reduction strategy. *Medium.com*.

Boin, A., Hart, P., Stern, E., & Sundelius, B. (2006). *The politics of crisis management: Public leadership under pressure*. Cambridge: Cambridge University Press.

Einfeld, C. (2019). Nudge and evidence based policy: Fertile ground. *Evidence & Policy*, 15(4), 509–524.

Elder, N., Thomas, A. H., & Arter, D. (1988). *The consensual democracies: The government and politics of the Scandinavian states*. Oxford: Blackwell.

Giesecke, J. (2020, May 5). Correspondence: The invisible pandemic. *The Lancet*, 395(10238), e98.

Granovetter, M. S. (1973). The strength of weak ties. *American Journal of Sociology*, 78(6), 1360–1380.

Jacobsson, B., & Sundström, G. (2015). Governing the state. In J. Pierre (Ed.), *The Oxford handbook of Swedish politics* (pp. 347–364). Oxford: Oxford University Press.

March, J. G., & Olsen, J. P. (1989). *Rediscovering institutions: The organizational dimension of politics*. New York: Free Press.

Niemann, C. (2013). *Villkorat förtroende: Normer och rollförväntningar i relationen mellan politiker och tjänstemän i Regeringskansliet* [Conditioned trust: Norms and role expectations in the relationship between politicians and civil servants in the central government office]. dissertation. Stockholm: Department of Political Science, Stockholm University.

Nyheter, D. (2020a). Folkhälsomyndigheten har misslyckats—nu måste politikerna gripa in [The Public Health Agency has failed, politicians must now step in] (op-ed), April 24.

Nyheter, D. (2020b). Flockimmunitet är en farlig och orealistisk coronastrategy [Herd immunity is a dangerous and unrealistic corona strategy] (op-ed), May 14.

Nyheter, D. (2020c). Annika Linde: En månads stängning hade gett oss tid [Annika Linde: A one month lockdown would have bought us time] (op-ed), May 19.

Orange, R. (2020). Anger in Sweden as elderly pay price for coronavirus strategy. *The Guardian*, April 19.

Page, E. C., & Jenkins, B. (2005). *Policy bureaucracy: Government with a cast of thousands*. Oxford: Oxford University Press.

Pierre, J. (ed). (2015). *The Oxford handbook of Swedish politics*. Oxford: Oxford University Press.

Rockman, B. A., & Weaver, R. K. (Eds.). (1993). *Do institutions matter: Government capabilities in the United States and abroad*. Washington, DC: The Brookings Institution.

Toshkov, D., Yesilkagit, K., & Carroll, B. (2020). *Government capacity, societal trust or party preferences? What accounts for the variety of national policy responses to the COVID-19 pandemic in Europe?* Unpublished paper. University of Leiden: Institute of Public Administration).

Trägårdh, L. (2020). Why might Sweden's Covid-19 policy work? Trust between citizens and state. *The Guardian*, April 21.

11 Herd Immunity or Suppression Strategy to Combat COVID-19

F. Jung, V. Krieger, F.T. Hufert, and J.-H. Küpper

Each state is currently pursuing its own strategies to cope with the SARS-CoV-2 pandemic that started in December 2019 in Wuhan, China. On January 21, the first imported case appeared in the USA and on January 24, SARS-CoV-2 emerged globally in many other countries including Europe where first cases were reported from France[1-4]. Some states, such as the Netherlands, Germany, Great Britain, Sweden and the USA initially focused on keeping the restrictions for economy and society as low as possible. Mass gatherings were initially neither prohibited nor were there strict regulations on social distancing or hygiene rules. The responsible authorities were of the opinion – and still are e.g. in Sweden – that it is sufficient to protect particularly vulnerable persons such as the elderly or people with pre-existing conditions. For the rest of the population, infection with the virus is certainly accepted, and even sought. The idea behind this is that as soon as 60 to 70 percent of the population is infected with a pathogen, a so-called "herd immunity" has developed. The procedure was as follows: The virus was to be suppressed only by gradual measures so that enough people could become infected. The strategy was an attempt to build up herd immunity so that "enough of us who will only show mild symptoms can become immune." This was the statement of Sir P. Vallance, the British government's chief scientific adviser on March 13, 2020. However, modelling studies of the epidemic by Imperial College London showed the expected overload of the hospitals. As a consequence, the British government abruptly changed the strategy March 16 and decided for a temporary lockdown. The Netherlands and Germany also left herd immunity strategy to cope with COVID-19. Figure 11.1 shows the clear reaction of the lockdown for Germany: the new infections per day in relation to the population of the respective country were continuously and significantly decreasing.

Sweden followed a strategy that is almost equivalent to the herd immunity. Restaurants, shops and fitness studios are also open. Border closures have not taken place. Only secondary schools and universities have been closed. Older people are advised to avoid social contacts. Those who feel symptoms of a possible COVID-19 disease should be placed in home quarantine.

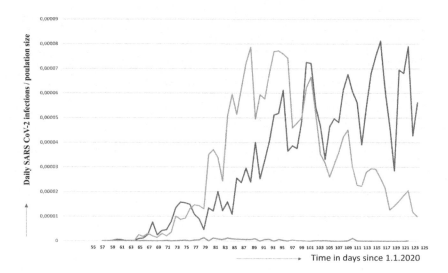

Figure 11.1 Daily SARS-COV-2 infections per respective number of inhabitants for Sweden (black line), Germany (light grey line) and Taiwan (dark grey line).

Data were obtained from the following source: ECDC (www.ecdc.europa.eu/en/ publications-data/download-todays-data-geographic-distribution-covid-19-cases-worldwide). See accompanying text for context of the data. Our policy regarding the information format is prioritizing Open Source and Free Software. We therefore make all data retrieved and analyzed hereby available at corona.milliways.online.

This figure clearly shows two findings. The course of the pandemic and the spread of the virus in those countries from day 56 (2020/25/2) until day 124 (2020/5/3). The course of the SARS-COV-2 pandemic in Sweden could be interpreted that a plateau has been reached. However, the further development of the situation remains to be elucidated. In any case, the Swedish health authority Folkhälsomyndigheten was wrong when it reported that the most new cases occurred on April 15. That was when the curve had reached its highest point. The further course of the curve indicates an ongoing increase, although the dynamic has slowed down. However, it is possible that a plateau-phase has been reached. In contrast, the cumulative graph of daily infections is still increasing in Sweden while in Germany almost, and more importantly in Taiwan, a plateau seems to be reached since many days (see Figure 11.2).

Sweden's advantages in fighting the pandemic are the high proportion of single households in large cities, the sparse population outside the conurbations around Stockholm (more than a third of those infected and more than half of those dying of COVID-19 are from the Stockholm area), Gothenburg and Malmö, and the generally high level of prosperity.

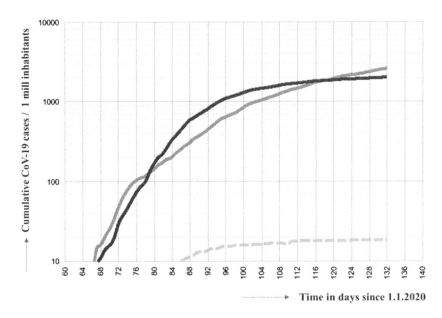

Figure 11.2 Cumulative case numbers of infections in Sweden (dark grey line), Germany (black line) and Taiwan (light grey line) in relation to 1 million people

Data were obtained from the following source: ECDC (www.ecdc.europa.eu/en/publications-data/download-todays-data-geographic-distribution-covid-19-cases-worldwide). See accompanying text for context of the data. Our policy regarding the information format is prioritizing Open Source and Free Software. We therefore make all data retrieved and analyzed hereby available at corona.milliways.online.

Based on the number of the total population, three times more people died from COVID-19 in Sweden (2,679 deaths per 10 million inhabitants) compared to Germany (6,848 deaths per 80 million inhabitants). The comparison of Sweden versus Taiwan is even worse because 1,072 times more people died in Sweden based on the number of the population (6 deaths per 24 million inhabitants in Taiwan).

The rise in the curve of normalized mortality rates for Sweden is still much steeper than for Germany (see Figure 11.3), so that the mortality rate is likely to drift even further apart (unless Sweden takes significant countermeasures).

This shows how effective the rigorous implementation of protective measures in Taiwan has been in preventing both infection and death. Unlike the European countries, Taiwan reacted very early[4]: Following the SARS experience of 2003, a National Health Command Centre (NHCC) was established with the Central Epidemic Command Centre (CECC) as the central coordinating body. The CECC has rapidly produced and

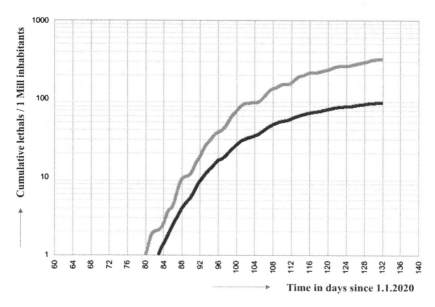

Figure 11.3 Cumulative deaths of SARS COV-2 infected patients in Sweden (dark grey line) and Germany (black line). Taiwan (until day 134 (2020/05/13) only 6 cases) cannot be shown in this representation. Data points lie almost on the x-axis).

Data were obtained from the following source: ECDC (www.ecdc.europa.eu/en/publications-data/download-todays-data-geographic-distribution-covid-19-cases-worldwide). See accompanying text for context of the data. Our policy regarding the information format is prioritizing Open Source and Free Software. We therefore make all data retrieved and analyzed hereby available at corona.milliways.online.

implemented a list of at least 124 action items including border control from the air and sea, case identification (using new data and technology), quarantine of suspicious cases, proactive case finding, resource allocation (assessing and managing capacity), reassurance and education of the public while fighting misinformation, negotiation with other countries and regions, formulation of policies toward schools and childcare, and relief to businesses[5]. These measures were so effective that only 6 patients died from a total of 397 confirmed infections in a population of more than 24 million people.

It is currently unclear how long immunity lasts after SARS-COV-2 infection. There are four other corona viruses circulating in the world population causing common cold, pneumonia and bronchitis. However, not much is known about cross-protection. Antibodies to SARS-CoV-1 have been described to be detected up to two years after infection; this might render people to be susceptible again for reinfection after three years[6]. A time-limited SARS-CoV-2 immunity would make it necessary that reinfection occurs to keep up herd immunity and the infestation of a country may take even longer than individual immunity. However, there are no data on the clinical course of reinfected people and the impact of T-cell immunity to prevent severe clinical outcome.

In the face of the lack of an antiviral treatment and the lack of a protective vaccine one must state Taiwan has made the best out of the pandemic situation whereas Sweden failed completely.

A lot of patients who survived the severe COVID-19 are suffering from severe sequelae especially after multiple thrombotic processes in the vascular system[7] involving lung, liver, spleen and kidney[8–10] and other organs. Today, prevention is the only and best tool we have to prevent severe COVID-19 cases and unnecessary late sequelae or deaths. The motto must be prevention first, since we all have only one life.

A recent simulation study by the universities of Uppsala and Stockholm[11] illustrated that if the current measures will be continued (day101), 100,000 people in Sweden would die of corona virus. If social distancing were to be implemented consistently, the study shows that the figure would be just over 20,000.

References

1. Kinross P, Suetens C, Gomes Dias J, et al. Rapidly increasing cumulative incidence of coronavirus disease (COVID-19) in the European Union/European Economic Area and the United Kingdom, 1 January to 15 March 2020. Euro Surveill. 2020;25.
2. Bernard Stoecklin S, Rolland P, Silue Y, et al. First cases of coronavirus disease 2019 (COVID-19) in France: surveillance, investigations and control measures, January 2020. Euro Surveill. 2020;25.
3. Johnson HC, Gossner CM, Colzani E, et al. Potential scenarios for the progression of a COVID-19 epidemic in the European Union and the European Economic Area, March 2020. Euro Surveill. 2020;25.
4. Jung F, Krieger V, Hufert FT, Küpper J-H. How we should respond to the Coronavirus SARS-CoV-2 outbreak: a German perspective. Clin Hemorheol Microcirc. 2020. https://doi.org/10.3233/CH-170277
5. Wang CJ, Ng CY, Brook RH. Response to COVID-19 in Taiwan. Big data analytics, new technology, and proactive testing. JAMA. 2020;323(14):1341–1342.
6. Wu L-P, Wang N-C, Chang Y-H, Tian X-Y, Na D-Y, Li-Zhang Y, Zheng L, Lan T, Wang L-F, Liang G-D. Duration of antibody responses after severe acute respiratory syndrome. Emerg Infect Dis. 2007;13:1562–1564.
7. Spiezia L, Boscolo A, Poletto F, et al. COVID-19-related severe hypercoagulability in patients admitted to intensive care unit for acute respiratory failure. Thromb Haemost. 2020.
8. Jung EM, Stroszczinski C, Jung F. Contrast enhanced ultrasonography (CEUS) to detect abdominal microcirculatory disorders in severe cases of COVID-19 infection: first experience. Clin Hemorheol Microcirc. 2020. https://doi.org/10.3233/CH-209003.
9. Borgel D, Bianchini E, Lasne D, Pascreau T, Saller F. Inflammation in deep vein thrombosis: a therapeutic target? Hematology. 2019;24(1):742–750.

10. Barco S, Russo M, Vicaut E, Becattini C, Bertoletti L, Beyer-Westendorf J, Bouvaist H, Couturaud F, Danays T, Dellas C, Duerschmied D, Empen K, Ferrari E, Galiè N, Jiménez D, Klok FA, Kostrubiec M, Kozak M, Kupatt C, Lang IM, Lankeit M, Meneveau N, Palazzini M, Pruszczyk P, Rugolotto M, Salvi A, Sanchez O, Schellong S, Sobkowicz B, Meyer G, Konstantinides SV. Incomplete echocardiographic recovery at 6 months predicts long-term sequelae after intermediate-risk pulmonary embolism. A post-hoc analysis of the Pulmonary Embolism Thrombolysis (PEITHO) trial. Clin Res Cardiol. 2019;108(7):772–778.

11. Gardner JM, Willem L, van der Wijngaart W, Kamerlin SCL, Brusselaers N, Kasson P. Intervention strategies against COVID-19 and their estimated impact on Swedish healthcare capacity. MedRxiv. https://doi.org/10.1101/2020.04.11.20062133.

Part IV

The United States and Canada

To many people in the United States, epidemics and pandemics were something that occurs someplace else—usually in some far away distant land. If a pandemic ever reached the United States, the quality of its health care system and the capability of producing a vaccine more rapidly and efficiently than other countries seemed likely to render its effects minimal. This outcome, however, as we now know, did not happen. Instead, the impact of COVID-19 in the United States resulted in more deaths than in any other country in the world. In October 2020, the United States had more than 8.4 million confirmed cases and over 221,000 deaths. Moreover, the President of the United States, Donald Trump, and several of his associates became infected from COVID-19. He was hospitalized for a few days with mild symptoms before being released. Trump was the tenth head of state to be infected by this global virus. Altogether, the United States had somewhat more cases (8.3 million) than all of Europe (nearly 8 million) but fewer deaths (221,000 versus 247,000) in October. The Centers for Disease Control and Prevention (CDC) predicted that the United States could have as many as 300,000 deaths from COVID-19 by December 2020.

COVID-19 Arrives

The first known human-to-human transmission in the United States occurred when a 60-year-old woman returned to Illinois from Wuhan, China, in mid-January 2020 after visiting relatives and subsequently infected her husband, who had not traveled with her (Ghinai et al. 2020). She tested positive for the virus on January 21 becoming the initial case. Both she and her husband recovered, tests on their social contacts proved negative, and the virus had apparently not spread. The Trump administration prohibited travel from China on January 31. However, the ban had holes in it as it did not apply to American citizens and their immediate family members or permanent residents returning from China. In the two months following the travel ban, almost 40,000 people arrived in the United States on direct flights from China (Leonhardt 2020). Travel from Europe was not restricted until March, and Britain was exempt although it later had the most deaths in Europe from the virus.

The virus again arrived in King County, Washington, in February with a 35-year-old Chinese man who had been in Wuhan. It then appeared in a long-term care skilled nursing home in King County, where a 73-year-old woman with several comorbid conditions became sick on February 19. She tested positive for COVID-19 on February 27 and died on March 2. By February 28, four more residents were ill, and altogether some 101 nursing home residents, 50 staff members, and 16 visitors tested positive for the virus. Some 34 residents and one staff member died.

Even though the first deaths were in the state of Washington and later California, the initial epicenter of the virus in the United States did not turn out to be the West Coast but New York City. The city had more than 30 percent of all cases nationwide by late April. At that time, New York state's more than 320,000 confirmed cases were greater than any country in the world with the exception of the United States as a whole. By summer the pandemic had eased in New York but by late October it had registered some 491,687 cases, with more than 60 percent in New York City alone. New York had the most deaths (more than 33,000) of any state in the country and about 24,000 of those deaths were in New York City. The opening reading in this section is by Anne Schuchat at CDC detailing the first public health response to the pandemic in the United States. She points out that contributing factors to the spread of COVID-19 in New York City were the density of its population, the weekly travel into the city by some 1.6 million persons mostly on mass transit and the 1 million weekly arrivals in its three airports, crowded settings and housing making it difficult to social distance, large vulnerable populations of elderly and persons with preexisting conditions, and large gatherings of people. As for the United States as a whole, travel from China and Europe (particularly Italy), community spread, and large gatherings (i.e., professional conferences, Mardi Gras in New Orleans), work settings, nursing homes, religious services, and funerals accelerated the spread of the virus. Travel restrictions, social distancing, and stay-at-home (shelter-in-place) orders were issued for varying time periods in varying places.

The next reading by Jonathan Wortham and his colleagues (2020) at CDC is an analysis of the demographic information on some 52,166 persons who died in the United States from COVID-19 during the February–May 2020 timeframe. The report focuses on a supplementary set of data within a larger study of some 10,647 decedents for whom there was more complete data on race/ethnicity, age, underlying medical conditions, the clinical course of the disease, and location (home, hospital, emergency room, etc.) of death. Most people in this supplementary data set (about 94 percent) were from New York City, New Jersey, and the state of Washington, which were among the earliest places experiencing a severe outbreak of the pandemic. Most of the decedents were male (60 percent), elderly (75 percent), and had a comorbid condition (76 percent), with cardiovascular disease the most common underlying ailment. Some 35 percent were white. Among those under the age of 65, Hispanics and non-whites were twice as likely as whites to die from COVID-19.

However, a summer surge in infections in younger adults packing bars, beaches, and entertainment venues following lockdown relaxations put Texas at the top in confirmed cases (over 896,000) by October in the United States, followed by California (about 894,000 cases), and Florida (over 772,000 cases). These figures undoubtedly increased during the publication of this book. Since the infected were largely younger, mortality remained well below that of New York. Nationwide, males were more likely to be infected than females and older people age 65 and above with preexisting health conditions were especially subject to infection and death. Nursing homes were a major site for infection with over 40 percent of all deaths nationally occurring among nursing home residents, while bars and meat-packing plants were other places in which exposure to the virus was prevalent.

Federalism

A significant issue affecting the U.S.' response to the pandemic has been its system of federalism. The responsibility for public health is divided at the federal, state, and local levels with the states having the most responsibility as public health is not a power reserved to the national government under the constitution. This legal structure created a highly decentralized system of public health governance in the United States with hundreds of state and local health departments across the country sharing responsibility for responding to the COVID-19 pandemic without a national mandate. As put by Sarah Gordon and her associates (Gordon, Huberfield, and Jones 2020), the federalist system implies that the public health response to the coronavirus in the United States depends on the zip code. Not surprisingly, this system led to a variety of different policy responses by American states.

A national response was also complicated by different levels of infection in different states warranting stringent measures in some localities and limited responses in others. Alaska, Maine, Hawaii, and Wyoming had few cases and few deaths, while Montana and Vermont also had few fatalities. In each of these states the death toll was less than 100 in October 2020, with Wyoming having a low of 53 deaths. Conversely, hundreds of thousands were infected in states with much larger populations and cities as seen in California, Florida, Texas, and New York.

In the third reading in this section, Donald Kettl (2020) observes that in the early stages of the pandemic, policy responses were based more on "broader policy streams" than evidence-based decision-making. His findings concluded that states that expanded Medicaid under the Affordable Care Act were more likely to lock down early in the pandemic. In addition, states that locked down in March tended to have better environmental performance, lower infant mortality rates, and lower poverty rates than those that did not. While Kettl acknowledges and discusses partisan political differences in these states, he argues the difference is based on more deeply rooted policy differences than just partisanship for the uneven response.

Although federalism is certainly an obstacle to a national response, a question that has emerged is whether the federal government should take a stronger role in coordinating a national strategy rather than leaving so much of the policy decisions to the states. Rebecca Haffajee and Michelle Mello (2020) suggested a number of measures that the federal government could employ to mount a more aggressive response. These measures include the White House using its bully pulpit to insist that states adopt more assertive measures to contain the spread of COVID. Congress, using the carrot and the stick of federal funding, along with its power to regulate interstate commerce to influence state action and the possibility of using federal emergency powers, could push some states into taking stronger actions. Getting Congress to act, however, is highly problematic because the Democrat-controlled House will likely oppose anything the Trump administration proposes to keep the President from taking credit and the Republican-controlled Senate will likely do likewise to prevent the Democrats from implementing their policies. The political divide in the country is that strong regardless of the pandemic as bipartisan action in Congress has been elusive in a variety of actions, including a second supplemental pay package for small businesses and workers. Moreover, it is not known whether a coherent, national response will prove to be a more effective response to the pandemic. With the United States suffering from a disproportionate amount of the world's cases and deaths from the pandemic in its early months, the fragmented and piecemeal policy approaches at the state and local levels of government have been suboptimal.

Even if the U.S. government were to push forward an aggressive national containment strategy, it would still need to address civil liberties limitations. A government mandated quarantine may only be constitutional if it can show by clear and compelling evidence that it is the least restrictive public health measure under the circumstances (Parmet and Sinha 2020). Even mandating social distancing measures could also possibly provoke a similar legal challenge. Due to these issues, Lawrence Gostin and his colleagues (Gostin, Friedman, and Wetter 2020) suggested that the government needs to rely as much as possible on voluntary compliance with quarantines and individual isolation. Government mandates for such actions are recommended only as a last resort based on assessments of the risk and likely effectiveness of the measure, and applied non-discriminatively. Such a mandate should also permit procedural due process and the guarantee of a safe environment for isolated individuals.

Nevertheless, state governments were able to issue short-term shelter-in-place orders, which included a variety of exceptions, and social distancing policies that did save lives. As detailed in the fourth reading in this section by Wei Lyu and George Wehby (2020), shelter-in-place orders did reduce COVID-19 mortality and lessen hospital admissions. It is suggested that shelter-in-place orders prevented up to 370,000 deaths from the coronavirus. In the fifth reading by Charles Courtemache et al. (2020), it was determined that social distancing mandates on the part of state and local governments in March and April of 2020 also helped contain the spread of the virus. There was no evidence of bans on large gatherings or school closures affecting the growth in COVID cases, but without social distancing, sheltering-in-place, and the closing of bars, restaurants, gyms, and entertainment venues it is estimated that the spread of the virus would have been 35 times greater than it was. Other research investigating mobility patterns at the county level in the United States strongly supported the role of social distancing as an effective method to contain COVID-19 in the United States (Badr et al. 2020).

Individualism

Why didn't the various measures put in place to contain the pandemic in the United States work as well as in some European countries? One reason may have been that perhaps only about 50 percent of the population followed lockdown orders compared to about 95 percent in Europe (Leonhardt 2020). As early as mid-April 2020, there were public protests and demonstrations in the United States against government-imposed lockdowns in some states. The protests ranged from only a few people to several thousand in a Michigan rally. In October, the FBI foiled a plot to kidnap the governor of Michigan by a right-wing group and put her on trial for her handling of the pandemic. There were also protests and public confrontations about having to wear protective masks in public places by individuals and groups—all of which is indicative of the influence of individualism as a powerful value in American culture. Individualism in the American context is the belief that people have the right to think for themselves, to live their lives as they see fit, and express themselves on the basis of their own opinions. Consequently, the individual has the right to make his or her decisions without undue interference from outside sources (Walls 2015). This belief is so strong in the United States that some studies suggest it lies at the heart of American culture and is emphasized more in America than in many other societies (Bellah et al. 1985; Walls 2015).

An example of this is seen in the French postmodern sociologist Jean Baudrillard's (1989) claim some years ago that American culture is the original version of modernity. Baudrillard said that Americans are not wrong in their conviction that their culture is at the center of the modern world and the model they believe every other society should emulate. Americans have constructed a society based on *ideals* of justice, law, wealth, and freedom that many people in other countries envy—even though the reality is far from perfect. American culture, in Baudrillard's view, is the only one that has dared to forge ahead and try to turn its values, which emphasize freedom and equality, into reality. As Baudrillard (1989:93) observed:

> You only have to see a French family settling in on a California beach to feel the abominable weight of our culture. The American group remains open; the French unit immediately creates a closed space. The American child roams far and wide; the French one hovers around its parents. The Americans see to it that they stay well stocked with ice and beer; the French see to it that social niceties are observed, and that they keep up a theatrical show of well-being. People move around a lot on American beaches; the Frenchman stays camped on his little sandy domain. The Frenchman makes quite a show on holiday, but the mediocrity of his petty-bourgeois space stays with him. Now you can say anything you like about Americans, . . . they certainly do not have aristocratic grace, but they have an ease that comes from space, the ease of those who have always had lots of space, and this makes up for manners and noble breeding.

While not everyone may agree with Baudrillard's assessment, his work suggests that culture influences the manner in which people from different nations develop a sense of themselves. He implies that the way Americans move about and use space reflects their sense of freedom and equality. When people begin life in a culture that promotes freedom, moving around in a relatively easy manner can be very natural. According to Baudrillard, freedom in American culture does not have a static meaning; instead, its meaning is spatial and mobile.

A major characteristic of a culture is that it typically forms a unity of perspective that is a specific expression of the society it represents. One difference between the United States and Europe in coping with the pandemic may therefore be cultural. That is, individualism in the United States may have been prioritized over government restrictions by some persons even in a pandemic (Leonhardt 2020). For a society used to mobility and spatial freedom, people can quickly get tired of staying at home and it becomes difficult to accept lockdowns, social distancing, and the wearing of masks for a lengthy period of time. When bars, restaurants, and beaches attracted large gatherings when social restrictions were relaxed, a resurgence of the virus took place in several locales as noted. The cultural value of individualism may have played a larger role in responding to the pandemic than generally recognized.

Anti-Racism Protests

Not only had there been public protests against lockdowns, but much larger-scale street protests erupted in several cities and abroad against the ill treatment and deaths of African Americans in police custody during the pandemic. The protests in support of the Black Lives Matter movement and demands for defunding police departments were highly energized after weeks of staying home and social distancing. In some cities, statues of historical figures associated with slavery were pulled down and damaged or destroyed. Some southern cities removed them because of the protests. Arrests and scuffles with police were common. There were also several instances of businesses being vandalized and looted during the protests. Cities like Seattle, Portland, Minneapolis, Chicago, and New York City had extensive damage. Even black-owned businesses were destroyed. While the protests against racism did not impact the COVID-19 pandemic, they nonetheless called attention to a significant social problem festering during the lockdowns.

As public demands for reducing a police presence and the underfunding of police departments was ongoing, crime rates in many of the same cities rose. In New York City, for example, the NYPD announced for the month of June 2020 during the pandemic that the number of people victimized by gun violence and murder increased significantly in comparison to the same period in 2019. Between June 1 and June 30, there was a 130 percent increase in the number of shootings across the city (205 versus 89) and 30 percent increase in the number of people murdered citywide (39 versus 30). For the following month of July 2020, there was an even higher 177 percent increase in the number of shooting incidents across the city (244 versus 88) and the number of people murdered increased by 59 percent (54 versus 34).

The number of burglaries also increased in June to 1,783 versus 817 (118 percent) and the number of auto thefts increased to 696 versus 462 (51 percent) citywide. However, the NYPD made some 40,000 fewer overall arrests in the first six months of 2020 compared with 2019, blaming legislative mandates for removing bail requirements for offenders allowing them back on the streets to be regularly rearrested and contributing to overall crime in the city. Another reason for the release of jail inmates was the pandemic itself, as penal facilities were another crowded setting for the spread of the virus. Other cities had problems as well, with the Seattle police chief resigning after funding cuts. Protestors in that city had been allowed by the mayor and city government to establish a police-free zone in a section of downtown until it was closed after three weeks when there were four shootings and two deaths.

Racial Minorities

A major issue embedded in the social protests in American society during the pandemic was opposition to racism disadvantaging racial minorities in a number of areas of social life, including a disproportionate level of infections and deaths from COVID-19. An early estimate is that the virus may be the third leading cause of mortality for African Americans in 2020 after heart disease and cancer (APM Research Lab 2020). Before the pandemic, non–Hispanic blacks had the worse overall health profile of any racial–ethnic group in the United States, with the highest rates of age–adjusted mortality from most causes of death, including heart disease and diabetes that are specifically linked to COVID-19 survival problems. The virus makes a bad situation worse and places a large number of blacks in double jeopardy from both a preexisting disease and COVID-19. Since there is greater exposure to the virus for many blacks and also Hispanics because of jobs lacking control over separating one's self from other people, there is a higher likelihood of being infected. Low incomes and less access to medical care are significant variables as well. Income during the pandemic is especially important for all earners, but especially for blacks as U.S. Census data shows the median income for blacks fell to $41,361 between 2000 and 2018 but rose to $70,642 for whites during the same period. This means that the typical black worker and family have less wealth to cushion losses in income and pay for expenses during the pandemic (Hardy and Logan 2020).

African Americans constitute 13.4 percent of the American population, but the proportion infected exceeded this percentage by far. One estimate is that the percentage of African Americans who were infected by the virus and died from it was more than twice as high as the proportion of blacks in the general population (Chowkwanyun and Reed 2020). In another example, as pointed out in Part I, blacks in Chicago constitute 30 percent of the population in that city but had 50 percent of the COVID-19 cases and almost 70 percent of the COVID-19 deaths by mid-May 2020 (Reyes et al. 2020). There was also the New Orleans study of patients in a local health care system, of whom 31 percent were black, that found some 76.9 percent of those hospitalized and 70.6 percent of deaths were those of blacks (Price-Hayward et al. 2020).

A problem, however, in documenting COVID-19 racial disparities is that much of the early data collected by states are incomplete and lack demographic information on race (Chowkwanyun and Reed 2020). Two studies that worked around this shortcoming were those of Gregorio Millett et al. (2020) on blacks and Carlos Rodriguez-Diaz et al. (2020) on Hispanics. These studies used county-level data from various sources to document whether COVID-19 diagnoses and deaths were higher in counties with higher proportions of these two racial minorities. The Rodriguez-Diaz study found that Hispanics had about a third of all COVID-19 diagnoses and a fifth of all deaths nationally but comprise only 18.5 percent of the population. The deaths were greatest in the Midwest and were associated with counties with higher household occupancy, air pollution, unemployment, monolingual Spanish speakers, and other variables.

The Millett et al. study found that almost 20 percent of U.S. counties are disproportionately black, but accounted for some 52 percent of COVID-19 diagnoses and 58 percent of COVID-19 deaths nationally. The deaths were highest in disproportionally black rural and small metro counties. Counties with higher proportions of black residents also had more comorbidities, elderly, uninsured and unemployed, and greater air pollution. Since both the Rodriguez-Diaz and Millett et al. studies are highly technical, the more easily readable article of Tonia Poteat, Gregorio Millett et al. on COVID-19 risks and vulnerabilities in black communities is included as the sixth reading in this section. This chapter addresses the effects of racism on blacks during the pandemic.

Gender Inequality

Included as the seventh reading is an article on how COVID-19 is promoting gender inequality in the labor force in the United States by Liana Landivar and her colleagues (2020). Their findings show that women workers are more negatively affected than men by the pandemic stay-at-home orders. This is particularly the case for mothers with young children at home trying work online without day care options. However, women generally, including those who are not a parent, are estimated to be confronting the greater likelihood of unemployment.

Canada

The first cases in Canada were linked to China. On January 25 a man in his 50s in Toronto who had returned the day before from Wuhan, China was identified as the first case and hospitalized. His wife was the second case on January 26 and put into home isolation. The third was a female university student in her 20s in British Columbia on January 31 who likewise had traveled to China. All three survived. Similar to the United States, the coronavirus pandemic was handled by local governments. The same containment measures as in the United States were applied by placing restrictions on travel into the country, while shelter-in-place and social distancing policies were implemented but varied. By late October 2020, Canada had over 212,000 confirmed cases of COVID-19 and some 9,888 deaths in a much smaller population than the United States of almost 38 million people. The provinces of Quebec (over 98,000 cases) and Ontario (over 68,000 cases) were the most affected. The fewest cases were in the northernmost provinces of Nunavut (0 cases), the Northwest Territories (8 cases), and Yukon (117 cases). The final and eighth reading in this section is by Patrick Denice et al. (2020) on the geographic and demographic distribution of COVID-19 in Canada. The analysis found that Canada is more similar to the United States than expected in that a much higher proportion of blacks than whites were infected.

Critical Thinking Questions

1. Why did New York City have so many cases of COVID-19?
2. How did federalism affect the response of the United States to the COVID-19 pandemic?

3. Do you agree or disagree with the view that individualism played an important role in the COVID-19 pandemic in the United States? Explain your answer.
4. Why are racial minorities particularly affected by the coronavirus pandemic?
5. What are COVID-10's effects of the status of gender equality in the workforce?

References

APM Research Lab. 2020. *The Color of Coronavirus: COVID-19 Deaths by Race and Ethnicity in the U.S.* Saint Paul, MN: APM Research Lab.

Badr, Hamada S., Hngru Du, Maximillian Marshall, Ensheng Dong, Marietta M. Squire, and Lauren M. Gardner. 2020. "Association Between Mobility Patterns and COVID-19 Transmission in the USA: A Mathematical Modelling Study." *Lancet Infectious Diseases* (July 1). https://doi.org/10.1016/S1473-3099(20)30553-3

Baudrillard, Jean. 1989. *America.* New York: Routledge.

Bellah, Robert N., Richard Madsen, William M. Sullivan, Ann Swidler, and Steven M. Tipton. 1985. *Habits of the Heart: Individualism and Commitment in American Life.* New York: Harper & Row.

Chowkwanyun, Merlin and Adolph L. Reed. 2020. "Racial Health Disparities and COVID-19." *New England Journal of Medicine* 383(3):201–3.

Courtemanche, Charles Joseph Garuccio, Anh Le, Joshua Pinkston, and Aaron Yelowitz. 2020. "Strong Social Distancing Measures in the United States Reduced the COVID-19 Growth Rate." *Health Affairs* 39(7):1–8.

Denice, Patrick, Kate H. Choi, Michael Haan, and Anna Zajacova. 2020. "Visualizing the Geographic and Demographic Distribution of COVID-19." *Socius* 6:1–3.

Ghinai, Issac, Tristan D. McPherson, Jennifer C. Hunter, Hannah L. Kirking et al. 2020. "First Known Person-to-Person Transmission of Severe Acute Respiratory Syndrome Coronavirus 2 (SARS-CoV-2) in the USA." *Lancet* 395:1137–44.

Gordon, Sarah H., Nicole Huberfield, and David K. Jones. 2020. "What Federalism Means for the US Response to the Coronavirus Disease 2019." *JAMA Network.* https://jamanetwork.com/channels/health-forum/fullarticle/2766033

Gostin, Lawrence O., Eric A. Friedman, and Sarah A. Wetter. 2020. "Responding to Covid-19: How to Navigate a Public Health Emergency Legally and Ethically." *Hastings Center Report* 50(2):8–12.

Haffajee, Rebecca L. and Michelle M. Mello. 2020. "Thinking Globally, Acting Locally—The U.S. Response to Covid-19." *New England Journal of Medicine* 382:e75.

Hardy, Bradley L. and Trevon D. Logan. 2020. *Racial Economic Inequality Amid the COVID-19 Crisis.* Washington, DC: Brookings Institution.

Kettl, Donald F. 2020. "States Divided: The Implications of American Federalism for COVID-19." *Public Administration Review* 80(4):595–602.

Landivar, Liana Christin, Leah Ruppanner, William J. Scarborough, and Caitlyn Collins. 2020. "Early Signs Indicate that COVID-19 Is Exacerbating Gender Inequality in the Labor Force." *Socius* 6:1–3.

Leonhardt, David. 2020. "The Unique U.S. Failure to Control the Virus." *New York Times* (August 6).

Lyu, Wei and George L. Wehby. 2020. "Shelter-In-Place Orders Reduced COVID-19 Mortality and Reduced the Rate of Growth in Hospitalizations." *Health Affairs* 39(9).

Millett, Gregorio A., Austin T. Jones, David Benkeser, Stefan Baral et al. 2020. "Assessing Differential Impacts of COVID-19 on Black Communities." *Annals of Epidemiology* 47:e37–e44.

Parmet, Wendy E. and Michael S. Sinha. 2020. "Covid-19—The Law and Limits of Quarantine." *New England Journal of Medicine* 382:e28.

Poteat, Tonia, Gregorio A. Millett, LaRon E. Nelson, and Chris Beyrer, 2020. "Understanding COVID-19 Risks and Vulnerabilities among Black Communities in America: The Lethal Force of Syndemics." *Annals of Epidemiology* 47:1–3.

Price-Hayward, Eboni G., Jeffrey Burton, Daniel Fort, and Leonardo Seoane. 2020. "Hospitalization and Mortality among Black Patients and White Patients with COVID-19." *New England Journal of Medicine* 382(June 25):2534–43.

Reyes, C., N. Husain, C. Gutowski, S. St. Clair, and G. Pratt. 2020. "Chicago's Coronavirus Disparity: Black Chicagoans are Dying at Nearly Six Times the Rate of White Residents, Data Show." *Chicago Tribune* (April 7).

Rodriguez-Diaz, Carlos E., Vincent Guilamo-Ramos, Leandro Mena, Eric Hall et al. 2020. "Risk for COVID-19 Infection and Death among Latinos in the United States: Examining Heterogeneity in Transmission Dynamics." *Annals of Epidemiology*. https://doi.org/10.1016/j.annepidem.2020.07.007

Walls, Stephanie M. 2015. Individualism in the United States: A Transformation *in American Political Thought*. New York: Bloomsbury Academic.

Wortham, Jonathan M., James T. Lee, Sandy Althomsons, Julia Latash et al. 2020. "Characteristics of Persons Who Died with COVID-19—United States, February 12–May 18, 2020." *CDC Morbidity and Mortality Weekly Report* (July 17) 69(28):923–29.

12 Public Health Response to the Initiation and Spread of Pandemic COVID-19 in the United States, February 24–April 21, 2020

Anne Schuchat

On May 1, 2020, this report was posted as an MMWR *Early Release on the* MMWR *website (www.cdc.gov/mmwr).*

From January 21 through February 23, 2020, a total of 14 cases of coronavirus disease 2019 (COVID-19) were diagnosed in six U.S. states, including 12 cases in travelers arriving from China and two in household contacts of persons with confirmed infections. An additional 39 cases were identified in persons repatriated from affected areas outside the United States (1). Starting in late February, reports of cases with no recent travel to affected areas or links to known cases signaled the initiation of pandemic spread in the United States (2). By mid-March, transmission of SARS-CoV-2, the virus that causes COVID-19, had accelerated, with rapidly increasing case counts indicating established transmission in the United States. Ongoing traveler importation of SARS-CoV-2, attendance at professional and social events, introduction into facilities or settings prone to amplification, and challenges in virus detection all contributed to rapid acceleration of transmission during March. Public health responses included intensive efforts to detect cases and trace contacts, and implementation of multiple community mitigation strategies. Because most of the population remains susceptible to infection, recognition of factors associated with amplified spread during the early acceleration period will help inform future decisions as locations in the United States scale back some components of mitigation and strengthen systems to detect a potential transmission resurgence. U.S. circulation of SARS-CoV-2 continues, and sustained efforts will be needed to prevent future spread within the United States.

The first cases of COVID-19 in the United States occurred in January and February 2020 in travelers from China's Hubei Province, where the virus was first recognized, and their household contacts (1). Beginning in late February, cases with no history of international travel and no contact with infected persons were recognized (1). By mid-March, transmission had become widespread, and by April 21, a total of 793,669 confirmed COVID-19 cases had been reported in the United States, the majority resulting from widespread community transmission (Figure 12.1). Factors that contributed

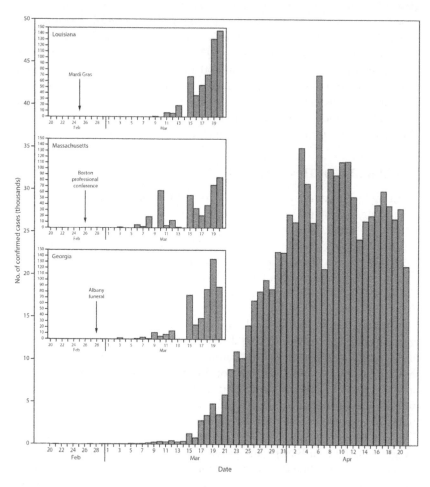

Figure 12.1 Number of confirmed COVID-19 cases, by date of report, in the United States during February 20–April 21, 2020,★ with initiation and early acceleration periods highlighted in Louisiana, Massachusetts, and Georgia.

Abbreviation: COVID-19 = coronavirus disease 2019.

★ Cumulative case count was 13 before February 20, 2020.

to the acceleration of dissemination in March included 1) continued importation of the virus by travelers infected elsewhere (e.g., on cruise ships or in countries experiencing outbreaks); 2) attendance at professional and social events, resulting in amplification in the host locations and multistate spread; 3) introduction of the virus into facilities or settings prone to amplification (e.g., long-term care facilities and high-density urban areas) with the potential for seeding the broader community; and 4) challenges in virus detection, including limited testing, emergence during the peak months of influenza circulation and influenza and pneumonia hospitalizations, and other cryptic transmission including from persons who were asymptomatic or presymptomatic. During March 2020, national, state, and local public health responses also intensified and adapted, augmenting case detection, contact tracing, and quarantine with targeted layered community mitigation measures. Because SARS-CoV-2, the virus that causes COVID-19, remains in circulation and a large proportion of the population remains susceptible, the potential for future acceleration remains.

Travel and COVID-19 Spread

Continued introductions of SARS-CoV-2 from outside the United States contributed to the initiation and acceleration of domestic COVID-19 cases in March. After Chinese authorities halted travel from Wuhan and other cities in Hubei Province on January 23, followed by U.S. restrictions on non-U.S. travelers from China issued on January 31 (effective February 2), air passenger journeys from China decreased 86%, from 505,560 in January to 70,072 in February. However, during February, 139,305 travelers arrived from Italy and 1.74 million from all Schengen countries,[1] where the outbreak was spreading widely and rapidly. Travelers from Italy and all Schengen countries decreased 74% to 35,877 and 50% to 862,432, respectively, in March.[2] Genomic analysis of outbreak strains suggested an introduction from China to the state of Washington around February 1.[3] However, examination of strains collected from northern California during early February to mid-March indicated multiple introductions resulting from international travel (from China and Europe) as well as from interstate travel.[4] Sequencing of strains collected in the New York metropolitan area in March also suggested origins in Europe and other U.S. regions.[5] Returning cruise ship travelers also contributed to amplification during this time (*3*). Persons from many countries are in close contact on cruises, and crew members continue to work on ships for multiple voyages. As a result, passengers returning from cruises contributed to the early acceleration phase. For example, 101 persons who had been on nine separate Nile River cruises during February 11–March 5 returned to 18 states and had a positive test result for SARS-CoV-2, nearly doubling the total number of known COVID-19 cases in the United States at that time (Figure 12.2).

Public health steps to mitigate continued importations of the virus included travel restrictions for non-U.S. citizens or permanent residents arriving from China beginning in early February and later expanded to include other countries with widespread sustained transmission (Table 12.1). Travel health notices were issued for countries with known outbreaks as the pandemic evolved, and ultimately warnings were issued to avoid nonessential international travel as well as all cruise ship travel (*1,4*). Quarantine measures were implemented for arriving international travelers with known

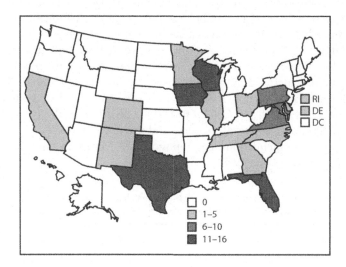

Figure 12.2 Number of confirmed COVID-19 cases (N = 101) linked to nine Nile River cruises held during February 11–March 5, 2020, by patient state of residence—18 states.

Abbreviations: COVID-19 = coronavirus disease 2019; DC = District of Columbia; DE = Delaware; RI = Rhode Island.

exposure to locations and settings of concern, such as Hubei Province and the *Diamond Princess* cruise ship docked off the coast of Yokohama, Japan. Screening and public health risk assessment of travelers in selected U.S. airports, initiated on January 17, were also expanded. As of April 21, 2020, CDC staff members and U.S. Customs and Border Protection officers had screened approximately 268,000 returning travelers, among whom testing confirmed 14 COVID-19 cases. State and local health departments were advised to supervise self-monitoring of travelers who had been directed to stay home after returning from countries with widespread sustained transmission. On March 14, 2020, the CDC Director issued a No Sail Order for cruise ships, suspending operation in U.S. waters; the order was renewed April 9, effective April 15.

Events and Gatherings

Various gatherings of persons from different locations, followed by return to their home communities, played a notable role in the early United States spread of COVID-19. During February 2020, the number of confirmed cases originating in the United States was low and appeared contained; thus, federal and local jurisdictions did not recommend restrictions on gatherings. However, during the last week of February, several large events led to further spread of the disease. These included Mardi Gras celebrations in Louisiana with more than 1 million attendees, an international professional conference held in Boston, Massachusetts, with approximately 175 attendees, and a funeral in Albany, Georgia, with more than 100 attendees (Figure 12.1). In the weeks after these events, amplifications in the host locations contributed to increasing U.S. case counts (5). Dougherty County, Georgia, a small rural county that includes Albany, had one of the highest cumulative incidences of COVID-19 (1,630/100,000 population) in the country. The substantial transmissibility of the virus and severity of COVID-19 triggered a series of recommendations, beginning in mid-March, to limit mass gatherings and travel (Table 12.1).

Table 12.1 Factors contributing to COVID-19 acceleration and corresponding public health actions—United States, January–April 2020.

Factor contributing to acceleration	Examples	Public health actions
Continued travel-associated importations of the virus	Travelers arriving from countries or cruise ships with ongoing transmission	Travel health notices, traveler screening (including risk assessment, public health management and monitoring), travel restrictions, federal isolation and quarantine orders, educating travelers and clinicians regarding symptoms and evaluation
Large gatherings	Social, cultural, and professional gatherings where persons convene and then disperse over broad areas	Restricting mass gatherings; global travel restrictions and domestic travel recommendations, recommending transition to virtual events
Introductions into high-risk workplaces/settings	Long-term care facilities, hospitals, correctional facilities, and homeless shelters	Restricting visitor access, establishing cohort units or facilities for residential settings, vigorous contact tracing around persons with confirmed cases, increased infection control, environmental surface cleaning, use of recommended personal protective equipment
Crowding and high population density	Densely populated areas, crowded workplaces, schools, and public spaces	Stay-at-home orders, recommendations for hand washing and social distancing, cloth face covering guidance, school dismissals, extended telework, environmental surface cleaning
Cryptic transmission	Presymptomatic or asymptomatic spread, limited testing, co-occurrence with circulation of other respiratory viruses	Increased testing, COVID-19–specific surveillance, cloth face covering guidance, aggressive contact tracing accompanied by quarantine and/or testing of asymptomatic contacts, stay-at-home orders

Note: **Abbreviation:** COVID-19 = coronavirus disease 2019.

Workplaces and Settings Contributing to Accelerated Spread

Skilled nursing and long-term care facilities (6) and hospitals (7) are settings in which persons at higher risk for severe COVID-19 illness are in close contact with staff members, many of whom work at multiple facilities. Other workplaces also facilitated amplification of virus transmission, including critical infrastructure sectors, such as multiple meat packing facilities in rural areas. Clusters of cases related to religious service attendance have been reported within the United States and worldwide (8). Congregate, high-density settings also might contribute to the spread of COVID-19 (9). For example, population density might account for the very high numbers of COVID-19 cases in the New York metropolitan area (Box 12.1). Public health actions aimed at reducing COVID-19 spread in high-risk settings have focused on infection control measures, including identifying and isolating ill persons, cleaning and disinfection, restricting visitors, physical distancing through shift work, and appropriate use of personal protective equipment (Table 12.1). To protect health care capacity and slow community spread of COVID-19, local, state, and federal authorities issued stay-at-home orders, and closed schools and nonessential workplaces. On April 3, CDC issued guidance for use of cloth face coverings in public areas to reduce spread, based on increasing evidence of transmission in the absence of symptoms.[6]

Cryptic Transmission

Unrecognized transmission played a key role in the initiation and acceleration phases of the U.S. outbreak. Cases were not detected during this time for various reasons. First, introduction of the virus into the United States occurred during the annual influenza season. Although syndromic surveillance systems tracked respiratory illness in outpatient settings and emergency departments in many U.S. jurisdictions, including areas where early COVID-19 clusters were detected, such as Seattle, Washington, none of these systems detected unusual trends during the early part of the acceleration period because of the preponderance of seasonal influenza illness. After the first community case in Santa Clara, California, was confirmed on February 27, the county conducted COVID-19 surveillance with polymerase chain reaction–based virus testing during March 5–14 at four urgent care centers. Influenza accounted for 23% of respiratory illnesses; among those who had a negative test result for influenza, 11% had a positive test result for SARS-CoV-2, representing approximately 8% of patients with respiratory symptoms (10). Seroprevalence data from Seattle during March 2020, a period when transmission of the virus was rapidly accelerating, suggested that there were limited undetected infections in healthy adults without respiratory illness (1 of 221 remnant clinical sera representing a convenience sample tested seropositive [Helen Chu, University of Washington School of Public Health, personal communication, April 2020]); at the population level, this still translates into substantial numbers of unrecognized community infections. No samples from 59 children with acute respiratory infections during January–March were seropositive (Janet Englund, Seattle Children's Hospital and University of Washington, personal communication, April 2020). Because the incidence of SARS-CoV-2 infections was still relatively low during the initiation and early acceleration periods, as evidenced by seroprevalence data, widespread testing would have been needed to detect all cases. The contribution of spread from persons without symptoms also complicated detection and containment (*11*). Public health actions included expanded surveillance and testing capacity and community measures, such as enhanced teleworking and stay-at-home orders, school closures, social distancing, and use of cloth face coverings (Table 12.1).

Discussion

The acceleration phase of a pandemic is complex and requires a multifaceted and rapidly adapting public health response. During a three-week period in late February to early March, the number of U.S. COVID-19 cases increased more than 1,000-fold. Various community mitigation interventions were implemented with the aim of reducing further spread and controlling the impact on health care capacity. Recognition of factors associated with amplified spread during this early acceleration period will help inform future decisions as locations in the United States scale back some components of mitigation and strengthen systems to detect transmission resurgence.

The findings in this report are subject to at least five limitations. First, the various factors facilitating viral spread described in this report occurred simultaneously; therefore, it is not possible to quantify the relative contribution of each to the outbreak trajectory in the United States. Second, the examples of factors contributing to amplification are illustrative and not meant to be comprehensive. Third, because the mitigation strategies highlighted here were implemented concurrently, the ability to estimate the relative impact of each intervention is limited. Fourth, the epidemic curve presented was likely affected by limited testing, particularly in the early phases of the outbreak. Finally, the case counts presented are an underestimate of the actual number of COVID-19 cases in the United States.

Summary

What Is Already Known About This Topic?

The first confirmed coronavirus disease 2019 (COVID-19) case in the United States was reported on January 21, 2020. The outbreak appeared contained through February, and then accelerated rapidly.

What Is Added by This Report?

Various factors contributed to accelerated spread during February–March 2020, including continued travel-associated importations, large gatherings, introductions into high-risk workplaces and densely populated areas, and cryptic transmission resulting from limited testing and asymptomatic and presymptomatic spread. Targeted and communitywide mitigation efforts were needed to slow transmission.

What Are the Implications for Public Health Practice?

Factors that amplified the March acceleration and associated mitigation strategies that were implemented can inform public health decisions as the United States prepares for potential re-emergences.

As the pandemic evolves, control efforts must be continuously refined. Certain interventions that were critical in the early stages, such as quarantine and airport screening, might have less impact when transmission is widespread in the community. However, many elements of the mitigation strategies used during the acceleration phase will still be needed in later stages of the outbreak. Preliminary results from serologic surveys suggest that even in the U.S. regions with the largest numbers of recognized cases, most persons have not been infected and remain susceptible.[7,8] Therefore, sustained and concerted efforts will be needed to prevent future spread of SARS-CoV-2 within the United States.

All authors have completed and submitted the International Committee of Medical Journal Editors form for disclosure of potential conflicts of interest. No potential conflicts of interest were disclosed.

**Box 12.1 Critical Factors Contributing to COVID-19
             Spread in New York**

Multiple interrelated factors that complicated identification and isolation of cases and tracing of contacts contributed to the COVID-19 outbreak in New York.

Population Density

- New York City's boroughs represent the top four population-dense U.S. counties.

- Reliance on mass transit (subways, buses, and ferries) results in frequent, prolonged close contact.
- High prevalence of apartment living contributed to household spread.

Domestic and Global Destination

- Three major airports serve as domestic and global hubs, serving >1 million air passengers per week.
- Approximately 1.6 million persons commute into Manhattan daily during the work week, primarily using mass transit.

Large Number of Crowded Settings Housing Vulnerable Populations

- Long-term care facilities, skilled nursing facilities: At least 80 facilities in the state have reported five or more cases as of April 21; initial infections were noted in early March.
- Correctional institutions: As of April 21, incidence in Department of Corrections and Community Supervision facilities was approximately seven times that in the state overall.
- Homeless shelters: As of the week of April 21, approximately 600 cases were confirmed among shelter residents and other persons experiencing homelessness.

Large Gatherings

- Initial cases in Westchester County were associated with attendance at large gatherings in late February.
- All types of large work and social gatherings accelerated transmission across jurisdictional boundaries.

Notes

1. Includes Austria, Belgium, Czech Republic, Denmark, Estonia, Finland, France, Germany, Greece, Hungary, Iceland, Italy, Latvia, Liechtenstein, Lithuania, Luxembourg, Malta, Netherlands, Norway, Poland, Portugal, Slovakia, Slovenia, Spain, Sweden, and Switzerland. Travel within the Schengen Area is permitted without border controls.
2. Air travel data provided by U.S. Customs and Border Protection's Office of Planning, Program Analysis, and Evaluation (PPAE).
3. www.medrxiv.org/content/10.1101/2020.04.02.20051417v2.
4. www.medrxiv.org/content/10.1101/2020.03.27.20044925v1.
5. www.medrxiv.org/content/10.1101/2020.04.08.20056929v2.
6. www.cdc.gov/coronavirus/2019-ncov/prevent-getting-sick/cloth-face-cover.html.

7. www.governor.ny.gov/news/video-audio-photos-rush-transcript-amid-ongoing-covid-19-pandemic-governor-cuomo-announces-12.
8. www.medrxiv.org/content/10.1101/2020.04.14.20062463v1.

References

1. Jernigan DB; CDC COVID-19 Response Team. Update: public health response to the coronavirus disease 2019 outbreak—United States, February 24, 2020. MMWR Morb Mortal Wkly Rep 2020;69:216–9. https://doi.org/10.15585/mmwr.mm6908e1

2. Qualls N, Levitt A, Kanade N, et al.; CDC Community Mitigation Guidelines Work Group. Community mitigation guidelines to prevent pandemic influenza—United States, 2017. MMWR Recomm Rep 2017;66(No. RR-1). https://doi.org/10.15585/mmwr.rr6601a1

3. Moriarty LF, Plucinski MM, Marston BJ, et al.; CDC Cruise Ship Response Team; California Department of Public Health COVID-19 Team; Solano County COVID-19 Team. Public health responses to COVID-19 outbreaks on cruise ships—worldwide, February–March 2020. MMWR Morb Mortal Wkly Rep 2020;69:347–52. https://doi.org/10.15585/mmwr.mm6912e3

4. Patel A, Jernigan DB; 2019-nCoV CDC Response Team. Initial public health response and interim clinical guidance for the 2019 novel coronavirus outbreak—United States, December 31, 2019–February 4, 2020. MMWR Morb Mortal Wkly Rep 2020;69:140–6. https://doi.org/10.15585/mmwr.mm6905e1

5. Bialek S, Bowen V, Chow N, et al.; CDC COVID-19 Response Team. COVID-19 Response Team. Geographic differences in covid-19 cases, deaths, and incidence—United States, February 12–April 7, 2020. MMWR Morb Mortal Wkly Rep 2020;69:465–71. https://doi.org/10.15585/mmwr.mm6915e4

6. McMichael TM, Currie DW, Clark S, et al. Epidemiology of Covid-19 in a long-term care facility in King County, Washington. N Engl J Med 2020;NEJMoa2005412. https://doi.org/10.1056/NEJMoa2005412

7. Heinzerling A, Stuckey MJ, Scheuer T, et al. Transmission of COVID-19 to health care personnel during exposures to a hospitalized patient—Solano County, California, February 2020. MMWR Morb Mortal Wkly Rep 2020;69:472–6. https://doi.org/10.15585/mmwr.mm6915e5

8. Pung R, Chiew CJ, Young BE, et al.; Singapore 2019 Novel Coronavirus Outbreak Research Team. Investigation of three clusters of COVID-19 in Singapore: implications for surveillance and response measures. Lancet 2020;395:1039–46. https://doi.org/10.1016/S0140-6736(20)30528-6

9. Rocklöv J, Sjödin H. High population densities catalyze the spread of COVID-19. J Travel Med 2020; Epub March 29, 2020. https://doi.org/10.1093/jtm/taaa038

10. Zwald ML, Lin W, Sondermeyer Cooksey GL, et al. Rapid sentinel surveillance for COVID-19—Santa Clara County, California, March 2020. MMWR Morb Mortal Wkly Rep 2020;69:419–21. https://doi.org/10.15585/mmwr.mm6914e3

11. Gandhi M, Yokoe DS, Havlir DV. Asymptomatic transmission, the Achilles' Heel of current strategies to control Covid-19. 2020. N Engl J Med 2020; Epub April 24, 2020. https://doi.org/10.1056/NEJMe2009758

13 Characteristics of Persons Who Died With COVID-19—United States, February 12–May 18, 2020

Jonathan M. Wortham, James T. Lee,
Sandy Althomsons, Julia Latash et al.

On July 10, 2020, this report was posted as an MMWR *Early Release on the* MMWR *website (www.cdc.gov/mmwr).*

During January 1, 2020–May 18, 2020, approximately 1.3 million cases of coronavirus disease 2019 (COVID-19) and 83,000 COVID-19–associated deaths were reported in the United States (*1*). Understanding the demographic and clinical characteristics of decedents could inform medical and public health interventions focused on preventing COVID-19–associated mortality. This report describes decedents with laboratory-confirmed infection with SARS-CoV-2, the virus that causes COVID-19, using data from 1) the standardized CDC case-report form (case-based surveillance) (www.cdc.gov/coronavirus/2019-ncov/php/reporting-pui.html) and 2) supplementary data (supplemental surveillance), such as underlying medical conditions and location of death, obtained through collaboration between CDC and 16 public health jurisdictions (15 states and New York City).

Case-Based Surveillance

Demographic and clinical data about COVID-19 cases are reported to CDC from 50 states, the District of Columbia, New York City, and U.S. territories using a standardized case-report form (case-based surveillance) or in aggregate. Data on 52,166 deaths from 47 jurisdictions among persons with laboratory-confirmed COVID-19 were reported individually to CDC via case-based surveillance during February 12–May 18, 2020. Among the 52,166 decedents, 55.4% were male, 79.6% were aged ≥65 years, 13.8% were Hispanic/Latino (Hispanic), 21.0% were black, 40.3% were white, 3.9% were Asian, 0.3% were American Indian/Alaska Native (AI/AN), 0.1% were Native Hawaiian or other Pacific Islander (NHPI), 2.6% were multiracial or other race, and race/ethnicity was unknown for 18.0% (Table 13.1). Median decedent age was 78 years (interquartile range (IQR) = 67–87 years). Because information about underlying medical conditions was missing for the majority of these decedents (30,725; 58.9%), data regarding medical conditions were not analyzed further using the case-based surveillance data set. Because most decedents reported to the supplementary data program were also reported to case-based surveillance, no statistical comparisons of the decedent characteristics between the data sets were made.

Supplemental Surveillance

To collect more complete data on race/ethnicity, selected underlying medical conditions[1] by age, and clinical course, CDC solicited supplementary information from medical charts and death certificates of decedents with laboratory-confirmed COVID-19 from state, territorial, and local public health departments. The supplementary data request also sought information on locations of death, which is not collected routinely on the CDC case-report form. Among 56 public health departments contacted by CDC, 16[2] provided supplementary data on 10,647 COVID-19 deaths that occurred during February 12–April 24, 2020.

Among the 10,647 COVID-19 decedents for whom supplementary data were collected, 60.6% were male, 74.8% were aged ≥65 years, 24.4% were Hispanic, 24.9% were black, 35.0% were white, 6.3% were Asian, 0.1% were AI/AN, 0.1% were NHPI, 2.9% were multiracial or other race, and race/ethnicity was unknown for 6.3% (Table 13.1). Decedent age varied by race and ethnicity; median age was 71 years (IQR = 59–81 years) among Hispanic decedents, 72 years (IQR = 62–81 years) among all non-white, non–Hispanic decedents, and 81 years (IQR = 71–88 years) among white decedents. The percentages of Hispanic (34.9%) and nonwhite (29.5%) decedents who were aged <65 years were more than twice those of white decedents (13.2%) (Figure 13.1).

At least one underlying medical condition was reported for 8,134 (76.4%) of decedents for whom supplementary data were collected, including 83.1% of decedents aged <65 years. Overall, the most common underlying medical conditions were cardiovascular disease (60.9%), diabetes mellitus (39.5%), chronic kidney disease (20.8%), and chronic lung disease (19.2%) (Table 13.2). Among decedents aged <65 years, 83.1% had one or more underlying medical conditions. Among decedents aged ≥85 years, 69.5% had one or more underlying medical conditions. Diabetes was more common among decedents aged <65 years (49.6%) than among those aged ≥85 years (25.9%).

Among decedents for whom supplementary data were reported, 8,976 (84.3%) were hospitalized. Among 3,021 (28.4%) with dates of illness onset and death reported, the median interval from illness onset to death was 10 days (IQR = 6–15 days); among 7,794 decedents with hospital admission and death dates, the median interval from hospital admission to death was 5 days (IQR = 3–8 days). Among the decedents, 62.0% died in hospitals. By age group, the largest percentage who died in the emergency department (6.8%) or at home (1.0%) was aged <65 years (combined total = 7.8%),

Table 13.1 Demographic characteristics of decedents reported through national COVID-19 case-based and supplemental surveillance, by data source—United States, February 12–May 18, 2020.

Characteristic	No. (%)	
	Case-based surveillance* N = 52,166	Supplemental surveillance[†] N = 10,647
Age, yrs (median, IQR)	78 (67–87)	75 (64–84)
Age group (yrs)		
All <65	10,626 (20.4)	2,681 (25.2)
<18	16 (<0.1)	5 (<0.1)
18–44	1,478 (2.8)	423 (4.0)
45–54	2,675 (5.1)	704 (6.6)
55–64	6,457 (12.4)	1,549 (14.5)
All ≥65	41,528 (79.6)	7,966 (74.8)
65–74	11,245 (21.6)	2,463 (23.1)
75–84	14,148 (27.1)	2,900 (27.2)
≥85	16,135 (30.9)	2,603 (24.4)
Unknown	12 (<0.1)	0 (0)
Sex		
Male	28,899 (55.4)	6,449 (60.6)
Female	22,798 (43.7)	4,194 (39.4)
Other/Unknown	469 (0.9)	4 (<0.1)
Race/Ethnicity		
Hispanic/Latino[§]	7,175 (13.8)	2,602 (24.4)
White	21,021 (40.3)	3,727 (35.0)
Nonwhite	14,590 (28.0)	3,653 (34.3)
Black	10,964 (21.0)	2,655 (24.9)
Asian	2,048 (3.9)	666 (6.3)
Multiracial/Other race[§]	1,578 (3.0)	332 (3.1)
Unknown	9,380 (18.0)	665 (6.3)

Notes: **Abbreviations**: COVID-19 = coronavirus disease 2019; IQR = interquartile range; NH = non-Hispanic.

* Includes data from laboratory-confirmed cases reported to CDC as of May 18, 2020.

† Data from laboratory-confirmed cases reported to CDC as of April 24, 2020, from these 16 public health jurisdictions: Alaska Department of Health and Social Services; Colorado Department of Public Health and Environment; Indiana State Department of Health; Louisiana Department of Health; Maine Center for Disease Control and Prevention; Michigan Department of Health and Human Services; Minnesota Department of Health; New Jersey Department of Health; New York City Department of Health and Mental Hygiene; North Carolina Department of Health and Human Services; Oregon Health Authority; Tennessee Department of Health; Utah Department of Health; Vermont Department of Health; Washington State Department of Health; Wisconsin Department of Health Services.

§ Persons who were not reported as Hispanic/Latino were all non-Hispanic.

¶ Includes persons reported as American Indian/Alaska Native (163 in case-based surveillance and 13 in supplementary data set), Native Hawaiian or other Pacific Islander (33 in case-based surveillance and eight in supplementary data set), multiracial, and persons of another race without further specification.

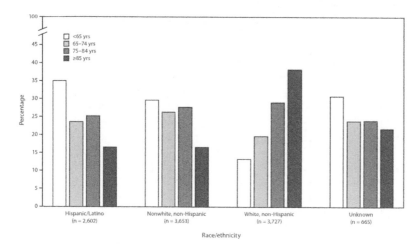

Figure 13.1 Decedent race/ethnicity,* by age group, reported to supplemental COVID-19 surveillance (N = 10,647)—16 U.S. public health jurisdictions,† February 12–April 24, 2020.

Abbreviation: COVID-19 = coronavirus disease 2019.

* The "Nonwhite, non-Hispanic" group includes persons who are black, white, Asian, American Indian/Alaska Native, or Native Hawaiian and other Pacific Islander; the "Unknown" group consists of persons for whom race/ethnicity data were not available.
† Alaska Department of Health and Social Services; Colorado Department of Public Health and Environment; Indiana State Department of Health; Louisiana Department of Health; Maine Center for Disease Control and Prevention; Michigan Department of Health and Human Services; Minnesota Department of Health; New Jersey Department of Health; New York City Department of Health and Mental Hygiene; North Carolina Department of Health and Human Services; Oregon Health Authority; Tennessee Department of Health; Utah Department of Health; Vermont Department of Health; Washington State Department of Health; Wisconsin Department of Health Services.

and decreased with increasing age group, whereas the percentage who died in long-term care facilities increased with increasing age and was highest among decedents aged ≥85 years (12.6%).

Among the decedents during February 12–April 24, 2020, for whom supplementary information was provided, 9,997 (93.9%) resided in New York City, New Jersey, or the state of Washington, three areas with early widespread circulation of SARS-CoV-2; the median age among decedents in these three jurisdictions was 75 years (IQR = 64–84 years). The median age among decedents residing in the other 13 jurisdictions was similar (78 years, [IQR = 68–85 years]).

Discussion

Using national case-based surveillance and supplementary data reported from 16 jurisdictions, characteristics of >10,000 decedents with laboratory-confirmed COVID-19 were described. More than one-third of Hispanic

Table 13.2 Clinical features of decedents collected through COVID-19 supplemental surveillance—16 public health jurisdictions,* United States, February 12–April 24, 2020.

Characteristic	No. (%)					
	Age group (yrs)					
	Overall	<65	≥65	65–74	75–84	≥85
	n = 10,647	n = 2,681	n = 7,966	n = 2,463	n = 2,900	n = 2,603
Race/Ethnicity						
Hispanic/Latino	2,602 (24.4)	908 (33.9)	1,694 (21.3)	611 (24.8)	652 (22.5)	431 (16.6)
White, NH	3,727 (35.0)	492 (18.4)	3,235 (40.6)	732 (29.7)	1,082 (37.3)	1,421 (54.6)
Nonwhite, NH	3,653 (34.3)	1,077 (40.2)	2,576 (32.3)	962 (39.1)	1,007 (34.7)	607 (23.3)
Black, NH	2,655 (24.9)	803 (30.0)	1,852 (23.3)	715 (29.0)	731 (25.2)	406 (15.6)
Asian, NH	666 (6.3)	164 (6.1)	502 (6.3)	157 (6.4)	189 (6.5)	156 (6.0)
Multiracial/Other race[†]	332 (3.1)	110 (4.1)	222 (2.8)	90 (3.7)	87 (3.0)	45 (1.7)
Unknown	665 (6.3)	204 (7.6)	461 (5.8)	158 (6.4)	159 (5.5)	144 (5.5)
≥ 1 underlying medical conditions[§]	8,134 (76.4)	2,228 (83.1)	5,906 (74.1)	1,922 (78.0)	2,175 (75.0)	1,809 (69.5)
≥ 2 underlying medical conditions[§]	5,772 (54.2)	1,647 (61.4)	4,125 (51.8)	1,403 (57.0)	1,549 (53.4)	1,173 (45.1)
≥ 3 underlying medical conditions[§]	3,269 (30.7)	1,012 (37.8)	2,257 (28.3)	803 (32.6)	844 (29.1)	610 (23.4)
Cardiovascular disease[¶]						
Yes[**]	6,481 (60.9)	1,633 (60.9)	4,848 (60.9)	1,565 (63.5)	1,773 (61.1)	1,510 (58.0)
No[††]	145 (1.4)	93 (3.5)	52 (0.7)	26 (1.1)	15 (0.5)	11 (0.4)
Unknown[§§]	4,021 (37.8)	955 (35.6)	3,066 (38.5)	872 (35.4)	1,112 (38.3)	1,081 (41.5)

Diabetes mellitus						
Yes**	4,210 (39.5)	1,330 (49.6)	2,880 (36.2)	1,107 (45.0)	1,098 (37.9)	675 (25.9)
No††	589 (5.5)	190 (7.1)	399 (5.0)	103 (4.2)	131 (4.5)	165 (6.3)
Unknown§§§	5,848 (54.9)	1,161 (43.3)	4,687 (58.8)	1,253 (50.9)	1,671 (57.6)	1,762 (67.7)
Chronic kidney disease¶¶						
Yes**	2,209 (20.8)	589 (22.0)	1,620 (20.3)	530 (21.5)	627 (21.6)	463 (17.8)
No††	711 (6.7)	308 (11.5)	403 (5.1)	129 (5.2)	137 (4.7)	137 (5.3)
Unknown§§§	7,727 (72.6)	1,784 (66.5)	5,943 (74.6)	1,804 (73.2)	2,136 (73.7)	2,002 (76.9)
End-stage renal disease						
Yes**	368 (3.5)	171 (6.4)	197 (2.5)	100 (4.1)	70 (2.4)	27 (1.0)
No††	373 (3.5)	211 (7.9)	162 (2.0)	67 (2.7)	46 (1.6)	49 (1.9)
Unknown§§§	9,906 (93.0)	2,299 (85.8)	7,607 (95.5)	2,296 (93.2)	2,784 (96.0)	2,526 (97.1)
Chronic lung disease*						
Yes**	2,047 (19.2)	561 (20.9)	1,486 (18.7)	504 (20.5)	574 (19.8)	408 (15.7)
No††	754 (7.1)	328 (12.2)	426 (5.4)	134 (5.4)	132 (4.6)	160 (6.2)
Unknown§§§	7,846 (73.7)	1,792 (66.8)	6,054 (76.0)	1,825 (74.1)	2,194 (75.7)	2,034 (78.2)
Neurologic conditions‡‡‡						
Yes**	1,376 (12.9)	314 (11.7)	1062 (13.3)	259 (10.5)	350 (12.1)	453 (17.4)
No††	501 (4.7)	220 (8.2)	281 (3.5)	117 (4.8)	86 (3.0)	78 (3.0)
Unknown§§§	8,770 (82.4)	2,147 (80.1)	6,623 (83.1)	2,087 (84.7)	2,464 (85.0)	2,071 (79.6)
Immunosuppression§§§§						
Yes**	1,661 (15.6)	470 (17.5)	1,191 (15.0)	441 (17.9)	445 (15.3)	305 (11.7)
Unknown§§§	8,986(84.4)	2,211 (82.5)	6,775 (85.0)	2,022 (82.1)	2,455 (84.7)	2,297 (88.3)

(Continued)

Table 13.2 (Continued)

Characteristic	No. (%)					
	Age group (yrs)					
	Overall	<65	≥65	65–74	75–84	≥85
	n = 10,647	n = 2,681	n = 7,966	n = 2,463	n = 2,900	n = 2,603
Chronic liver conditions[¶¶¶]						
Yes[★★]	247 (2.3)	111 (4.1)	136 (1.7)	67 (2.7)	50 (1.7)	19 (0.7)
No[††]	705 (6.6)	262 (9.8)	443 (5.6)	146 (5.9)	139 (4.8)	158 (6.1)
Unknown[§§]	9,695 (91.1)	2,308 (86.1)	7,387 (92.7)	2,250 (91.4)	2,711 (93.5)	2,425 (93.2)
Obesity[★★★★]						
Yes[★★]	918 (8.6)	575 (21.4)	343 (4.3)	182 (7.4)	103 (3.6)	58 (2.2)
No[††]	168 (1.6)	127 (4.7)	41 (0.5)	28 (1.1)	9 (0.3)	4 (0.2)
Unknown[§§]	9,561 (89.8)	1,979 (73.8)	7,582 (95.2)	2,253 (91.5)	2,788 (96.1)	2,540 (97.6)
Clinical course						
Illness duration[††††]	10 days (6–15)	11 days (7–16)	9 days (6–14)	10 days (7–15)	10 days (6–14)	8 days (5–12)
Hospitalized[§§§§]						
Yes[★★]	8,976 (84.3)	2,375 (88.6)	6,601 (82.9)	2,170 (88.1)	2,449 (84.4)	1,981 (76.1)
Unknown[§§]	1,671 (15.7)	306 (11.4)	1,365 (17.1)	293 (11.9)	451 (15.6)	621 (23.9)

Required ICU admission

Yes**	2,401 (22.6)	1,094 (40.8)	1,307 (16.4)	629 (25.5)	470 (16.2)	208 (8.0)
No††	1,239 (11.6)	464 (17.3)	775 (9.7)	185 (7.5)	272 (9.4)	318 (12.2)
Unknown§§	7,007 (65.8)	1,123 (41.9)	5,884 (73.9)	1,649 (67.0)	2,158 (74.4)	2,076 (79.8)

Required mechanical ventilation

Yes**	2,994 (28.1)	1,322 (49.3)	1,672 (21.0)	803 (32.6)	588 (20.3)	281 (10.8)
No††	914 (8.6)	263 (9.8)	651 (8.2)	141 (5.7)	228 (7.9)	282 (10.8)
Unknown§§	6,739 (63.3)	1,096 (40.9)	5,643 (70.8)	1,519 (61.7)	2,084 (71.9)	2,039 (78.4)

Length of hospital stay, days (median, IQR)¶¶¶¶

	5 (3–8)	6 (3–9)	5 (2–8)	5 (3–9)	5 (3–8)	4 (2–7)

Location of death

Hospital	6,604 (62.0)	1,575 (58.8)	5,029 (63.1)	1,630 (66.2)	1,884 (65.0)	1,515 (58.2)
Long-term care facility*****	567 (5.3)	31 (1.2)	536 (6.7)	60 (2.4)	148 (5.1)	328 (12.6)
Emergency department	549 (5.2)	181 (6.8)	368 (4.6)	134 (5.4)	138 (4.8)	96 (3.7)
Home	79 (0.7)	27 (1.0)	52 (0.7)	††††	††††	††††
Hospice	28 (0.3)	††††	††††	††††	††††	††††
Other/Unknown§§§§§	2,820 (26.5)	866 (32.3)	1,954 (24.5)	619 (25.1)	703 (24.2)	632 (24.3)

Notes: **Abbreviations:** COVID-19 = coronavirus disease 2019; ICU = Intensive care unit; IQR = Interquartile range; NH = non-Hispanic.

* Alaska Department of Health and Social Services; Colorado Department of Public Health and Environment; Indiana State Department of Health; Louisiana Department of Health; Maine Center for Disease Control and Prevention; Michigan Department of Health and Human Services; Minnesota Department of Health; New Jersey Department of Health; New York City Department of Health and Mental Hygiene; North Carolina Department of Health and Human Services; Oregon Health Authority; Tennessee Department of Health; Utah Department of Health; Vermont Department of Health; Washington State Department of Health; Wisconsin Department of Health Services.

† Includes persons reported as American Indian/Alaska Native (130), Native Hawaiian or other Pacific Islander (8), multiracial, and persons reported as being of another race without further specification.

Table 13.2 (Continued)

§ Includes decedents for whom at least one of the following conditions were reported: cardiovascular disease, diabetes mellitus, chronic kidney disease (including end-stage renal disease), neurologic conditions, immunosuppression, chronic liver conditions, or obesity. Conditions are not mutually exclusive; decedents might have more than one underlying condition.

¶ Includes decedents with hypertension, coronary artery disease, congenital heart disease, congestive heart failure, cerebrovascular accident/stroke, valvular heart diseases, conduction disorders, or other cardiovascular diseases.

** Includes only decedents for whom the condition within the specified category was collected from reviews of medical records.

†† Includes only decedents for whom data abstractors indicated did not have any condition within the specified category.

§§ Includes decedents for whom no data were available to indicate whether the decedent had any of the condition(s) within the specified category.

¶¶ Includes decedents with chronic kidney disease and end-stage renal disease.

*** Includes decedents with chronic obstructive pulmonary disease/emphysema, asthma, and tuberculosis.

††† Includes decedents with dementia, seizure disorders, and other neurologic conditions.

§§§ Includes decedents with any history of cancer, HIV/AIDS, or identified as being immunosuppressed.

¶¶¶ Includes decedents with cirrhosis, alcoholic hepatitis, chronic liver disease, end-stage liver disease, hepatitis B, hepatitis C, or non-alcoholic steatohepatitis.

**** Includes persons with body mass index ≥30 kg/m2.

†††† Among 3,021 (28.4%) persons for whom illness onset and death dates were reported; these data were available for 1,363 decedents aged <65 years, 557 decedents aged 65–74 years, 551 decedents aged 75–84 years, and 550 decedents aged ≥85 years.

§§§§ Includes decedents with a reported hospital admission date or who were reported to have died in a hospital.

¶¶¶¶ Among 7,794 (73.2%) persons with available data regarding time from admission to death; these data were available for 2,178 decedents aged <65 years, 1,909 decedents aged 65–74 years, 2,065 decedents aged 75–84 years, and 1,642 decedents aged ≥85 years.

***** Includes decedents who died in a long-term care facility, skilled nursing facility, assisted living facility, or nursing home.

††††† Cells with numbers <20 were suppressed.

§§§§§ Includes decedents for whom no data on location of death were reported and those for whom "other" was specified for death location without any more specific information.

decedents (34.9%) and nearly one-third (29.5%) of nonwhite decedents were aged <65 years, but only 13.2% of white decedents were aged <65 years. Consistent with reports describing the characteristics of deaths in persons with COVID-19 in the United States and China (2–5), approximately three-fourths of decedents had one or more underlying medical conditions reported (76.4%) or were aged ≥65 years (74.8%). Among reported underlying medical conditions, cardiovascular disease and diabetes were the most common. Diabetes prevalence among decedents aged <65 years (49.6%) was substantially higher than that reported in an analysis of hospitalized COVID-19 patients aged <65 years (35%) and persons aged <65 years in the general population (<20%) (5–7). Among decedents aged <65 years, 7.8% died in an emergency department or at home; these out-of-hospital deaths might reflect lack of health care access, delays in seeking care, or diagnostic delays. Health communications campaigns could encourage patients, particularly those with underlying medical conditions, to seek medical care earlier in their illnesses. Additionally, health care providers should be encouraged to consider the possibility of severe disease among younger persons who are Hispanic, nonwhite, or have underlying medical conditions. More prompt diagnoses could facilitate earlier implementation of supportive care to minimize morbidity among individuals and earlier isolation of contagious persons to protect communities from SARS-CoV-2 transmission.

The relatively high percentages of Hispanic and nonwhite decedents aged <65 years were notable. The median age of nonwhite persons (31 years) in the United States is lower than that of white persons (44 years); these differences might help explain the higher proportions of Hispanic and nonwhite decedents among those aged <65 years. The median ages among Hispanic and nonwhite decedents (71 and 72 years, respectively) were 9–10 years lower than that of white decedents (81 years). However, the percentage of Hispanic decedents aged <65 years (33.9%) exceeded the percentage of Hispanic persons aged <65 years in the U.S. population (20%); the percentage of nonwhite COVID-19 decedents aged <65 years (40.2%) also exceeded the overall percentage of nonwhite decedents aged <65 years (23%) in the U.S. population (8). Further study is needed to understand the reasons for these differences. It is possible that rates of SARS-CoV-2 transmission are higher among Hispanic and nonwhite persons aged <65 years than among white persons; one potential contributing factor is higher percentages of Hispanic and nonwhite persons engaged in occupations (e.g., service industry) or essential activities that preclude physical distancing (9). It is also possible that the COVID-19 pandemic disproportionately affected communities of younger, nonwhite persons during the study period (10). Although these data did not permit assessment of interactions between race/ethnicity, underlying medical conditions, and nonbiologic factors, further studies to understand and address these racial/ethnic differences are needed to inform targeted efforts to prevent COVID-19 mortality.

The findings in this report are subject to at least five limitations. First, despite >90% completeness for age and race/ethnicity variables in the supplementary data set, the proportion of missing data for some variables, such as underlying medical conditions, clinical course, and race/ethnicity in case-based surveillance, and location of death, was higher than that for other variables; accordingly, the proportions reported for these variables should be considered minimum proportions rather than robust estimates. Second, reporting practices varied by jurisdiction, and several states bundled underlying medical conditions into organ system–specific categories (e.g., hypertension was included as cardiovascular disease) or did not code specifically for a given condition (e.g., immunosuppression was only specifically coded in 10 of the jurisdictions). These differences in reporting structure precluded evaluations of specific conditions other than diabetes using the entire data set. Third, generalizability of the findings from either data set to all deaths among persons with COVID-19, either within the individual jurisdictions or across the United States, is unknown; COVID-19 testing practices for decedents might differ among jurisdictions. Fourth, information from the supplementary data set provides additional insight into decedent demographic and clinical characteristics; however, these data are a convenience sample from 16 public health jurisdictions. Therefore, because the age-race structure of the underlying population is not known, age-standardized mortality rates could not be calculated. Although more than 90% of decedents resided in just three jurisdictions, and most are represented in case-based surveillance, they represent a subset of deaths reported during this period. Therefore, neither calculations of mortality rates nor statistical comparisons between the demographic characteristics of the decedents with available supplementary data and those from case-based surveillance were possible. Finally, these data were collected during a period before dexamethasone was shown to reduce deaths among ventilated patients; implementation of dexamethasone and other therapeutics, as well as shifts in the ages of patients and geographic locations of cases might affect the generalizability of these data to the current period.

Despite these limitations, this report provides more detailed demographic and clinical information on a subset of approximately 10,000 decedents with laboratory-confirmed COVID-19. Most decedents were aged >65 years and had underlying medical conditions. Compared with white decedents, more Hispanic and nonwhite decedents were aged <65 years. Additional studies are needed to elucidate associations between age, race/ethnicity, SARS-CoV-2 infection, disease severity, underlying medical conditions (especially diabetes), socioeconomic status (e.g., poverty and access to health care), behavioral factors (e.g., ability to comply with mitigation recommendations and maintain essential work responsibilities), and out-of-hospital deaths. Regional and state level efforts to examine the roles of these factors in SARS-CoV-2 transmission and COVID-19-associated deaths could lead to targeted, community-level, mortality prevention initiatives. Examples include health communication campaigns targeted towards Hispanics and nonwhite persons aged <65 years. These campaigns could encourage social distancing and the need for wearing cloth face coverings in public settings. In addition, health care providers should be encouraged to consider the possibility of disease progression, particularly in Hispanic and nonwhite persons aged <65 years and persons of any race/ethnicity, regardless of age, with underlying medical conditions, especially diabetes.

Summary

What Is Already Known About This Topic?

COVID-19 mortality is higher in persons with underlying medical conditions and in those aged ≥85 years.

What Is Added by This Report?

Analysis of supplementary data for 10,647 decedents in 16 public health jurisdictions found that a majority were aged ≥65 years and most had underlying medical conditions. Overall, 34.9% of Hispanic and 29.5% of nonwhite decedents were aged <65 years, compared with 13.2% of white, non-Hispanic decedents. Among decedents aged <65 years, a total of 7.8% died in an emergency department or at home.

What Are the Implications for Public Health Practice?

Understanding factors contributing to racial/ethnic mortality differences and out-of-hospital deaths might inform targeted communication to encourage persons in at-risk groups to practice preventive measures and promptly seek medical care if they become ill.

Notes

1. Underlying medical conditions include cardiovascular disease (congenital heart disease, coronary artery disease, congestive heart failure, hypertension, cerebrovascular accident/stroke, valvular heart disease, conduction disorders or dysrhythmias, other cardiovascular disease); diabetes mellitus; chronic lung disease (chronic obstructive pulmonary disease/emphysema, asthma, tuberculosis, other chronic lung diseases); immunosuppression (cancer, human immunodeficiency virus [HIV] infection, identified as being immunosuppressed); chronic kidney disease (chronic kidney disease, end-stage renal disease, other kidney diseases); neurologic conditions (dementia, seizure disorder, other neurologic conditions); chronic liver disease (cirrhosis, alcoholic hepatitis, chronic liver disease, end-stage liver disease, hepatitis B, hepatitis C, nonalcoholic steatohepatitis, other chronic liver diseases); obesity (body mass index ≥30 kg/m2). Information was collected from decedent medical records or death certificates. For 10 states (10,461 decedents), information was abstracted into state surveillance data structures and transmitted to CDC. For six states (186 decedents), the medical records and death certificates were sent to CDC and abstracted using a standardized form.

2. Alaska Department of Health and Social Services; Colorado Department of Public Health and Environment; Indiana State Department of Health; Louisiana Department of Health; Maine Center for Disease Control and Prevention; Michigan Department of Health and Human Services; Minnesota Department of Health; New Jersey Department of Health; New York City Department of Health and Mental Hygiene; North Carolina Department of Health and Human Services; Oregon Health Authority; Tennessee Department of Health; Utah Department of Health; Vermont Department of Health; Washington State Department of Health; Wisconsin Department of Health Services.

References

1. CDC. Coronavirus disease 2019: cases in U.S. Atlanta, GA: US Department of Health and Human Services, CDC; 2020. www.cdc.gov/coronavirus/2019-ncov/cases-in-us.html
2. Bialek S, Boundy E, Bowen V, et al.; CDC COVID-19 Response Team. Severe outcomes among patients with coronavirus disease 2019 (COVID-19)—United States, February 12–March 16, 2020. MMWR Morb Mortal Wkly Rep 2020;69:343–6. https://doi.org/10.15585/mmwr.mm6912e2
3. Chen T, Wu D, Chen H, et al. Clinical characteristics of 113 deceased patients with coronavirus disease 2019: retrospective study. BMJ 2020. Epub March 26, 2020. https://doi.org/10.1136/bmj.m1091
4. Du Y, Tu L, Zhu P, et al. Clinical features of 85 fatal cases of COVID-19 from Wuhan: a retrospective observational study. Am J Respir Crit Care Med 2020;201:1372–9. https://doi.org/10.1164/rccm.202003-0543OC
5. Gold JAW, Wong KK, Szablewski CM, et al. Characteristics and clinical outcomes of adult patients hospitalized with COVID-19—Georgia, March 2020. MMWR Morb Mortal Wkly Rep 2020;69:545–50. https://doi.org/10.15585/mmwr.mm6918e1
6. CDC. National diabetes statistics report, 2020. Atlanta, GA: US Department of Health and Human Services, CDC; 2020. www.cdc.gov/diabetes/pdfs/data/statistics/national-diabetes-statistics-report.Pdf
7. Garg S, Kim L, Whitaker M, et al. Hospitalization rates and characteristics of patients hospitalized with laboratory-confirmed coronavirus disease 2019—COVID-NET, 14 states, March 1–30, 2020. MMWR Morb Mortal Wkly Rep 2020;69:458–64. https://doi.org/10.15585/mmwr.mm6915e3
8. US Census Bureau. Annual population estimates. Washington, DC: US Census Bureau; 2019. www.census.gov/newsroom/press-kits/2019/national-state-estimates.html
9. Bureau of Labor Statistics. Labor force characteristics by race and ethnicity, 2018. Washington, DC: US Department of Labor, Bureau of Labor Statistics; 2019. www.bls.gov/opub/reports/race-and-ethnicity/2018/home.htm
10. Chowkwanyun M, Reed AL Jr. Racial health disparities and Covid-19—caution and context. N Engl J Med 2020. Epub May 6, 2020. https://doi.org/10.1056/NEJMp2012910

14 States Divided

The Implications of American Federalism for COVID-19

Donald F. Kettl

As the United States tackled the COVID-19 outbreak, it could have traveled down several different roads. In South Korea, the national government took strong action with aggressive testing. In Germany, Angela Merkel's aggressive embrace of science produced a relatively successful early campaign against the virus (Miller 2020). In the United States, however, President Donald Trump consciously avoided carving out a clear role for the federal government. Instead, as he wrote in a letter to Senator Charles E. Schumer (D-NY), "the Federal Government is merely a back-up for state governments."[1] The federal response was to avoid a national strategy on what was clearly a national problem.

That puts the American response apart from the rest of the world. There was a different response in every state—as well as in the District of Columbia and in territories across the world from Guam to Puerto Rico. In no other country was the level of friction between the national and subnational governments as high as in the United States. Even in the United Kingdom, where an election weeks before the outbreak of the virus led to a wrenching national debate over keeping the country together, national unity was substantially higher. At the core of these differences—and these frictions—is America's system of governance and, especially, its deep-rooted traditions of federalism. These traditions, in turn, shaped two important patterns. First, the decisions in each state were not just reactions to the virus but were embedded in a far longer and much wider policy stream. Second, these decisions clustered in important ways, with groups of states following different tactics. A careful look at these interrelated forces provides keen insight into the policy streams of American federalism—and to examine American federalism is to provide insight into the differences in the state responses.

The States as Laboratories

There were many arguments for allowing the states to take the lead. To begin with, the virus did not flare up uniformly. It first hit in Washington State, then in California, and then emerged with a horrible vengeance in New York State. For some states, especially in the middle part of the country, the virus came much later. As the disease developed, it often had surprising patterns, hitting both urban areas and rural hot spots, especially around food processing plants. Crafting a single strategy to try to get ahead of these fast-moving problems proved extraordinarily difficult.

Then there was the long-standing argument that the states should lead because they are "laboratories of democracy," the phrase coined by U.S. Supreme Court Justice Louis Brandeis.[2] Brandeis enthusiastically argued for experimentation in the states, and David Osborne's (1990) book of the same name reinforced the case. COVID-19 seemed to be a problem tailor-made for state-based laboratories: individual states could experiment; they could assess what produced the best outcomes; successful experiments could be shared with other states; less successful experiments would be discarded; and the federal government could lead the national effort based on evidence about what worked. COVID-19 was a policy problem of enormous complexity and uncertainty. No one knew quite what it was, how it behaved, or how best to treat it. Why not allow the states that confronted it first try different strategies so that other states, with cases that developed later, could benefit from the successes? Indeed, there is strong evidence that the state-by-state decisions to invoke shelter-in-place orders significantly reduced the spread of the virus (Courtemanche et al. 2020). But the bigger question remains: Was it advisable for the federal government to rely on the decisions of state and local governments to frame policies to control and mitigate a virus that was truly national in scope? That is a question that framed the initial debates about how best to respond to pandemic, and it will cast a deep shadow over American federalism for a very long time.

Then there is the enduring argument for "sorting out" government's functions. Is COVID-19 a problem that state officials ought best to manage, since the most important resources in tackling it lie at the state and local levels? In *Federalist* No. 51, after all, James Madison argued for the virtues of a "compound republic" with "two distinct governments," federal and state. Martha Derthick embraced that sorting-out notion and argued for clear lines of responsibility between the federal government and the states (Derthick 2001; see also Anrig 2010; Bednar 2011; Edwards 2009; Hoover Institution Task Force on K–12 2012; Kendall 2004; Nivola 2005; Oates 1972). The debate, of course, was rooted in the remarkably "ambiguous division of authority" at the core of American federalism, as John Donahue (1997, 5) contended. Perhaps in the ambiguity of legal and constitutional documents, there was authority—perhaps even a mandate—for state governments to carve out their own paths.

And that is just what they did, most notably in the early weeks of the crisis, through governors' decisions about whether—and when—to lock down their economies. Indeed, in the first phase of the outbreak, the lockdown decision was the central public policy action. Because there was no proven treatment for the virus and no vaccine to prevent it, the best way to prevent its spread was to keep people far enough away from each other to reduce its spread. Otherwise, public health officials warned, the disease would over-run communities and overwhelm hospital emergency rooms, intensive care units, and the supply of ventilators. Reducing economic activity and social interaction was, public health officials believed, the only real line of defense.

One of the first lockdown decisions came from National Collegiate Ath-letic Association (NCAA) president Mark Emmert, who announced on March 11 that the men's and women's basketball tournaments would be played to empty arenas. That decision startled the country, since a March without March Madness crowds seemed unthinkable. But then a few days later, the NCAA canceled the entire tournament, in response to what NCAA vice president Dan Gavitt called a "global health crisis" (Gavitt 2020). Within days, the governors began locking down their states, begin-ning on March 19 in California and rippling from there across the country. By the end of March, 32 states had issued lockdown orders. Eleven more states followed in the first week of April, but in the end, seven states (Arkan-sas, Iowa, Nebraska, North Dakota, South Dakota, Utah, and Wyoming) decided not to lock down at all (Ballotopedia 2020). The lockdown deci-sion was invariably one of the most difficult decisions most governors had ever had to make. And the decision to lock down before the end of March proved an important measure of the states' decisions about responding to the outbreak.

What forces shaped these decisions? It is possible to imagine two approaches. One is that the governors' decisions would be built on evidence from public health experts. The other is that these decisions would, instead, flow from the broader stream of public policy decisions over the years. It is certainly the case that, especially for the handful of states in which the virus proved especially virulent in its opening weeks, public health experts shaped the strategy. But, as we shall see, as the outbreak spread, it was the broader policy stream, not evidence-based policies, that dominated. The state-by-state decisions about locking down the economy by the end of March pro-vides the important touchstone.

The pivotal question was whether the lockdown decisions followed the seriousness of the outbreak. In fact, the 10 states that experienced the high-est death rate by mid-April were, in fact, far more likely to lock down by the end of March. The death rate provided, sadly, the best evidence of the seri-ousness of the disease, and it was the most uniform national measure, even though reporting problems made even this measure hard to collect. Because the disease can take several weeks to incubate and inflict its most serious damage, this April death rate provides an indicator of the decisions that the governors faced at the end of March. For the rest of the states, however, there was no pattern between the death rate and the lockdown decision. In fact, the states with the lowest death rate were about as likely to lock down early as those with much higher death rates (see Table 14.1). Moreover, by the middle of May, the rate of new deaths was 12 percent higher in the states that did not lock down in March (Fox et al. 2020).

Table 14.1 Governors' Decisions to Lock Down Their States Compared with the Death Rate.

Deaths/100,000	Locked Down in March
Highest 10	9 of 10
Next-highest 10	6 of 10
Middle 10	6 of 10
Next-lowest 10	7 of 10
Lowest 10	5 of 10

Source: COVID-19 Tracking Project, www.washingtonpost.com/graphics/2020/national/coronavirus-us-cases-deaths/?itid=hp_hp-banner-low_web-gfx-death-tracker%3Ahomepage%2Fstory-ans. Data as of April 26, 2020.

Table 14.2 Governors' Decisions to Lock down their States Compared with Partisan Control.

	Republicans Control Governorship, Both Houses of State Legislature	Democrats Control Governorship, Both Houses of State Legislature	Split Partisan Control	Nonpartisan (Nebraska)	Trump Vote
March lockdown	6	13	13	0	45.7
No March lockdown	14	2	1	1	55.3

Source: For state partisan control, Nuttycombe (2020).

The timing of the governors' decisions, therefore, was not directly connected with the seriousness of problems they faced. What, then, were they connected with? The states were not operating as "laboratories of democracy," with different states experimenting with different policy decisions depending on the seriousness of the problem they faced. COVID-19 created a laboratory, but one without experimentation. The states' decisions flowed instead from a different pattern.

Systematic Variations

Although the early focus of the crisis centered on a handful of states with a big surge in cases, it quickly became clear that the virus was a genuine emergency, a national crisis instead of a regional outbreak. No part of the country, no matter how far removed from the first cases, was immune. Officials in Iowa discovered 16 cases among travelers recently back from a cruise on Egypt's Nile River. The same trip sparked cases in Texas and Maryland (Helderman et al. 2020). COVID-19 proved an angry aggressor that paid no attention to borders of any kind.

The pattern of state responses, however, followed the broader stream of political and policy choices that were already in place. Table 14.2 shows that the states that locked down in March voted for President Trump at a much lower rate and tended to have weaker Republican control of their state governments.

The lockdown decisions were also consistent with a broad collection of disparate policy decisions over a far longer time. For example, consider the connection between governors' lockdown decisions and the states' previous decisions to expand Medicaid as part of the Affordable Care Act (ACA), passed in 2010. Barack Obama came into office committed to providing health care for all Americans, but he faced two inescapable forces: opposition to the federal government providing health care, which meant he needed to focus on creating a program of health insurance, and opposition to the federal government providing health insurance, which meant he needed to craft a strategy that relied heavily on the states. The ACA thus was not so much a program of federal health insurance as a federal program encouraging the states to create their own state-based health insurance exchanges and to decide whether to expand the Medicaid program to more recipients. As Sommer (2013) pointed out, the program was "a patchwork of related but not identical strategies, solutions, and regulations." Some states embraced the ACA and used it to expand health care coverage to their citizens. Others strongly pushed back and refused to expand their Medicaid programs under the ACA's provisions.

The previous decisions about expanding Medicaid tended to match the governors' decisions to lock down their states. In the states where governors locked down their economies in March, 87.5 percent had earlier decided to expand Medicaid under the ACA. In the states where the governors did not lock down in March, almost two-thirds had decided not to expand Medicaid (see Table 14.3). There were also stark differences in the states' investment in their public health programs. As Figure 14.1 shows, the states that locked down in March also spent significantly more on public health spending—44.4 percent more per capita, in fact.

The differences in public health investments spilled over into a remarkably broad range of other policy outcomes. Consider a wide collection of policy areas: environmental performance, infant mortality, eighth-grade reading proficiency, poverty rate, the condition of the state's infrastructure (as measured by the percentage of the total bridges that were judged deficient).

Table 14.3 Medicaid expansion under the Affordable Care Act.

	Expansion	No Expansion	Total
March lockdown	28	4	32
No March lockdown	7	11	18

Source: Calculated by author.

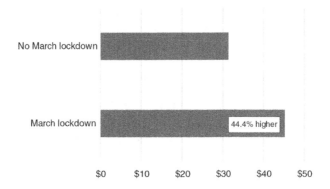

Figure 14.1 Public health spending per capita.
Source: Robert Wood Johnson Foundation (2020). Data are for 2018.

Table 14.4 Differences between states that locked down in March and those that did not.

	Environmental performance (ACE Index)	Infant mortality rate (per 1,000 live births)	Eighth-grade reading proficiency (NAEP Index)	Poverty rate 2014–16, average (% of people in poverty)	Deficient bridges (% of total)
March lockdown	15.96	5.7	33.9	12.7	7.5%
No March lockdown	7.51	6.4	31.2	13.7	8.1%
Difference for March lockdown states	112.4% higher	11.0% lower	8.7% higher	6.8% lower	6.9% lower

Sources: Environmental performance: index compiled by Frost and Fiorino (2018); infant mortality: CDC (2020); eighth-grade reading proficiency: Nation's Report Card (2020); poverty rate: U.S. Census Bureau (2017). Deficient bridges: American Road Transportation Builders Association (2020).

Table 14.4 shows a consistent and significant difference in the two groups of states. The states that locked down their economies in March fared better on all of these indicators. Policy outcomes in the states not only vary widely, but the differences among them are growing (Kettl 2020).

In the states' response to the virus, there certainly were partisan differences. The early-outbreak states—especially Washington, California, and New York—tended to disproportionately lean Democratic, and their Democratic governors tended to be among the first and most vocal champions of an aggressive governmental response. The states where the virus hit latest tended to lean Republican. But it is much too simple to argue that the most important strategic decisions were purely the product of partisanship. They are embedded in a much wider, much deeper, and even more important policy stream that has been reshaping American public policy for a far longer time.

The Silent Tsunami

The governors' decisions about locking down their economies arose out of a silent tsunami. America, of course, is no stranger to disasters, both man-made and natural. That is why, in fact, Congress created the Department of Homeland Security in the aftermath of the September 11 terrorist attacks, and why the states have followed suit. Emergency management experts have long embraced the idea of an "all-hazards" approach to disasters: create a robust but nimble capacity to respond to disasters, however they emerge, because it is impossible to guess which disaster will occur next and because the response to many disasters builds on a core collection of resources.

The COVID-19 assault fits within the all-hazards approach. Indeed, emergency planners had built the capacity for a strong public health response into their response strategy, especially since the September 11 terrorist attacks, and experts had warned about the risks of a global pandemic (Center for Health Security 2019; Nuki 2020). Compared with most of the all-hazard planning, however, COVID-19 was a silent tsunami, in several important respects. First, unlike the terrorist attacks or Hurricane Katrina, which followed four years later, the virus was *invisible to the public*. An invisible microscopic killer, it took a skilled team of artists at the Centers for Disease Control and Prevention (CDC) to bring it to life with an artistic rendition that quickly became iconic (Kallingal 2020). That stood in dramatic contrast to the terrorist attacks and Hurricane Katrina, where the scale and importance of the disasters were both clear to all and unmistakable in scope. Second, *the root of the problem was unclear*, as was what to do about it. Compared with Hurricane Katrina, where the nature of the problem (epic flooding and wind damage) and how to attack it (rescue those the storm had left isolated and devastated), COVID-19 generated only uncertainty. That carried over, third, to the question of how to create a longer-term strategy because, the deeper state officials got into the crisis, the more *uncertainty they faced about the disease*: what it was, how to slow it, how to recover from it, and how to rebuild communities in the long term. Fourth, the *scale of the problem* was far greater than any previous recent disaster. COVID-19 hit with a force of 1,000 or more Katrinas, leaving no part of the country unspared. The governors were faced not only with a vast array of problems they could scarcely identify (compare Kettl 2014). They were overwhelmed with what Donald Rumsfeld would have called both "known unknowns" and "unknown unknowns" (Graham 2014).

Confronting enormous punctuations to their equilibrium (see Baumgartner and Jones 1993; Baumgartner, Jones, and Mortensen 2014; Jones and Baumgartner 2005), the governors could have used the virus to trigger big changes to their states' existing policy regimes. Rather, they fell quickly back to the established and accepted patterns of the political culture and policy decisions that had grown up within their states. Indeed, the larger the crisis became, the stronger the incentives were for governors to slide back into the relatively familiar, politically proven policy streams, shaped by the problems, policies, and politics of the past (Kingdon 1984). Even though these past practices risked falling badly out of sync with what an effective response to the disease demanded, it was far less risky to fall onto what the policy streams in each of their states had produced over the years. However, because these policy streams have becoming increasingly divided over the years, with the United States becoming a land of divided states (Kettl 2020), COVID-19 served only to reinforce the divisions that had already developed in the country. That, in turn, reinforced the growing inequality among the states that had emerged on a wide policy front.

Intergovernmental Friction

The outbreak of COVID-19 has laid bare a trio of fundamental—and fundamentally important—issues at the core of modern American democracy: the relationship between the federal government and the states, the relationship among the states, and the relationship between the state governments and their localities. In the 1960s, there was a budding consensus that the federal government should take a strong steering role, shaping national policy through a robust system of grants that state and local governments were bound to find irresistible. In part, that was because the federal government came to channel the nation's ambition in fighting wars against problems ranging from poverty to health care. In part, that was also because of lingering distrust of state and local governments flowing from the days of segregation. There was a strong sense that if the nation was going to make large strides, the federal government would need to strap on the boots and fund the effort.

In the decades that followed, however, there was a growing concern that the federal government had overreached, that state and local governments had powerful administrative machinery of their own, and that for both political and policy reasons it made sense to match national programs to local conditions. Along the way, it became increasingly hard for the federal government to reach consensus on any decision of major import. Congress became, as Mann and Ornstein (2006) put it, a "broken branch," often struggling to move important pieces of legislation. Any major proposal for domestic initiatives immediately became wrapped up in fierce battles about the size of the government and, in the pre-COVID-19 days, the size of the deficit.

That increasingly left domestic policy leadership to the states, and the states' preeminence in turn produced a widely varying patchwork of state government responses to COVID-19. The federal government did not speak with a single voice, and the president often downplayed the seriousness of the outbreak. At the end of February, President Trump called the virus the "new hoax" of the Democrats, and he suggested that "the press is in hysteria mode" (Palma 2020). Meanwhile, different messages came from the National Institutes of Health, the CDC, the Food and Drug Administration, the Federal Emergency Management Agency, and the cabinet secretaries overseeing them. Of course, the federal government's power to lock down the states was limited, even with President Trump's decision on March 13 to invoke the Stafford Act, which declared a national emergency. But from the procurement of tests to the distribution of ventilators, the states remained largely on their own and often in competition with each other. Without national coordination of the production, price, and allocation of scarce medical supplies, the states ended up competing with each other, and with the federal government, for ventilators and personal protective equipment. "We are literally bidding up the prices ourselves," complained Governor Andrew Cuomo (D-NY), pointing to an increase of ventilator prices from $25,000 to $40,000. The result was what economists would predict: escalating demand, in the absence of much greater supply, produced a rapid increase in the price (Feldman 2020). Within states like Georgia and, especially, Texas, moreover, the frictions between the state and local governments boiled over, with fierce battles over who had the authority to set rules for citizens—and which businesses could open when, and under what circumstances.

Even the basic question of where the problem was most serious and how fast it was spreading was impossible to answer because there was no common language for charting the problem, as what defined the problem depended on tests for the virus and different states had different strategies for testing. Some states reported only tests that produced positive results. Some states included negative tests, while others (including Maryland and Ohio) did not. Some states had a significant lag in reporting test results, and some states were reluctant to report test results at all. Some states reported results differently from public and private labs. Virginia at first combined results from antibody and diagnostic tests, an approach that compared apples with oranges, and then changed its reporting metrics as the virus wore on. In some states, officials reported the number of positive results compared with the number of specimens taken, which produced a higher infection rate than reporting on the number of individuals tested, because many individuals often had many tests over the course of their disease. Georgia officials admitted that they had bungled a chart that incorrectly showed a downward trend. "Our mission failed. We apologize," the governor's spokesperson said (Mariano and Trubey 2020). The architect of Florida's virus dashboard was removed, leading critics to charge that the state government was attempting to censor science (Sassoon 2020). Across the states, the infection rate ranged from 5 to 10 percent of tests conducted, even though it was highly unlikely, of course, that the infection rate was twice as high in some states than others (Schulte 2020).

The intergovernmental confusion meant that it was impossible to get a full and accurate picture of the disease, its spread, and its health implications. In fact, the benchmark data for tracking COVID-19 increasingly came not from governmental sources but, instead, from private and nonprofit organizations. Johns Hopkins University's Coronavirus Resource Center (https:// coronavirus. jhu.edu) was the touchstone for most analysis and reporting. At the University of Washington, the Institute for Health Metrics and Evaluation (www.healthdata.org/covid) produced the models estimating the likely spread of the disease, on which many federal and state officials depended. At the University of Texas, data scientists developed a separate model because they were unhappy with methodological changes in some of the other tracking systems (https://covid-19/tacc.utexas.edu). A collaborative of media organizations created their own COVID Tracking Project (https:// covidtracking.com).

Many of the data flowed from health care providers to county health departments, from these county health departments to state health departments, and from there to the CDC. The CDC data, in turn, helped fuel the analytical engines at Johns Hopkins, the University of Washington, and the media conglomerates. But when it became apparent that the illness affected minority populations more than others, only 35 states reported the death rate by race, and just two shared information on testing by race.[3] Other data came from social distancing measures derived from mobile phones (Woody et al. 2020), but relying on those data generated debates about privacy.

The federal government played a weak steering role for the nation's COVID-19 response. Indeed, it never framed a truly national strategy to deal with the virus or spoke with a clear national voice on how best to handle it. That left each state to steer its own course, often without a sound base of evidence on which to make decisions. States competed against each other and often moved in very different directions. Other nations, of course, struggled mightily to deal with the large and uncertain course of the disease. But in no other country were the frictions between the national and subnational governments or the variations in strategies among the regions so great. In a mid-2020 survey, the Edelman Trust Barometer found a larger gap in trust between the national and local governments in the United States than in any other government—four times higher, in fact, than the average of 11 other countries that were surveyed.[4] Moreover, in no other country with a federal system of government was the death rate in the first two months of the pandemic as high as in the United States (see Figure 14.2).

Time will chart the broader implications of the tensions within America's system of government, but the evidence is clear that the intergovernmental frictions—between the federal and the state governments, between the state

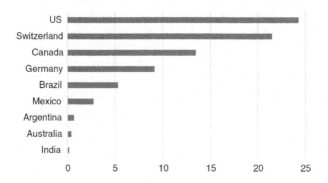

Figure 14.2 COVID-19 death rate per 100,000 population.

Source: Johns Hopkins University Coronavirus Resource Center, "Mortality Analyses," https//coronavirus.jhu.edu/map.html. Data as of May 10, 2020.

governments, and between state and local governments—were high and that these frictions had real impact on the health of Americans.

The evidence from the critical initial decisions to lock down the states revealed stark differences among the states. Indeed, the best predictor of the states' decisions was where the states had already stood in the broad stream of policy decisions and outcomes, ranging from whether to expand Medicaid and how much to invest in public health to their ongoing policies about environmental quality and infrastructure investment. America might be a land where all people are created equal. But with respect to COVID-19, as in many other policy areas, the risks citizens took and the government they got increasingly depended on where they lived. Indeed, the early evidence from the stark differences between the states was that the effectiveness of the state governments' responses varied widely, and that Americans in some states were exposed to far greater risks because of the decisions their state governments made.

One of the enduring questions that emerges from the COVID-19 outbreak is whether governance in the United States failed—or at least did not succeed as Americans needed it to—precisely because it relied so heavily on the states as laboratories, which produced such wide-ranging experiments. Did some states develop strategies that, given the problems they faced, produce significantly better outcomes? Did frictions in the system—between Washington and some states, between many states, and between some state capitols and their local governments—create much higher risks and cost more lives?

In particular, it will be important to probe the central question of American federalism in the case of COVID: Should the federal government have played a far stronger leadership role? One argument is that a more aggressive federal government could have devised a testing regimen much earlier, ensured that the country geared up its production of testing supplies and personal protective equipment, reduced the competition among the states for supplies, developed a national dashboard for measuring the spread of the virus and the effectiveness of interventions, and directed resources where they were most needed. A counterargument is that a stronger federal role would only have escalated dysfunction, immobilizing the states that developed early and aggressive actions and subjecting the national response to epic problems of coordination. These questions are urgent and require searching, sustained examination, because it is impossible to escape the conclusion that the country's initial response was significantly less successful than in other countries and that its system of federalism lies at the roots. Its clumsy response, in turn, weakened the public's trust and widened political polarization, at precisely the time that citizens and business leaders struggled to determine who to believe as the even tougher decisions about reopening the economy came to center stage. These are issues that cut to the heart of governance in the United States and frame the twenty-first century's version of the debates that have been at the core of democracy in America since the nation's founding.

The Public Interest on a Wobbly Foundation

The COVID-19 outbreak was, by any measure, one of the most challenging public policy problems in American history—and indeed one of the most complex that modern governments anywhere have faced. But amid the global challenges, the United States stands apart because of the highly devolved nature of its response. Although COVID-19 became a clearly national problem, the country did not meet it with a national response. Indeed, the *Washington Post's* editorial board argued that creating a robust national testing system was "a uniquely federal responsibility," a strategy that should have been "a Manhattan Project for the pandemic age." Instead, President Trump "left the job to governors, and the nation is staggering under the consequences" (*Washington Post* 2020). For the success that the governors did have, the president took credit. He tweeted, "Remember this, every Governor who has sky high approval on their handling of the Coronavirus, and I am happy for them all, could in no way have gotten those numbers, or had that success, without me and the Federal Governments help. From Ventilators to Testing, we made it happen!"[5]

The nation's strategy was built on a wobbly foundation, riven by great tensions of federal versus state power, and then with the states pulling in different directions. The state reactions, in turn, matched the different policy strategies of the states in many other policy areas as well. It is one thing to rely on "laboratories of democracy" to experiment with policy initiatives and determine which ones deserve wider adoption. But it is quite another for the nation's response to a truly national problem to vary so greatly. The

American response to COVID-19 underlines a growing truth about American public policy: The United States is a country with states moving in different directions, and these different directions have grave consequences for the well-being of Americans. The nation faced fundamental choices at the start of the pandemic: first, whether the federal government would lead on issues that were truly national in scope, but instead it pushed responsibility to the states; and then whether the states would seize the punctuation of the equilibrium to create a new governance regime, but instead they slid back into long-established and increasingly disparate patterns. At the core, this is the price of American federalism. The virus frames the question of whether that price is simply too high to pay when faced with the biggest policy challenges of the twenty-first century.

Is this price the inevitable result of James Madison's strategy in 1787 to balance federal and state power, to nudge the Constitution toward ratification? The long history of American democracy is, in fact, one in which the original compromise has fed division as well as experimentation in the laboratories of democracy. But during the COVID-19 pandemic, that grand compromise exacted a big price, with a federal government unwilling to act to frame a genuine national policy, with states going down different roads, and where the entire creaky system was too slow to act on a problem that paid no attention to state boundaries and that moved faster than government's ability to keep up. Alexander Hamilton framed an alternative vision, of a robust federal government powerful enough to push forward national policies to attack national problems. That, indeed, was the approach advanced with great success in the first weeks by Germany's Angela Merkel, who took on her own state governments (Kupferschmidt and Vogel 2020). Even in Germany, tensions between the central government and the states began rising, although the national government was not shy about forcefully crafting a robust national policy, calling out the states for reopening too quickly and for protecting the strong results that the country won in the important early weeks of the very long campaign against the virus.

The insidious complexity of the virus quickly demonstrated that the first decisions made by government officials were only the initial salvos in a far longer war that was to test the systems of government around the world. But it is impossible to escape the conclusion that the United States faced the virus with a system of governance that was not up to the job, in part because the initial outcomes were less positive than in other federal systems and in part because the treatment of citizens varied so greatly across the country. And the widely—sometimes wildly—varying responses of its governance meant that citizens suffered more than they needed to—and that they suffered more in some places than others.

Decisions about COVID-19 followed the broader strategies already in place: for the federal government to pass the buck to the states, and for the states to go their own ways, often in different directions. The result was a system of states divided, with deep and enduring implications for Americans and the pursuit of "equal protection of the laws," as the Fourteenth Amendment to the Constitution so elegantly puts it.

Notes

1. Letter to Senator Charles E. Schumer, April 2, 2020, www.politico.com/f/?id=00000171-3f7b-d6b1-a3f1-fffb5e270000&nname=playbook&nid=0000014f-1646-d88f-a1cf-5f46b7bd0000&nrid=00000159-176e-db99-ab5d-bffe84ac0002&nlid=630318 (accessed May 29, 2020).
2. *New State Ice Co. v. Lieberman*, 285 U.S. 262 (1932).
3. Johns Hopkins University Coronavirus Resource Center, "State COVID-19 data by Race," https://coronavirus.jhu.edu/data/racial-data-transparency (accessed May 29, 2020).
4. Edelman Trust Barometer 2020, www.edelman.com/sites/g/files/aatuss191/files/2020-05/2020%20Edelman%20Trust%20Barometer%20Spring%20Update.pdf (accessed May 29, 2020).
5. Donald J. Trump (@realDonaldTrump), "Remember this, every Governor who has sky high approval on their handling of the Coronavirus, and I am happy for them all, could in no way have gotten those numbers, or had that success, without me and the Federal Governments help. From Ventilators to Testing, we made it happen!," Twitter, May 12, 2020, 7:56 a.m., https://twitter.com/realDonaldTrump/status/1260177007490600960.

References

American Road Transportation Builders Association. 2020. ARTBA 2020 Bridge Report. https://artbabridgereport.org/reports/ARTBA%202020%20Bridge%20Report%20-%20State%20Ranking.pdf [accessed May 29, 2020].

Anrig, Greg. 2010. Federalism and Its Discontents. *Democracy: A Journal of Ideas*, no. 15. https://democracyjournal.org/magazine/15/federalism-and-its-discontents/ [accessed May 29, 2020].

Ballotopedia. 2020. State Government Responses to the Coronavirus (COVID-19) Pandemic, 2020. https://ballotpedia.org/State_government_responses_to_the_coronavirus_(COVID-19)_pandemic,_2020 [accessed May 29, 2020].

Baumgartner, Frank R., and Bryan D. Jones. 1993. *Agendas and Instability in American Politics*. Chicago: University of Chicago Press.

Baumgartner, Frank R., Bryan D. Jones, and Peter B. Mortensen. 2014. Punctuated-Equilibrium Theory: Explaining Stability and Change in Public Policymaking. In *Theories of the Policy Process*, 3rd ed., edited by Paul Sabatier and M. Christopher Weible, 155–187. Boulder, CO: Westview Press.

Bednar, Jenna. 2011. The Political Science of Federalism. *Annual Review of Law and Social Science* 7: 269–88. https://doi.org/10.1146/annurev-lawsocsci-102510-105522.

CDC. 2020. *Infant Mortality in the United States, 2018*. Atlanta, GA: CDC.

Center for Health Security. 2019. Event 201. www.centerforhealthsecurity.org/event201/ [accessed May 29, 2020].

Courtemanche, Charles, Joseph Garuccio, Anh Le, Joshua Pinkston, and Aaron Yelowitz. 2020. Strong Social Distancing Measures in the United States Reduced the COVID-19 Growth Rate. *Health Affairs*. Published online May 14. https://doi.org/10.1377/hlthaff.2020.00608.

Derthick, Martha. 2001. *Keeping the Compound Republic: Essays on American Federalism.* Washington, DC: Brookings Institution Press.

Donahue, John D. 1997. *Disunited States: What's at Stake as Washington Fades and the States Take the Lead.* New York: Basic Books.

Edwards, Chris. 2009. Fiscal Federalism. In *Cato Handbook for Policymakers*, 7th ed., 63–71. Washington, DC: Cato Institute. www.cato.org/sites/cato.org/files/serials/files/cato-handbook-policymakers/2009/9/hb111-5.pdf [accessed May 29, 2020].

Feldman, Amy. 2020. States Bidding against Each Other Pushing Up Prices of Ventilators Needed to Fight Coronavirus, NY Governor Cuomo Says. *Forbes*, March 28. www.forbes.com/sites/amyfeldman/2020/03/28/states-bidding-against-each-other-pushing-up-prices-of-ventilators-needed-to-fight-coronavirus-ny-governor-cuomo-says/#1dd9926f293e [accessed May 29, 2020].

Fox, Joe, Brittany Renee Mayes, Kevin Schaul, and Leslie Shapiro. 2020. 78,890 People Have Died from Coronavirus in the U.S. *Washington Post*, May 10. www.washingtonpost.com/graphics/2020/national/coronavirus-us-cases-deaths/?itid=hp_hp-banner-low_web-gfx-death-tracker%3Ahomepage%2Fstory-ans [accessed May 29, 2020].

Frost, Riordan, and Daniel Fiorino. 2018. The State Air, Climate, and Energy (ACE) Index. Email communication with the author, March 13.

Gavitt, Dan. 2020. NCAA SVP Dan Gavitt: No DI Men's and Women's Basketball Brackets Will Be Released This Year. *NCAA*, March 15. www.ncaa.com/live-updates/basketball-men/d1/ncaa-cancels-mens-and-womens-basketball-championships-due [accessed May 29, 2020].

Graham, David A. 2014. Rumsfeld's Knowns and Unknowns: The Intellectual History of a Quip. *The Atlantic*, March 27. www.theatlantic.com/politics/archive/2014/03/rumsfelds-knowns-and-unknowns-the-intellectual-history-of-a-quip/359719/ [accessed May 29, 2020].

Helderman, Rosalind S., Hannah Sampson, Dalton Bennett, and Andrew Ba Tran. 2020. The Pandemic at Sea. *Washington Post*, April 25. www.washingtonpost.com/graphics/2020/politics/cruise-ships-coronavirus/?itid=hp_hp-top-table-high_cruisefallout-1020am%3Ahomepage%2Fstory-ans [accessed May 29, 2020].

Hoover Institution Task Force on K–12 Education. 2012. *Choice and Federalism: Defining the Federal Role in Education.* Stanford, CA: Stanford University. www.hoover.org/sites/default/files/research/docs/choice-and-federalism.pdf [accessed May 29, 2020].

Jones, Bryan D., and Frank R. Baumgartner. 2005. *The Politics of Attention: How Government Prioritizes Problems.* Chicago: University of Chicago Press.

Kallingal, Mallika. 2020. Meet the Illustrators Who Gave the Coronavirus Its Face. *CNN*, April 18. www.cnn.com/2020/04/17/us/coronavirus-cdc-design-trnd/index.html [accessed May 29, 2020].

Kendall, Douglas T., ed. 2004. *Redefining Federalism: Listening to the States in Shaping "Our Federalism."* Washington, DC: Environmental Law Institute.

Kettl, Donald F. 2014. *System under Stress: Homeland Security and American Politics*, 3rd ed. Washington, DC: CQ Press.

———. 2020. *The Divided States of America: Why Federalism Doesn't Work.* Princeton, NJ: Princeton University Press.

Kingdon, John W. 1984. *Agendas, Alternatives and Public Policies.* Boston: Little, Brown.

Kupferschmidt, Kai, and Gretchen Vogel. 2020. Reopening Puts Germany's Much-Praised Coronavirus Response at Risk. *Science*, April 27. www.sciencemag.org/news/2020/04/reopening-puts-germany-s-much-praised-coronavirus-response-risk [accessed May 29, 2020].

Mann, Thomas E., and Norman J. Ornstein. 2006. *The Broken Branch: How Congress Is Failing America and How to Get It Back on Track.* Oxford: Oxford University Press.

Mariano, Willoughby, and J. Scott Trubey. 2020. "It's Just Cuckoo": State's Latest Data Mishap Causes Critics to Cry Foul. *Atlanta Journal-Constitution*, May 13. www.ajc. com/news/state-regional-govt-politics/just-cuckoo-state-latest-data-mishap-causes-critics-cry-foul/182PpUvUX9XEF8vO11NVGO/ [accessed May 29, 2020].

Miller, Saskia. 2020. The Secret to Germany's COVID-19 Success: Angela Merkel Is a Scientist. *The Atlantic*, April 20. www.theatlantic.com/international/archive/2020/04/angela-merkel-germany-coronavirus-pandemic/610225/ [accessed May 29, 2020].

Nation's Report Card. 2020. National Assessment of Educational Progress (NEAP) Results. www.nationsreportcard.gov/profiles/stateprofile?chort=2&sub=RED&sj=AL&sfj=NP&st=MN&year=2019R3 [accessed May 29, 2020].

Nivola, Pietro. 2005. Why Federalism Matters. Policy Brief Series, Brookings Institution, October 1. www.brookings.edu/research/why-federalism-matters/ [accessed May 29, 2020].

Nuki, Paul. 2020. Exercise Cygnus Uncovered: The Pandemic Warnings Buried by the Government. *The Telegraph*, March 28. www.telegraph.co.uk/news/2020/03/28/exercise-cygnus-uncovered-pandemic-warnings-buried-government/ [accessed May 29, 2020].

Nuttycombe, Chaz. 2020. The State of the States: The Legislatures. University of Virginia Center for Politics, May 7. http://centerforpolitics.org/crystalball/articles/the-state-of-the-states-the-legislatures/ [accessed May 29, 2020].

Oates, Wallace E. 1972. *Fiscal Federalism.* New York: Harcourt, Brace, Jovanovich.

Osborne, David. 1990. *Laboratories of Democracy.* Boston: Harvard Business School Press.

Palma, Bethania. 2020. Did President Trump Refer to the Coronavirus as a "Hoax"? *Snopes*, March 2. www.snopes.com/fact-check/trump-coronavirus-rally-remark/ [accessed May 29, 2020].

Robert Wood Johnson Foundation. 2020. Per Person State Public Health Funding. http://statehealthcompare.shadac.org/rank/117/per-person-state-public-health-funding#2,3,4,5,6,7,8,9,10,11,12,13,14,15,16,17,18,19,20,21,22,23,24,25,26,27,28,29,30,31,32, 33,34,35,36,37,38,39,40,41,42,43,44,45,46,47,48,49,50,51,52/a/25/154/false/location [accessed May 29, 2020].

Sassoon, Alessandro Marazzi. 2020. Florida COVID-19 Response Loses Data Chief and Transparency. *Governing*, May 19. www.governing.com/next/Florida-COVID-19-Response-Loses-Data-Chief-and-Transparency.html?utm_term=Florida%20COVID-19%20Response%20Loses%20Data%20Chief%20and%20Transparency&utm_campaign=Drawing%20Lessons%20from%20a%20Government%20Protest%20in%20North%20Dakota&utm_content=email&utm_source=Act-On+Software&utm_medium=email [accessed May 29, 2020].

Schulte, Fred. 2020. Some States Are Reporting Incomplete COVID-19 Results, Blurring the Full Picture. *Kaiser Health News*, March 25. https://khn.org/news/some-states-are-reporting-incomplete-covid-19-results-blurring-the-full-picture/ [accessed May 29, 2020].

Sommer, Alexander H. 2013. State Implementation of the Affordable Care Act. *AMA Journal of Ethics*, July. https://journalofethics.ama-assn.org/article/state-implementation-affordable-care-act/2013-07 [accessed May 29, 2020].

U.S. Census Bureau. 2017. Percentage of People in Poverty by State. www.census.gov/data/tables/2017/demo/income-poverty/p60-259.html [accessed May 29, 2020].

Washington Post. 2020. This Is Trump's Greatest Failure of the Pandemic. May 11. www.washingtonpost.com/opinions/this-is-trumps-greatest-failure-of-the-pandemic/2020/05/11/29f22f7c-93ae-11ea-82b4-c8db161ff6e5_story.html [accessed May 29, 2020].

Woody, Spencer, Mauricio Tec, Maytal Dahan, Kelly Gaither, Michael Lachmann, Spencer J. Fox, Lauren Ancel Meyers, and James Scott. 2020. Projections for First-Wave COVID-19 Deaths across the US Using Social-Distancing Measures Derived from Mobile Phones. https://covid-19.tacc.utexas.edu/media/filer_public/87/63/87635a46-b060-4b5b-a3a5-1b31ab8e0bc6/ut_covid-19_mortality_forecasting_model_latest.pdf [accessed May 29, 2020].

15 Shelter-in-Place Orders Reduced COVID-19 Mortality and Reduced the Rate of Growth in Hospitalizations

Wei Lyu and George L. Wehby

The coronavirus disease 2019 (COVID-19) pandemic has placed unprecedented challenges on governments to mitigate its spread. As of May 15, the end date for our study data, the US had over 1.5 million confirmed cases, over 198,000 hospitalizations and over 83,000 deaths; updates to this data indicate over 2.5 million cases, 320,000 hospitalizations, and 120,000 deaths.[1,2] Following the experience of countries hit earlier by the pandemic, it became clear that social distancing measures are critical for effective mitigation.[3,4] States closed schools, banned in-restaurant dining and large gatherings, and closed non-essential businesses. Most states also adopted shelter-in-place orders (SIPOs), also known as stay-at-home orders. SIPOs added further restrictions such as closures of all non-essential businesses, bans on small group gatherings, and limited outdoor time to essential activities.[5] By April 6, 42 states plus DC had statewide SIPOs in place.[5]

Recent evidence from the United States suggests that social distancing measures, especially more restrictive measures, such as SIPOs, were successful in reducing COVID-19 cases.[6–13] One of the latest US national studies using data through April 27 reports that the daily growth rate of COVID-19 cases dropped by 8.6 percentage points three weeks after states issued SIPOs.[9]

There is less evidence thus far on how social distancing measures including SIPOs have affected COVID-19 deaths and hospitalizations. Evidence from California's SIPO, the earliest statewide SIPO, indicates more than 1,600 deaths averted after one month.[6] Another study examining SIPO effects on deaths across multiple states through April 20 finds a statistically insignificant decline in deaths.[8] To our knowledge, at the time of writing this chapter, there is little additional direct evidence on how social distancing measures have affected COVID-19 deaths and hospitalizations.

We examine the effects of statewide SIPOs on COVID-19 deaths and hospitalizations using quasi-experimental models capturing variation within and between states in enacting these orders and their timing. We focus on SIPOs because of the converging evidence on their effects on case spread,[9] while adjusting for other social distancing measures. The pandemic has placed unprecedented pressure on states and hospitals to ensure adequate resources for COVID-19 hospitalizations.[14] Therefore, understanding effects of social distancing restrictions on deaths and hospitalizations allows for more accurate forecasting of needed hospital resources in case of future waves.[15]

Hospitalization risks are greater among older adults, those with chronic conditions, American Indians or Alaska Natives, Blacks, and Hispanics.[1,16] Deaths are also disproportionally higher in nursing homes.[17] How SIPOs affect deaths and hospitalizations is, therefore, partly dependent on how they affect case spread among higher risk individuals, which is not well known. Higher risk individuals may be more likely to take protective measures to reduce infection risk, irrespective of SIPOs; they may also be more likely to comply with SIPOs. These responses are further complicated by socioeconomic factors that may influence compliance, such as local poverty rate,[18] and are associated with chronic conditions.[19] Therefore, it is important to obtain direct evidence on how social distancing measures, such as SIPOs, impact deaths and hospitalizations beyond effects on the number of cases.

Study Data and Methods

Data

Daily cumulative state-level COVID-19 deaths come from a repository by *The New York Times* based on reports from state and local health agencies.[20] Because we examine effects of statewide SIPOs, we exclude Oklahoma, Utah, and Wyoming, which have issued local but not statewide SIPOs. The analytical sample for the mortality outcome includes 42 states plus the District of Columbia (DC) that had statewide SIPOs and five states (Arkansas, Iowa, Nebraska, North Dakota, and South Dakota) without SIPOs. Data on state-level COVID-19 hospitalizations come from The COVID Tracking Project, which collects COVID-19 related data from state public authorities.[21] Not all states systematically report data on hospitalizations. Data on hospitalizations in this dataset is first available on March 21, although start date varies by state. At the time of the study, this dataset included hospitalization data for 37 states. Of those, 25 states have data reports on hospitalizations over a long enough period needed for the study design and analysis (described in following sections). We exclude Oklahoma, Utah, and Wyoming for the same reasons already noted. The analytical sample for hospitalizations includes data from 22 states, 19 with statewide SIPOs, and three with no SIPOs.

Research Design and Empirical Models

▶ SIPO Effects on COVID-19 Deaths

We employ an event study to examine whether statewide SIPOs affect COVID-19 deaths. This approach is generally similar to a difference-in-differences design, but more flexible, to evaluate how effects evolve over time. The outcome is the daily growth rate in state cumulative deaths, similar to two other studies on COVID-19 cases.[9,10]

We begin the event study model on March 21 (the first day with hospitalization data available) to keep the same period for estimated effects on deaths and hospitalizations and include data through May 15. Another reason is the low number of national deaths before that date. By March 21, the US had 356 confirmed deaths from COVID-19 in states in the analytical sample; many states had no confirmed COVID-19 deaths in early to mid-March.

We evaluate two measures of the daily state-level mortality growth rate. The first is the natural log of cumulative deaths on a day minus the natural log of cumulative deaths on the prior day; multiplying the difference by 100 gives the growth rate in percentage points. Mathematically this requires changing days of 0 deaths to 1 death. Because of the relatively large number of 0 deaths earlier in the study (85 out of 2688 state-day observations), we alternatively use an inverse hyperbolic sine (IHS) transformation, which handles zeroes without changing the data, and allows for a similar interpretation of the daily growth rate.[9,22]

We do not expect SIPOs to affect COVID-19 deaths immediately after their enactment because of the virus incubation period before symptoms appear and because it may take time for symptoms to worsen and for the illness to eventually lead to death. Estimates from China indicate median incubation period of around 5 days[23] and median time from illness to death of 18.5 days.[24] At the same time, the daily COVID-19 case growth rate appears to significantly decline with SIPOs 6–10 days after enactment.[9]

Therefore, we use the first 7 days after SIPO enactment as the reference period and define six post-SIPO periods including 8–14, 15–21, 22–28, 29–35, 36–42, and 43–plus days *after* SIPOs become effective. We also define two pre-SIPOs periods, 1–7 days and 8 or more days *prior to* enactment to test for systematic pre-trends in daily mortality growth rates before SIPOs are enacted.

The model controls for state fixed effects capturing time-invariant differences between states, and day fixed effects capturing daily trends in deaths shared across states. States enacted other measures to mitigate COVID-19. Therefore, the model also flexibly controls for the following six state measures (by including multiple post-enactment indicators for each measure as done for SIPOs): state COVID-19 major disaster declarations, K–12 school closures, large gathering bans, travel restrictions by mandating traveler quarantine for 14 days, banning visitors to nursing homes, and restaurant/gym/entertainment venue closures. Also included is the daily growth rate of COVID-19 tests.

▶ *SIPO Effects on COVID-19 Hospitalizations*

Similar to deaths, we model the daily state-level growth rate of COVID-19 hospitalizations based on the difference in natural logs of daily cumulative hospitalizations between consecutive dates; all sample states had non-zero hospitalizations on the first day of data, so the natural log and the IHS transformation give similar estimates. The model for hospitalization growth rate is estimated for 19 states with SIPOs with daily data beginning at least one day before the first SIPO effective date and three states with no state-wide SIPOs. We follow a similar regression and specification of the post-enactment periods as for deaths. However, unlike the mortality model, we cannot directly test for hospitalization pre-trends within the event study model as multiple states have insufficient pre-SIPO data. However, studies examining case changes following SIPOs have found no evidence of significant differential pre-trends before SIPOs were enacted.[8,9] In addition, for nine states with at least 4 days of data before SIPO enactment, we examine changes in hospitalization growth rates over 4 days before enactment and find no evidence of systematic pre-trend differences.

Limitations

There are no data on demographic and clinical risk factors among deaths and hospitalizations to assess how SIPOs affect case compositional changes. Also, the data are based on confirmed deaths and hospitalizations and there are unconfirmed/undiagnosed deaths and cases that could have needed hospitalizations and were not hospitalized. There is emerging evidence of thousands of "excess" deaths during this period with pneumonia and influenza-like symptoms that were not tested or confirmed for COVID-19.[25] Furthermore, our estimates for hospitalizations are specific to 22 states with currently available daily data.

Study Results

SIPO Effects on COVID-19 Deaths

There are no significant differential trends in mortality growth rates before enacting SIPOs, lending support to the event study estimates. Within 22–28 days after SIPOs are effective, there is a significant decline ($p < 0.05$) in the daily mortality growth rate. The effect gradually increases over time. Specifically, the daily COVID-19 mortality growth rate declines by 2.9, 3.6, 4.7, and 6.1 percentage points within 22–28, 29–35, 36–42, and 43 or more days after enacting SIPOs, respectively. To put these numbers in perspective, the baseline average daily mortality growth rate (over the first 7 days after enacting SIPOs) is 20.5%.

There is an increasing difference in mortality growth rates between these scenarios in April and May. And while the mortality growth rate started declining at the end of March, SIPOs have accelerated the decline over time. By May 15, the event study estimates indicate that the average daily death growth rate would have been 8.6% without SIPOs instead of 2.8%

with SIPOs, and the projections suggest as many as 250,000–370,000 deaths possibly averted with SIPOs in place.

SIPO Effects on COVID-19 Hospitalizations

Again, these estimates of COVID-19 hospitalizations are based on 22 states, 19 of which imposed SIPOs. There is a significant decline ($p < 0.05$) in the daily hospitalization growth rate at 15 days after SIPOs, with the effect generally increasing over time and remaining statistically significant ($p < 0.05$, except for the period of 29–35 days during which the decline is marginally significant, $p < 0.10$). Specifically, the daily COVID-19 hospitalization growth rate declines by 3.2, 5.5, 5.4, 6.9, and 8.4 percentage points within 15–21, 22–28, 29–35, 36–42, and 43 or more days after enacting SIPOs, respectively. As a comparison, the average daily hospitalization growth rate in the reference period is 17.5%. The confidence intervals for changes in hospitalizations are wider than those for mortality, as expected from the smaller sample of states.

We also project the number of averted COVID-19 hospitalizations in those 19 states with SIPOs included in the hospitalization analysis by comparing observed daily cumulative daily hospitalizations (up to 126,704 hospitalizations by May 15) with predicted hospitalizations without SIPOs. By May 15, the model predicts as many as 750,000–840,000 COVID-19 hospitalizations possibly averted in those 19 states passing SIPOs.

Discussion

In response to the COVID-19 pandemic, the majority of states in the United States issued statewide SIPOs. Building on the evidence of declines in COVID-19 case spread with SIPOs[6–13] and using the variation in issuing SIPOs and timing across states, we employ event study models to examine the effects of statewide SIPOs on death and hospitalization growth rates. We find that SIPOs reduced the daily mortality growth rate after nearly three weeks from enactment, and the daily hospitalization growth rate after two weeks after enactment. Effects on mortality and hospitalization growth rates intensify over time from SIPO enactment. After 42 days from enactment, the average daily mortality growth rate has declined by 6.1 percentage points (in 42 states and DC with SIPOs), while the average hospitalization growth rate has declined by 8.4 percentage points (in 19 states with SIPOs and hospitalization data).

By May 15, projections of SIPO effects on the daily growth rates suggest 250,000–370,000 deaths averted in the 42 states plus DC with statewide SIPOs, and 750,000–840,000 averted hospitalizations in 19 states with statewide SIPOs and hospitalization data. We can compare the projection of averted deaths to projected averted cases from another study with a generally similar model.[9] By April 27, that study projects nearly 10 million averted cases with SIPOs; that study examines both state and county issued SIPOs and includes all states so this is not an exact comparison. The ratio of projected 250,000–370,000 averted deaths to 10 million cases is 0.025–0.037. On May 15, the ratio of cumulative deaths to cumulative cases in the 42 states plus DC with statewide SIPOs is 0.062 (ratio would be higher if deaths on May 15 are divided by cases on an earlier date to allow for some lag). Therefore, averted death projections seem reasonable and within range of that study's projections.

Comparing the projection on hospitalizations is less straightforward since it is only for 19 states with SIPOs and effects might vary across states. Those 19 states account for 52.5% of cumulative cases by April 27 in the 42 states plus DC with statewide SIPOs. If those 19 states represent a similar proportion of the projected 10 million averted cases from the other study (which might be a strong assumption since that study includes county-level SIPOs and all states),[9] this would imply as many as 5.25 million cases averted in those 19 states. On May 15, the ratio of cumulative hospitalizations to cumulative cases in those 19 states is 0.181. Applying that ratio of 0.181, one would expect about 950,000 averted hospitalizations of the assumed 5.25 million averted cases. Therefore, the projections of 750,000–840,000 averted hospitalizations also seem reasonable and within range of the other study's projection on averted cases.[9]

The timing of effects are largely consistent with hospitalizations lagging cases, and deaths lagging hospitalizations. They are also consistent with studies in the United States finding significant reductions in cases beginning within 6–10 days after SIPOs.[8,9] Data from New York City shows median inpatient stay for in-hospital deaths between 2.8 to 5.9 days (depending on age), suggesting relatively short periods from symptoms to death for some patients.[26] In some of the robustness checks however, effects on deaths become statistically significant around 15–21 days when effects on hospitalizations are observed. This may not necessarily imply inconsistency in deaths lagging hospitalizations. The timing of SIPO effects from the event study models can vary between hospitalizations and deaths (other than due to the lagging effect) depending on how SIPOs affect the distribution of case severity. If younger and healthier individuals comply less with SIPOs than older individuals and those with chronic conditions (who are at greater risk of death if infected), infection rate may decline less among individuals who are at low risk of mortality if infected but who may still need hospital care. If so, effects on hospitalizations and deaths could emerge at relatively close periods, as we observe in some of the models. Clinical data suggest that the proportion of low-risk individuals among hospitalized cases is not small. For example, in Georgia, over 25% of adult COVID-19 admissions were without conditions considered high risk for severe COVID-19.[27] In New York City, 6.1% of admitted patients had no comorbidities.[26] In any case, the observed hospitalization and mortality declines indicate that SIPOs reduce case spread broadly in the population including among groups with high risk for health complications from COVID-19. If SIPOs only reduced COVID-19 among young healthy adults, SIPO effects on hospitalizations and deaths would have been small.

The findings have major implications for public health and health care systems. The primary goal of SIPOs and other social distancing measures is flattening the incidence curve of COVID-19 cases and hospitalizations so that hospitals are not overwhelmed by very high acute surges of cases and admissions. We find evidence that SIPOs played an important role in decelerating the growth curve for COVID-19 deaths and hospitalizations. The estimates imply that the inpatient care burden on hospitals and medical staff would have been much larger without SIPOs. Had this excess burden not been averted, mortality from other conditions might have also increased due to overcrowded hospitals.

Our findings and those from prior studies on case spread emphasize the importance of examining the mechanisms through which social distancing measures like SIPOs generate effects.[6–13] There is emerging but mixed evidence on foot traffic changes following SIPOs and other social distancing measures. Some suggest little effect of SIPOs on foot traffic,[28] while others show significant effects of statewide SIPOs on proportion staying home using state-level data.[8] The effects of SIPOs on case spread and on mortality and hospitalizations depend on compliance (staying at home) but could also develop in other ways. For example, SIPOs may send a strong message about infection risk, leading individuals to be more cautious and alert even when outside (keeping distance from others, washing hands frequently, etc.). Such potential behavioral effects deserve future research. Another dynamic for future research is whether and how spillover effects develop across states that differ in their social distancing measures, and how they may influence estimated effects on cases, deaths, and hospitalizations.

Conclusion

Our study shows that statewide SIPOs issued by 42 states plus DC have reduced the daily growth rates of COVID-19 deaths by up to 6.1 percentage points after 42 days from enactment. SIPOs also reduced the daily hospitalization growth rate, by up to 8.4 percentage points after 42 days in 19 states with SIPOs and hospitalization data. These estimates indicate that SIPOs played a key role in flattening the curves not only for cases, but also for deaths and hospitalizations, and eased pressure on hospitals from avoided COVID-19 admissions. Of course, SIPOs also generate a large economic toll and are not sustainable over extensive periods. Understanding their effects on cases, deaths, and hospitalizations can help inform policy responses.

References

1. Centers for Disease Control and Prevention. COVIDView: a weekly surveillance summary of U.S. COVID-19 activity [Internet]. Atlanta (GA): CDC; [updated 2020 Jun 26; cited 2020 Jun 29]. Available from: www.cdc.gov/corona virus/2019-ncov/covid-data/covid view/index.html

2. Johns Hopkins University and Medicine, Coronavirus Resource Center. COVID-19 dashboard by the Center for Systems Science and Engineering (CSSE) at Johns Hopkins University (JHU) [Internet]. Baltimore (MD): Johns Hopkins University; 2020 [cited 2020 Jun 29]. Available from: https://corona virus.jhu.edu/map.html

3. Pan A, Liu L, Wang C, Guo H, Hao X, Wang Q, et al. Association of public health interventions with the epidemiology of the COVID-19 outbreak in Wuhan, China. JAMA. 2020;323(19):1–9.

4. Kraemer MUG, Yang C-H, Gutierrez B, Wu C-H, Klein B, Pigott DM, et al. The effect of human mobility and control measures on the COVID-19 epidemic in China. Science. 2020 May 1;368(6490):493–7.

5. Mervosh S, Lu D, Swales V. See which states and cities have told residents to stay at home. New York Times [serial on the internet]. Updated 2020 Apr [cited 2020 May 15]. Available from: www.nytimes.com/interactive/2020/us/coronavirus-stay-at-home-order.html

6. Friedson AI, McNichols D, Sabia JJ, Dave D. Did California's shelter in place order work? Early Evidence on coronavirus-related health benefits [Internet]. Cambridge (MA): National Bureau of Economic Research; 2020 Apr [cited 2020 May 15]. (NBER Working Paper No. 26992). Available from: www.nber.org/papers/w26992

7. Fowler JH, Hill SJ, Levin R, Obradovich N. The effect of stay-at-home orders on COVID-19 infections in the United States. medRxiv [serial on the Internet]. 2020 May 13 [cited 2020 May 15]. Available from: www.medrxiv.org/content/10.1101/2020.04.13.20063628v3

8. Dave DM, Friedson AI, Matsuzawa K, Sabia JJ. When do shelter-in-place orders fight COVID-19 best? Policy heterogeneity across states and adoption time [Internet]. Cambridge (MA): National Bureau of Economic Research; 2020 May [cited 2020 May 15]. (NBER Working Paper No. 27091). Available from: www.nber.org/papers/ w27091

9. Courtemanche C, Garuccio J, Le A, Pinkston J, Yelowitz A. Strong social distancing measures in the United States reduced the COVID-19 growth rate. Health Aff (Millwood) 2020 May 14. [Epub ahead of print].

10. Siedner MJ, Harling G, Reynolds Z, Gilbert RF, Venkataramani A, Tsai AC. Social distancing to slow the U.S. COVID-19 epidemic: an interrupted time-series analysis. medRxiv [serial on the Internet]. 2020 Apr 15 [cited 2020 May 15]. Available from: www.medrxiv.org/content/ 10.1101/2020.04.03.20052373v2

11. Lasry A, Kidder D, Hast M, Poovey J, Sunshine G, Zviedrite N, et al. Timing of community mitigation and changes in reported COVID-19 and community mobility—four US metropolitan areas, February 26–April 1, 2020. MMWR Morb Mortal Wkly Rep. 2020;69(15):451–457.

12. Wagner AB, Hill EL, Ryan SE, Sun Z, Deng G, Bhadane S, et al. Social distancing has merely stabilized COVID-19 in the US. medRxiv [serial on the Internet]. 2020 Apr 30 [cited 2020 May 15]. Available from: www.medrxiv.org/content/10.1101/2 020.04.27.20081836v1

13. Lyu W, Wehby GL. Comparison of estimated rates of Coronavirus Disease 2019 (COVID-19) in border counties in Iowa without a stay-at-home order and border counties in Illinois with a stay-at-home order. JAMA Netw Open. 2020;3(5): e2011102.

14. Burns K. Governors plead with other states for more health care workers to fight coronavirus. Vox [serial on the internet]. 2020 Mar 31 [cited 2020 May 15]. Available from: www.vox.com/policy-and-politics/2020/3/31/21201281/coronavirus-staffing-shortage-governors-health-care-workers-help

15. Sun LH. CDC director warns second wave of coronavirus is likely to be even more devastating. The Washington Post [serial on the internet]. 2020 Apr 21 [cited 2020 May 15]. Available from: www.washingtonpost.com/health/2020/04/21/coronavirus-second wave-cdcdirector/

16. Centers for Disease Control and Prevention. COVID-19 in racial and ethnic minority groups [Internet]. Atlanta (GA): CDC; [updated 2020 Jun 25; cited 2020 Jun 29]. Available from: www.cdc.gov/corona virus/2019-ncov/need-extra-precautions/racial-ethnicminorities.html

17. Chidambaram P. State reporting of cases and deaths due to COVID-19 in long-term care facilities [Internet]. San Francisco (CA): Kaiser Family Foundation; 2020 Apr 23 [cited 2020 May 15]. Available from: www.kff.org/medicaid/issue-brief/state-reporting-of-cases-and-deaths-due-to-covid-19-in-longterm-care-facilities/

18. Wright AL, Sonin K, Driscoll J, Wilson J. Poverty and economic dislocation reduce compliance with COVID-19 shelter-in-place protocols [Internet]. Chicago (IL): University of Chicago, Becker Friedman Institute for Economics; 2020 Apr 29 [cited 2020 May 15]. (Working Paper No. 2020-40). Available from: https://papers.ssrn.com/sol3/papers.cfm?abstract_id=3573637

19. Shaw KM, Theis KA, Self-Brown S, Roblin DW, Barker L. Chronic disease disparities by county economic status and metropolitan classification, behavioral risk factor surveillance system, 2013. Prev Chronic Dis. 2016;13:E119.

20. The New York Times. An ongoing repository of data on coronavirus cases and deaths in the U.S. Github [serial on the Internet]. 2020 [cited 2020 May 15]. Available from: https://github.com/nytimes/covid-19-data

21. The COVID Tracking Project [serial on the Internet]. 2020 [cited 2020 May 15]. Available from: https://covidtracking.com/data

22. Burbidge JB, Magee L, Robb AL. Alternative transformations to handle extreme values of the dependent variable. J Am Statistic Assoc. 1988; 83(401):123–7.

23. Lauer SA, Grantz KH, Bi Q, Jones FK, Zheng Q, Meredith HR, et al. The incubation period of Coronavirus Disease 2019 (COVID-19) from publicly reported confirmed cases: estimation and application. Ann Intern Med. 2020;172(9):577–82.

24. Zhou F, Yu T, Du R, Fan G, Liu Y, Liu Z, et al. Clinical course and risk factors for mortality of adult inpatients with COVID-19 in Wuhan, China: a retrospective cohort study. The Lancet. 2020;395(10229): 1054–62.

25. National Vital Statistics System. Provisional death counts for Coronavirus Disease (COVID-19) [Internet]. Atlanta (GA): Centers for Disease Control and Prevention; [updated 2020 May 15; cited 2020 May 15]. Available from: www.cdc.gov/nchs/nvss/vsrr/covid19/index.htm

26. Richardson S, Hirsch JS, Narasimhan M, Crawford JM, McGinn T, Davidson KW, et al. Presenting characteristics, comorbidities, and outcomes among 5700 patients hospitalized with COVID-19 in the New York City area. JAMA. 2020;323(20):2052–59.

27. Gold JAW, Wong KK, Szablewski CM, Patel PR, Rossow J, da Silva J, et al. Characteristics and clinical outcomes of adult patients hospitalized with COVID-19—Georgia, March 2020. MMWR Morb Mortal Wkly Rep. 2020;69(18):545–50.

28. Gupta S, Nguyen TD, Rojas FL, Raman S, Lee B, Bento A, et al. Tracking public and private response to the COVID-19 epidemic: evidence from state and local government actions [Internet]. Cambridge (MA): National Bureau of Economic Research; 2020 Apr [cited 2020 May 15]. (NBER Working Paper No. 27027). Available from: www.nber.org/papers/ w27027

16 Strong Social Distancing Measures in the United States Reduced the COVID-19 Growth Rate

Charles Courtemanche, Joseph Garuccio, Anh Le, Joshua Pinkston, and Aaron Yelowitz

A critical question during the COVID-19 pandemic is the effectiveness of the social distancing policies adopted by US states and localities in bending the curve. Although these policies take a variety of forms—such as imposing shelter-in-place orders (SIPOs); restricting dine-in at restaurants; closing other non-essential business such as bars, entertainment venues, and gyms; banning large social gatherings; and closing public schools—their effectiveness depends critically on the cooperation of the public. For example, although California's first-in-the-nation SIPO carries threats of fines and incarceration, its effectiveness fundamentally relies on social pressure.[1] Compliance with social distancing orders appears to be related to local income, partisanship, and political beliefs in the United States; and compliance with self-quarantines is related to potential losses in income in Israel.[2–4]

Some epidemiological models forecast the eventual number of COVID-19 cases and fatalities based on untested assumptions about the impact of social distancing policies in contemporary society. The widely cited Imperial College London model assumes contact outside the home, school or workplace declines by 75 percent, school contact rates are unchanged, workplace contact rates fall by 25 percent, and household contact rates rise by 25 percent.[5] Another study assumes social distancing measures will reduce the average contact rate by 38 percent, based on evidence from the 1918 influenza pandemic.[6]

In the United States the literature on models of social distancing during the COVID-19 pandemic is evolving rapidly, and at the time of our writing, we were aware of several working papers that examined the consequences of social distancing policies. Recent work found significant effects of stronger measures (like SIPOs) on movement using difference-in-differences methods and state-level data from Google.[7] Similar findings have been obtained in a study with SafeGraph mobility data,[8] although a different study using PlaceIQ and SafeGraph data found strong measures were not important.[9] Another paper used synthetic control methods to show that California's SIPO significantly reduced COVID-19 cases.[1] A study of SIPOs across the United States also found a reduction in cases, as well as higher rates of staying home full-time.[10] Other authors used interrupted time-series methods and found that early statewide social distancing measures were associated with decreases in states' COVID-19 growth rates, but later SIPOs did not lead to further reductions.[11]

At issue is not whether isolation works to limit the spread of disease, but rather whether the particular government restrictions designed to encourage social distancing in the United States reduced spread relative to simply providing information and recommendations. Individuals may voluntarily engage in avoidance behavior, such as hand washing or wearing masks, once they fully perceive the risks of contagion.[12,13] Critics of more stringent government measures highlight Sweden's less intrusive response to COVID-19, although Sweden's strategy is increasingly questioned.[14] Rigorous empirical research is needed to determine the impacts of the various aspects of state and local governments' responses in the United States.

Our work—which leveraged both state and county policy variation and used a flexible event-study method that allowed for effects to vary across measures and over time—estimated the impacts of four types of social distancing measures on confirmed COVID-19 case growth rates through April 27, 2020. The reduced-form approach captures any potential pathways driven by these mandates, including complementary avoidance behaviors that the public may engage in if these orders provide an informational shock in addition to increasing social distancing.

Study Data and Methods

Study Data

The unit of observation was daily US county/county equivalents. Although there are 3,142 counties in the United States, official COVID-19 records report New York City as a whole rather than dividing it into five counties, reducing this number to 3,138. Our dataset tracked counties over 58 days from March 1, 2020 to April 27, 2020, leading to a sample size of 182,004. We chose March 1 as the start date because no new cases were reported in the entire United States on most days in January and February. The April 27 end date was chosen to coincide with the first removal of one of four types of restrictions we analyzed (the reopening of restaurants and other entertainment facilities in Georgia).[15] Each county observation was weighted by population using 2018 estimates from the US Department of Agriculture's Economic Research Service.[16]

Outcome of Interest

We examined the daily growth rate in confirmed COVID-19 cases at the county level, which originated from the 2019 Novel Coronavirus COVID-19 Data Repository provided by the Johns Hopkins Center for Systems

Science and Engineering. This repository collected data on COVID-19 cases worldwide from a range of sources including government and independent health institutions.[17]

The daily exponential growth rate was calculated as the natural log of cumulative daily COVID-19 cases minus the log of cumulative daily COVID-19 cases on the prior day. We chose this functional form because epidemiological models predict exponential growth in the absence of intervention. Percent growth in cases is identical to percent growth in cases per capita since reported county populations did not vary during the sample period. The growth rate was multiplied by 100 and can be read as percentage point changes. In computing the growth rate, we followed a recent COVID-19 study and added one to the case counts to avoid dropping counties that started with zero cases.[18]

Covariates

The data on the timing of state and local government social distancing interventions was gathered from a host of sources and made available by Johns Hopkins University.[19]

We focused on four government-imposed interventions: SIPOs, public school closures, bans on large social gatherings, and closures of entertainment-related businesses. For large gatherings, we used the date of the first prohibition that was at least as restrictive as 500 people. Most of the bans were much more restrictive: 95 percent of the time (in our population-weighted sample) the prohibition extended to 50 people. For entertainment-related businesses, we used the date of the first closure of either restaurant dining areas (including bars) or gyms/entertainment centers. If one such prohibition was in place, 96 percent of the time, the other was in place as well.

We included control variables related to the availability of COVID-19 tests. The same data repository that provides cases also includes daily counts of positive, negative, and pending tests in each state on each day, which we added together.[17] To mirror our measure of cases, we converted this testing variable to the exponential daily growth rate of cumulative tests performed. Since COVID-19 test results are generally not available immediately, we also included the one-day lag of this growth rate. Further lags (out to 10 days) were considered but always statistically insignificant, so we did not include them. Most states did not report any pending tests, meaning that they did not officially record tests until the results were obtained. This likely explains the lack of a longer lag between testing growth and case growth.

Methods

We estimated the relationship between social distancing policies and the exponential growth rate of confirmed COVID-19 cases using an event-study regression with multiple treatments. Statistical analysis was conducted using

Stata MP (version 15). This approach is akin to difference-in-differences but more flexible, as it interacts the treatment variables with multiple indicators of time since implementation, thereby tracing out the evolution of the treatment effects over time.[20]

For each of the four policies, we include seven variables: whether it was implemented 1–5, 6–10, 11–15, 16–20, or more than 20 days ago; and whether it will be implemented 5–9 or 10 or more days later. Implementation on the current day through four days from now was, therefore, the reference group. If a county never adopted the policy, each of these variables was set to zero throughout the sample period.

An event study model is particularly useful to study the impact of social distancing policies on COVID-19 cases for two reasons. First, after accounting for the incubation period and time between onset of first symptoms and positive test result, such policies likely only affect official cases after a considerable lag.[21] Additionally, the inclusion of variables reflecting future implementation allows for an analysis of pretreatment trends. Since it is not plausible for policies that have not yet been implemented to causally affect current cases, finding such associations could suggest misspecification. For instance, one might expect counties with rapidly growing case counts to be the most likely to enact these measures, leading to a reverse-causal relationship between current cases and future policies that would be detected by our model.

Each policy was implemented at least 10 days after the start of the sample period and at least 20 days prior to the end. Therefore, each policy contributes to the identifying variation for all coefficients except those for more than 20 days ago and 10 or more days from now. Since the estimated policy effects at those two "catch-all" time periods could partially reflect compositional changes, they should therefore be interpreted with more caution than the estimates for the other time intervals.

In addition to the testing controls just discussed, the model also included fixed effects for geography and time. County fixed effects accounted for the likelihood that, even aside from differences in policies, case growth rates may have varied due to a number of county characteristics. These characteristics include population density and residents' education, political orientation, and age.[3,4] Fixed effects for each day in each of the nine US Census Divisions (522 fixed effects in total) allowed for flexible underlying trends in growth rates that could vary in different parts of the country, helping to account for the staggered nature of the outbreak across locations.[22] We report 95% confidence intervals, with standard errors robust to heteroskedasticity and clustered by state, the level of most of the policy variation.

Limitations

There are several limitations to our analysis. Official COVID-19 case counts are known to understate the true prevalence of the disease, as they do not include asymptomatic carriers, those who are not ill enough to seek medical care, and those who are unable to obtain a test due to supply constraints.[1] Nonetheless, confirmed case counts are crucial to the Trump administration's "Opening Up America Again" plan, which proposes either a "downward trajectory of documented cases within a 14-day period" or "downward trajectory of positive tests as a percent of total tests within a 14-day period (flat or increasing volume of tests)" as criteria to loosening social distancing measures.[23] Moreover, to the extent that testing shortages led to only the sickest individuals receiving them, official case counts can loosely be interpreted as the prevalence of moderate-to-severe illnesses, a relevant metric for policy purposes.

A related caveat is that, ideally, we would like to be able to control more precisely for access to testing. Available data only allowed us to control for number of tests performed at the state, rather than county, level. However, most of our policy variation is at the state level, so state-level testing should go a long way towards alleviating bias. Additionally, number of tests performed is not an ideal measure of the ease of obtaining a test because it also reflects the level of illness in the community.

Also, we might ideally want to estimate a richer econometric model. It would be interesting to trace out the timing of impacts more exactly and study the policies' interactions with each other or county characteristics. Future work should also examine the impacts of other social distancing policies such as closing public parks and beaches, the requirement to wear masks in public, restrictions on visitors in nursing homes, state announcements of first cases or fatalities, and federal government actions such as prohibiting international travel.[9] However, it is difficult to include numerous correlated treatment variables without reducing precision to the point where statistical inference is uninformative.

Finally, as is typical of observational data analyses, we cannot rule out all possible threats to causal inference. Numerous possible confounders could vary across time and space, including the other policies already mentioned, informal encouragement by government officials to wear masks or improve hygiene, changing business practices, and social norms regarding distancing. That said, including Census-Division-by-day and county fixed effects in our model and examining pretreatment trends helped us to push in the direction of causality.

Study Results

Descriptive Information

Confirmed COVID-19 cases grew rapidly during the sample period, from just 30 on March 1 to 978,047 on April 27. On March 1, the vast majority of counties had zero cases, and across all days, 49 percent of unweighted county-by-day observations were zero. However, counties with zero cases tended to have low populations, so our population weights limited the influence of these counties on the results.

The SIPO was generally the last policy to be implemented, and adoption was uniformly lower than the other policies. On March 1, no jurisdiction had implemented all four measures. By March 22, nearly 25 percent of the US population was covered by all the measures, growing to approximately 65 percent by March 29 and 95 percent by April 7, when the last SIPO took effect.

Impact of Social Distancing Policies

Relative to the reference category of 0–4 days before implementation, SIPOs lead to statistically significant ($p < 0.01$) reductions in the COVID-19 case growth rate of 3.0 percentage points after 6–10 days, 4.5 after 11–15 days, 5.9 after 16–20 days, and 8.6 from day 21 onward. Because the model held constant the other types of policies, these estimates should be interpreted as the additional effect of SIPOs *beyond* shutting down schools, large gatherings, and entertainment-related businesses. This additional effect may come from either the requirement/strong advisement to shelter-in-place aside from "essential" activities or the accompanying closure of any "non-essential" businesses that remained open. We did not observe any statistically significant "placebo" effects of SIPOs in the periods prior to implementation, giving credence to a causal interpretation of our main results. If anything, the pre-trend appears to point upward, which would make our estimates in the post-treatment period conservative.

We found no evidence that bans on large social gatherings influenced the growth rate. The point estimates for banning gatherings were statistically insignificant ($p > 0.56$ in all cases). However, the 95% confidence intervals included reductions of up to 3–6 percentage points, so the lack of evidence of an effect should not be misinterpreted as clear evidence of no effect. Also, the lack of a statistically significant reduction in the post-treatment period could potentially be due to an upward (though not statistically significant) pre-treatment trend. However, results from the aforementioned event study with separate variables for each day showed that the pre-trend disappeared four days prior to implementation.

Closing restaurant dining rooms/bars and/or entertainment centers/gyms led to statistically significant reductions in the growth rate of COVID-19 cases in all time periods after implementation ($p < 0.05$). The estimated effect was 4.4 percentage points after 1–5 days, 4.7 after 6–10 days, 6.1 after 11–15 days, 5.6 after 16–20 days, and 5.2 after 21 or more. Prior to implementation, policies related to businesses showed no effect on the growth rate, again passing the "placebo" test.

In contrast, we found no evidence that school closures influenced the growth rate. The point estimates were never close to statistically significant

(p > 0:37 in all cases), but the 95% confidence intervals meant that we could not rule out reductions of up to 4–5 percentage points.

Adding the coefficient estimates for each policy gives the combined effect of implementing all four social distancing policies. In days 1–5 after implementation, the bundle of restrictions reduced the growth rate of COVID-19 cases by 5.4 percentage points. In days 6–10 after implementation, the growth rate fell by 6.8 percentage points. This reduction grew to 6.8 percentage points after 6–10 days, 8.2 percentage points after 11–15, 9.1 after 16–20, and 12.0 after 21 or more. As discussed previously, the estimate for 21+ days should be viewed with caution, as it did not utilize the same geographic balance of treatments as the estimates for the other time intervals. A conservative interpretation of these results would therefore be that the impact reached 9.1 percentage points after 16–20 days and appeared to remain at least as high after that.

Simulations that we conducted showed that cases would have been 10 times higher without SIPOs (10,224,598) and 35 times higher (35,257,098) without any social distancing restrictions. Interestingly, the closures of restaurants/entertainment facilities accounted for a larger share of the reduction in cases than SIPOs, despite SIPOs having larger coefficient estimates. This is because closures of restaurant/entertainment facilities were implemented earlier and in more places than SIPOs.

Discussion

While our results suggest both SIPO and non-SIPO measures can be effective at averting COVID-19 cases, the lack of evidence of effects of school closures or bans on large social gatherings is noteworthy. We cannot rule out the possibility that these null results are due to statistical imprecision, but it is also possible that both policies may displace social interaction rather than reducing it. For example, school closures may have led families to continue social interactions outside of the school setting, such as at day care centers or parks. Google mobility data through April 5, 2020, show increases of 10 percent or more in visits to parks in 28 states.[24] A new study finds that schools are only slightly more dangerous than parks and playgrounds for COVID-19 transmission, supporting this explanation.[25] Alternatively, school closures primarily affect children and the vast majority of children experience mild symptoms and therefore may not be included in confirmed cases.[26] While asymptomatic children can pass the virus to adults who become more severely ill, our results imply that the extent to which this led to confirmed cases did not change when schools were closed.

Similarly, official group events may have simply been replaced by informal gatherings. Alternatively, official prohibitions may have been largely redundant since the largest events (such as college and professional sports) were already being cancelled due to CDC guidance or other information.

Also note that school closures and large event bans occurred prior to the implementation of SIPOs, meaning substitute types of social gatherings were still allowed. Our results, therefore, should not be interpreted as a forecast about what would happen if schools were reopened or certain large gatherings were allowed while other aspects of SIPOs remained in place.

Conclusion

We estimated the separate and combined impact of four widely adopted social distancing policies. Both SIPOs and closures of restaurants/bars/entertainment-related businesses substantially slowed the spread of COVID-19. We did not find evidence that bans on large events and closures of public schools also did, though the confidence intervals cannot rule out moderately sized effects. Interestingly, two recent papers on the effect of social distancing restrictions on mobility found the same pattern as we did in terms of which restrictions mattered and which ones did not, suggesting that null effects of gathering bans and school closures on case growth are at least plausible.[7,8]

Our contribution was to provide credible empirical evidence on whether US social distancing measures worked as intended in flattening the curve. Estimating other important benefits and costs from social distancing, including the total lives saved and economic harm, was beyond the scope of our study. Other work has attempted to estimate job losses, simulate effects on the overall economy and economic growth, or estimate distributional consequences from current and past pandemics.[1,6,27–30]

Nonetheless, we provide important information about benefits of social distancing for policymakers to consider as they decide on strategies for restarting economic activity. For instance, our results argue against returning to partial measures such as school closures and restrictions on large gatherings, while removing the restrictions that prevent the redirection of social activity to other settings. At issue moving forward is whether cases averted simply turn into cases delayed, and a premature return to light measures would make this more likely. At the same time, our results are not informative about the effectiveness of intermediate measures, such as lifting a SIPO but requiring masks in public or opening restaurants at reduced capacity. Further research is needed as gradual, untested steps toward reopening are taken across the country.

References

1. Friedson AI, McNichols D, Sabia JJ, Dave D. Did California's Shelter in Place Order Work? Early Evidence on Coronavirus-Related Health Benefits [Internet]. Cambridge (MA): National Bureau of Economic Research; 2020 Apr [cited 2020 May 11]. (NBER Working Paper No. 26992). Available from: www.nber.org/papers/w26992

2. Bodas M, Peleg K. Self-Isolation Compliance in the COVID-19 Era Influenced by Compensation: Findings From a Recent Survey in Israel. Health Aff (Millwood). 2020 Apr 9. DOI: 10.1377/hlthaff.2020.00382. [Epub ahead of print].

3. Painter M, Qiu T. Political Beliefs affect Compliance with COVID-19 Social Distancing Orders [Internet]. St. Louis (MO): Saint Louis University; 2020 Apr 30 [cited 2020 May 11]. Available from: https://papers.ssrn.com/sol3/papers.cfm?abstract_id=3569098

4. Wright AL, Sonin K, Driscoll J, Wilson J. Poverty and Economic Dislocation Reduce Compliance with COVID-19 Shelter-in-Place Protocols [Internet]. Chicago (IL): University of Chicago, Becker Friedman Institute for Economics; 2020 Apr 29 [cited 2020 May 11]. (Working Paper No. 2020-40). Available from: https://papers.ssrn.com/sol3/papers.cfm?abstract_id=3573637

5. Ferguson NM, Laydon D, Nedjati-Gilani G, Imai N, Ainslie K, Baguelin M, et al. Report 9: Impact of Non-Pharmaceutical Interventions (NPIs) to Reduce COVID19 Mortality and Healthcare Demand [Internet]. London: Imperial College London; 2020 Mar 16 [cited 2020 May 11]. Available at: www.imperial.ac.uk/media/imperial-college/medicine/sph/ide/gida-fellowships/Imperial-College-COVID19-NPI-modelling-16-03-2020.pdf

6. Thunstrom L, Newbold S, Finnoff D, Ashworth M, Shogren JF. The Benefits and Costs of Using Social Distancing to Flatten the Curve for COVID-19 [Internet]. Laramie (WY): University of Wyoming; 2020 Mar 27 [cited 2020 May 11]. Available from: https://papers.ssrn.com/sol3/papers.cfm?abstract_id=3561934

7. Abouk R, Heydari B. The Immediate Effect of COVID-19 Policies on Social Distancing Behavior in the United States [Internet]. Wayne (NJ): William Paterson University; 2020 Apr 8 [cited 2020 May 11]. Available from: https://papers.ssrn.com/sol3/papers.cfm?abstract_id=3571421

8. Andersen M. Early Evidence on Social Distancing in Response to COVID-19 in the United States [Internet]. Greensboro (NC): University of North Carolina Greensboro; 2020 Apr 6 [cited 2020 May 11]. Available from: https://papers.ssrn.com/sol3/papers.cfm?abstract_id=3569368

9. Gupta S, Nguyen TD, Rojas FL, Raman S, Lee B, Bento A, et al. Tracking Public and Private Responses to the COVID-19 Epidemic: Evidence from State and Local Government Actions [Internet]. Cambridge (MA): National Bureau of Economic Research; 2020 Apr [cited 2020 May 11]. (NBER Working Paper No. 27027). Available from: www.nber.org/papers/ w27027

10. Dave DM, Friedson AI, Matsuzawa K, Sabia JJ. When Do Shelter-in-Place Orders Fight COVID-19 Best? Policy Heterogeneity Across States and Adoption Time [Internet]. Cambridge (MA): National Bureau of Economic Research; 2020 May [cited 2020 May 11]. (NBER Working Paper No. 27091). Available from: www.nber.org/papers/ w27091

11. Siedner MJ, Harling G, Reynolds Z, Gilbert RF, Venkataramani A, Tsai AC. Social Distancing to Slow the U.S. COVID-19 Epidemic: An Interrupted Time-Series Analysis [Internet]. Boston (MA): Massachusetts General Hospital; 2020 [cited 2020 May 11]. Available for download from: www.researchgate.net/publication/340518052_Social_distancing_to_slow_the_US_COVID-19_epidemic_an_interrupted_time-series_analysis

12. Abaluck J, Chevalier JA, Christakis NA, Forman HP, Kaplan EH, Ko A, et al. The Case for Universal Cloth Mask Adoption and Policies to Increase Supply of Medical Masks for Health Workers [Internet]. New Haven (CT): Yale University; 2020

Apr 1 [cited 2020 May 11]. Available from: https://papers.ssrn.com/sol3/papers.cfm?abstract_id=3567438

13. Harris JE. The Coronavirus Epidemic Curve is Already Flattening in New York City [Internet]. Cambridge (MA): National Bureau of Economic Research; 2020 Apr [cited 2020 May 11]. (NBER Working Paper No. 26917). Available from: www.nber.org/papers/w26917

14. Ahlander J, O'Connor P. Sweden's Liberal Pandemic Strategy Questioned as Stockholm Death Toll Mounts. Reuters [serial on the Internet]. 2020 Apr 3 [cited 2020 May 7]. Available from: www.reuters.com/article/us-health-coronavirus-sweden/swedens-liberal-pandemic-strategy-questioned-as-stockholm-death-toll-mounts-idUSKBN21L23R

15. The State of Georgia. Providing Guidance for Reviving a Healthy Georgia in Response to COVID-19 [Internet]. Atlanta (GA): Governor's Office; 2020 Apr 23 [cited 2020 May 11]. (Executive Order). Available for download from: https://gov.georgia.gov/executive-action/executive-orders/2020-executive-orders

16. US Department of Agriculture, Economic Research Service. Population Estimates for the U.S., States, and Counties, 2010–18 [Internet]. Washington (DC): USDA; [updated 2019; cited 2020 May 11]. Available from: https://data.ers.usda.gov/reports.aspx?ID=17827

17. Johns Hopkins University and Medicine, Coronavirus Resource Center. COVID-19 Dashboard by the Center for Systems Science and Engineering (CSSE) at Johns Hopkins University (JHU) [Internet]. Baltimore (MD): Johns Hopkins University; 2020 [cited 2020 May 11]. Available from: https://coronavirus.jhu.edu/map.html

18. Bursztyn L, Rao A, Roth C, Yanagizawa-Drott D. Misinformation During a Pandemic [Internet]. Chicago (IL): University of Chicago, Becker Friedman Institute for Economics; 2020 Apr [cited 2020 May 11]. (Working Paper No. 2020-44). Available from: https://bfi.uchicago.edu/wp-content/uploads/BFI_WP_202044.pdf [accessed 2020 7 May].

19. Killeen BD, Wu JY, Shah K, Zapaishchykova A, Nikutta P, Tamhane A, et al. A County-level Dataset for Informing the United States' Response to COVID-19 [Internet]. Baltimore (MD): Johns Hopkins University; 2020 [cited 2020 May 11]. Available from: https://arxiv.org/pdf/2004.00756v1.pdf

20. Saloner B, Maclean JC. Specialty Substance Use Disorder Treatment Admissions Steadily Increased in the Four Years After Medicaid Expansion. Health Aff (Millwood). 2020;39(3):453–61.

21. Lauer SA, Grantz KH, Bi Q, Jones FK, Zheng Q, Meredith HR, et al. The Incubation Period of Coronavirus Disease 2019 (COVID-19) From Publicly Reported Confirmed Cases: Estimation and Application. Ann Intern Med. 2020 Mar 10. [Epub ahead of print].

22. US Census Bureau. Census Regions and Divisions of the United States [Internet]. Washington (DC): Census Bureau; [cited 2020 May 11]. Available from: www2.census.gov/geo/pdfs/maps-data/maps/reference/us_regdiv.pdf

23. White House. Opening Up America Again. Washington (DC): White House; 2020.

24. Google. COVID-19 Community Mobility Report [Internet]. [Updated 2020 Apr 5; cited 2020 May 11]. Available from: https://www.gstatic.com/covid19/mobility/2020-04-05_US_Mobility_Report_en.pdf

25. Benzell S, Collis A, Nicolaides C. Rationing Social Contact During the COVID-19 Pandemic: Transmission Risk and Social Benefits of US Locations

[Internet]. Cambridge (MA): Massachusetts Institute of Technology; 2020 Apr 18 [cited 2020 May 11]. Available from: https://papers.ssrn.com/sol3/papers.cfm?abstract_id=3579678

26. Editorial. Pandemic School Closures: Risks and Opportunities. The Lancet Child & Adolescent Health. 2020; 4(5):341.

27. Scherbina AD. Determining the Optimal Duration of the COVID-19 Suppression Policy: A Cost-Benefit Analysis [Internet]. Boston (MA): Brandeis University; 2020 Mar 24 [cited 2020 May 11]. Available from: https://papers.ssrn.com/sol3/papers.cfm?abstract_id=3562053

28. Hall RE, Jones CI, Klenow PJ. Trading Off Consumption and COVID-19 Deaths [Internet]. Stanford (CA): Stanford University; 2020 Apr 24 [cited 2020 May 11]. (Working Paper). Available from: https://web.stanford.edu/~chadj/Consumption_v_Covid.pdf

29. Greenstone M, Vishan N. Does Social Distancing Matter? [Internet]. Chicago (IL): University of Chicago, Becker Friedman Institute for Economics; 2020 Mar 30 [cited 2020 May 11]. (Working Paper No. 2020-26). Available from: https://papers.ssrn.com/sol3/papers.cfm?abstract_id=3561244

30. Correia S, Luck S, Verner E. Pandemics Depress the Economy, Public Health Interventions Do Not: Evidence from the 1918 Flu [Internet]. Washington (DC): Board of Governors of the Federal Reserve System; 2020 Mar 26 [cited 2020 May 11]. Available from: https://papers.ssrn.com/sol3/papers.cfm?abstract_id=3561560

17 Understanding COVID-19 Risks and Vulnerabilities Among Black Communities in America

The Lethal Force of Syndemics

Tonia Poteat, Gregorio A. Millett, LaRon E. Nelson, and Chris Beyrer

As COVID-19 cases have exploded in the United States, stark racial disparities in morbidity and mortality have emerged. The burden is most pronounced for black Americans who make up 13% of the U.S. population but 30% of COVID-19 cases in the 14 states for which racial data were available[1]. Rates of exposure and infection with the novel pathogen may also differ by race; however, the lack of widespread testing and limited reporting of racial data make this difficult to ascertain. A variety of explanations have been offered for this emerging health inequity: Black Americans experience a higher prevalence of underlying chronic conditions, such as hypertension (57%)[2], diabetes (18%)[3], and obesity (50%)[4], which predispose individuals to poorer clinical outcomes, including death, in the event of COVID-19 disease[5]. Black Americans are 1.5 times more likely to be underinsured or lack health insurance altogether than whites[6], contributing to delayed access to lifesaving care[7]. On April 17, 2020, U.S. Surgeon General Jerome Adams even suggested black Americans have higher substance use rates and recommended they reduce substance use, alcohol consumption, and smoking to prevent COVID-19 deaths[8]. While these factors may play a role in why black American communities face greater losses in this pandemic, decades of research to understand the disproportionate burden of HIV among black Americans may help unmask the drivers of this inequity and improve efforts to mitigate it.

It is a longstanding paradox that black Americans carry the highest burdens of HIV while also reporting similar rates of HIV risk behaviors as other groups. This holds true for black American men who have sex with men as well as for black American women[9,10]. Syndemic theory has provided a useful framework for understanding this paradox[11]. Anthropologist Merrill Singer first proffered syndemic theory as a way "to elucidate the tendency for multiple co-terminus and interacting epidemics to develop under conditions of health and social disparity"[12]. The high rate of COVID-19 exposure, acquisition, and mortality among black Americans represents "multiple co-terminus and interacting epidemics" occurring within persistent national health and social inequities already impacting black communities. Multiple historical and present-day factors have created the syndemic conditions within which black Americans experience the lethal force of COVID-19.

The health impact of social and political decisions outweighs the impact of individual choices, and these decisions have a historical context. Sociological and economic studies have shown correlations between modern-day attitudes and policies in former confederate states and policies that disenfranchise black Americans[13]. Of 677 disproportionally black counties (≥13% black Americans), 91% are concentrated in the southern United States[14]. Strikingly, not only are rates of unemployment and uninsurance high in those counties, but also diabetes, heart disease, and HIV (Figure 17.1). It is likely that these preexisting conditions play an important role in poor clinical outcomes from COVID-19 in these counties.

State governments in the South have fiercely resisted the Medicaid expansion component of the Affordable Care Act (ACA), thereby limiting health insurance access for many of the working poor. It is not lost on many black Americans that part of the repudiation of the ACA—a policy that provided insurance to an additional 20 million Americans—is a direct repudiation of Barack Obama (our country's first black president)[15]. Such corrosive politics have health consequences. Uninsured or underinsured Americans often delay seeking timely health care because of costs and are more likely to present when a disease has progressed.

Delays in access to COVID-19 testing is also a function of the intersection of economics and racism. Recent data on testing availability have demonstrated the lack of testing options in low-income neighborhoods, and "drive-by" sites are only accessible to people with a private car. One analysis found six-fold higher rates of COVID-19 testing in high-income neighborhoods in Philadelphia despite higher COVID-19-positive tests in poorer black neighborhoods[16]. Such inequities are magnified by medical provider bias. A long legacy of medical mistreatment, present day racial bias in clinical decision making, and minimization of black American patients' symptoms impact access to health technologies[17]. This dynamic is evident in the limited availability of COVID-19 testing and media reports of hospitals that refused to test and/or turned away black Americans with COVID-19 symptoms[18-20].

Black Americans are overrepresented in essential service industries, including low-wage health care sectors such as home health aides, nursing home staff, and hospital janitorial, food service, laundry, and other sectors[21]. Many of these low-wage jobs do not provide adequate, if any, health insurance, sick leave, childcare, or other benefits which protect higher wage workers from COVID-19 exposures. Moreover, the surrounding environment magnifies risk. Black Americans are more likely to live in crowded settings such as public housing where the ability to practice social distancing

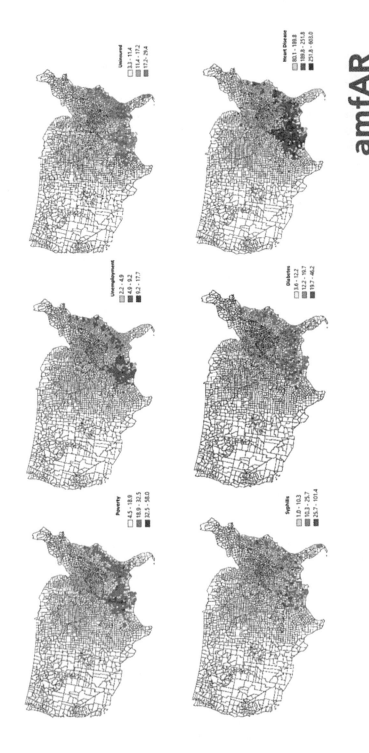

Figure 17.1 Overlapping socioeconomic and health conditions (syndemic) in counties with a disproportionate (≥13%) black population.

Figure courtesy of amfAR, excerpted from Greg Millett's July AIDS 2020 plenary.

is quite limited, if not impossible[22]. The preponderance of black Americans in occupations, environments, and situations that increase exposure to the novel coronavirus is not accidental but grounded in the historical and modern-day structural violence of racism. Racism is a form of structural violence because it produces socially unjust conditions that predispose black communities to disability and death—a reality that is both normalized and reproduced within the practices and policies of enduring public and private institutions[23]. Examples range from historical mortgage redlining that undermined black economic progress to current attempts at racial gerrymandering to disenfranchise black political power[24,25].

The partisan politicization of COVID-19 is also a detriment to black Americans. A Princeton professor who analyzed cell phone data to assess social distancing patterns in the United States found a striking pattern that exemplifies the sociopolitical drivers of syndemic conditions. Counties with the greatest share of votes for Trump in the 2016 election were least likely to practice social distancing, and the greater the share of residents who denied climate change, the worse the county scored on social distancing[26]. Repudiation of science related to both climate change and COVID-19 is encouraged by the Trump administration, and both have disproportionate impacts on black communities[27-29]. Resistance to climate change and Trump support are both high among white people in the southern United States[30,31], and it is no coincidence that the push to suspend stay-at-home orders and to prematurely reopen economies are being led by governors of southern states (e.g., Georgia, Texas, South Carolina). Ironically, Georgia (which has been among the most aggressive in suspending public health practices implemented to curb COVID-19 transmission) is not only the home to the Centers for Disease Control and Prevention, but also where one of the most devastating COVID-19 outbreaks nationwide has taken place among black residents[32]. Dougherty County, Georgia, has a per-capita COVID-19 death rate of 27 per 100,000 with 81% of deaths among black Americans who make up 69% of the population[33]. Relaxing public health measures will undoubtedly exacerbate existing racial disparities.

As a discipline, epidemiology aims to produce information for action. Improving reporting of race in surveillance and screening programs is an essential step to ensure disparities are accurately tracked. However, we do not need to wait for surveillance programs to act. The pattern is clear. To address these disparities in the short term, we must compensate low-wage service workers who have not had the option to stay at home and have kept our society functioning through this devastating pandemic. We must push for a living wage for all workers; provide universal health care access that is not tethered to employment or income; and demand personal protective equipment, access to testing, paid sick leave, and other basic minimums for essential workers who face life-threatening occupational exposures. Although important, these actions are insufficient to address the inequities rooted in syndemic conditions.

We all are not at equal risk for COVID-19. Like other conditions, this is decidedly a racialized disease. The racial health inequities that we are seeing have not emerged randomly nor passively; rather, they are actively produced through anti-black racism institutionalized within the American political system. The field of epidemiology must now reckon with a heightened awareness that the system of racism is more than a passive backdrop; it is a dynamic functioning epidemic that has converged with the COVID-19 pandemic to accelerate exposure, disease, and mortality among black people in America. While science endeavors to remain nonpartisan, its effectiveness in protecting the health of populations will be minimized if it is silent on the influence of politics on the disproportionate rates of illness and death experienced by black people in this country. Our scientific approach to addressing drivers of these inequities must change in response to our awareness of systemic racism. The timeframe for change is up to us. Better to embrace the fierce urgency of now.

Acknowledgments

Supported by the Desmond M. Tutu Professorship in Public Health and Human Rights at Johns Hopkins University.

References

1. Centers for Disease Control and Prevention. Cases of Coronavirus Disease (COVID-19) in the U.S. www.cdc.gov/coronavirus/2019-ncov/cases-updates/cases-in-us.html. [Accessed 24 April 2020].

2. Ostchega Y, Fryar CD, Nwankwo T, Nguyen DT. Hypertension prevalence among adults aged 18 and over: United States, 2017–2018. NCHS Data Brief No. 364. Hyattsville, MD: National Center for Health Statistics; 2020.

3. Mendola ND, Chen T-C, Gu Q, Eberhardt MS, Saydah S. Prevalence of total, diagnosed, and undiagnosed diabetes among adults: United States, 2013–2016. NCHS Data Brief No. 319. Hyattsville, MD: National Center for Health Statistics; 2018.

4. Hales CM, Carroll MD, Fryar CD, Ogden CL. Prevalence of obesity and severe obesity among adults: United States, 2017–2018. HCHS Data Brief No. 360. Hyattsville, MD: National Center for Health Statistics; 2020.

5. Marron MM, Ives DG, Boudreau RM, Harris TB, Newman AB. Racial differences in cause-specific mortality between community-dwelling older black and white adults. J Am Geriatr Soc 2018;66(10):1980–6.

6. Artiga S, Orgera K, Damico A. Changes in health coverage by race and ethnicity since implementation of the ACA, 2013–2017. In: Kaiser Family Foundation, Issue Brief; 2019. www.kff.org/disparities-policy/issue-brief/changes-in-health-coverage-by-race-and-ethnicity-since-the-aca-2010-2018/. [Accessed 29 April 2020].

7. Stimpson JP, Wilson FA. Medicaid expansion improved health insurance coverage for immigrants, but disparities persist. Health Aff (Millwood) 2018;37(10):1656–62.

8. Kayla B, Nikki S. Surgeon General is under fire for telling Black Americans not to smoke, drink or take drugs and 'highly offensive' use of 'big momma' as coronavirus pandemic hits black community hardest. Daily Mail; 2020. www.dailymail.co.uk/

news/article-8210359/Surgeon-general-fire-offensive-instruction-black-Americans-not-smoke-drink.html. [Accessed 29 April 2020].

9. Adimora AA, Cole SR, Eron JJ. US black women and human immunodeficiency virus prevention: time for new approaches to clinical trials. Clin Infect Dis 2017;65(2): 324–7.

10. Millett GA, Jeffries WLt, Peterson JL, Malebranche DJ, Lane T, Flores SA, et al. Common roots: a contextual review of HIV epidemics in black men who have sex with men across the African diaspora. Lancet 2012;380(9839):411–23.

11. Dyer TP, Shoptaw S, Guadamuz TE, Plankey M, Kao U, Ostrow D, et al. Application of syndemic theory to black men who have sex with men in the Multicenter AIDS Cohort Study. J Urban Health 2012;89(4):697–708.

12. Singer MC, Erickson PI, Badiane L, Diaz R, Ortiz D, Abraham T, et al. Syndemics, sex and the city: understanding sexually transmitted diseases in social and cultural context. Soc Sci Med 2006;63(8):2010–21.

13. Williams RA. Historical perspectives of healthcare disparities. In: Eliminating healthcare disparities in America. Totowa, NJ: Humana Press Inc; 2007. p. 3–19.

14. Schaeffer K. In a rising number of U.S. counties, Hispanic and black Americans are the majority. Washington, DC: Pew Research Center; 2019. www.pewresearch.org/fact-tank/2019/11/20/in-a-rising-number-of-u-s-counties-hispanic-and-black-americans-are-the-majority/. [Accessed 27 April 2020].

15. Jeffries MP. Obamacare repeal is based on racial resentment. www.bostonglobe.com/opinion/2017/05/05/obamacare-repeal-based-racial-resentment/iVNtB9fpr3JNm7IKfYyorK/story.html. [Accessed 4 May 2020].

16. Lubrano A. High-income Philadelphians getting tested for coronavirus at far higher rates than low-income residents. The Philadelphia Inquirer. www.inquirer.com/news/philadelphia/coronavirus-testing-inequality-poverty-philadelphia-health-insurance-20200406.html. [Accessed 27 April 2020].

17. van Ryn M, Burgess DJ, Dovidio JF, Phelan SM, Saha S, Malat J, et al. The impact of racism on clinician cognition, behavior, and clinical decision-making. Du Bois Rev 2011;8(1):199–218.

18. Mitropoulos A, Moseley M. Beloved Brooklyn teacher, 30, dies of coronavirus after she was twice denied a COVID-19 test. ABC News. https://abcnews.go.com/Health/beloved-brooklyn-teacher-30-dies-coronavirus-denied-covid/story?id=70376445. [Accessed 29 April 2020].

19. Shamus KJ. Family ravaged by coronavirus begged for tests, hospital care but was repeatedly denied. USA Today. www.usatoday.com/story/news/nation/2020/04/20/coronavirus-racial-disparity-denied-tests-hospitalization/5163056002/. [Accessed 29 April 2020].

20. Lothian-Mclean M. Black woman in US dies after being turned away from hospital she worked at for 31 years. Independent. www.indy100.com/article/coronavirus-black-health-care-worker-dies-test-detroit-deborah-gatewood-9485341. [Accessed 29 April 2020].

21. U.S. Bureau of Labor Statistics. Characteristics of minimum wage workers, 2018. In: BLS Reports; 2019. www.bls.gov/opub/reports/minimum-wage/2018/pdf/home.pdf. [Accessed 27 April 2020].

22. U.S. Department of Housing and Urban Development. Resident Characteristic Report [database on the Internet]. 2020. https://pic.hud.gov/pic/RCRPublic/rcrmain.asp. [Accessed 26 April 2020].

23. Farmer PE, Nizeye B, Stulac S, Keshavjee S. Structural violence and clinical medicine. PLoS Med 2006;3(10):e449.

24. Massey DS, Denton NA. American apartheid: segregation and the making of the underclass. Cambridge, MA: Harvard University Press; 1993.

25. Durst NJ. Racial gerrymandering of municipal borders: direct democracy, participatory democracy, and voting rights in the United States. Ann Am Assoc Geogr 2018;108(4):938–54.

26. Sharkey P. The US has a collective action problem that's larger than the coronavirus crisis: data show. one of the strongest predictors of social distancing behavior is attitudes toward climate change. Vox. www.vox.com/2020/4/10/21216216/coronavirus-social-distancing-texas-unacast-climate-change. [Accessed 26 April 2020].

27. Macdonald M. We must treat climate change as a racial justice issue. 2019. https://changewire.org/we-must-treat-climate-change-as-a-racial-justice-issue/. [Accessed 4 May 2020].

28. Shear MD, Mervosh S. Trump encourages protest against governors who have imposed virus restrictions. New York Times. www.nytimes.com/2020/04/17/us/politics/trump-coronavirus-governors.html. [Accessed 4 May 2020].

29. Trump on climate change report: 'I don't believe it'. BBC News. www.bbc.com/news/world-us-canada-46351940. [Accessed 4 May 2020].

30. Ballew M, Maibach E, Kotcher J, Bergquist P, Rosenthal S, Marlon J, et al. Which racial/ethnic groups care most about climate change? Yale Program on Climate Change Communication. https://climatecommunication.yale.edu/publications/race-and-climate-change/. [Accessed 4 May 2020].

31. Reality check: Who voted for Donald Trump? BBC News. www.bbc.com/news/election-us-2016-37922587. [Accessed 4 May 2020].

32. Fowler M. 'It Hit Like a Bomb'. A Georgia coroner on how the coronavirus is ravaging his community. Time. https://time.com/collection/coronavirus-heroes/5816891/coroner-georgia-coronavirus/. [Accessed 26 April 2020].

33. Dougherty County, GA. Census Reporter. https://censusreporter.org/profiles/05000US13095-dougherty-county-ga/. [Accessed 29 April 2020].

18 Early Signs Indicate That COVID-19 Is Exacerbating Gender Inequality in the Labor Force

Linda Christin Landivar, Leah Ruppanner, William J. Scarborough, and Caitlyn Collins

We draw upon the Current Population Survey for February and April 2020 to compare employment trends by gender and parental status. These data were strategically selected to capture a distinct coronavirus 2019 (COVID-19) time frame: the period before and during the peak of the first wave and associated pandemic lockdowns. Drawing upon a representative sample of the U.S. workforce, we find that women report higher unemployment than men and that mothers are exiting the labor force and reducing work hours to a greater extent than fathers (Figure 18.1). The long-term impacts of the COVID-19 lockdowns on gender inequality are paramount and require strategic policy intervention.

Labor Force Participation

Mothers of young children experienced the largest reduction in labor force participation between February and April 2020 (a 3.2 percentage point reduction among mothers with children younger than 6 and a 4.3 percentage point reduction among those with children 6 to 12). Fathers have also exited the labor force, but their exit rates are 1 to 2 percentage points lower, which means that nearly 250,000 more mothers than fathers with children younger than 13 left the labor force between February and April.

Unemployment

The economic fallout from COVID-19 has already been labeled a "shecession" (Gupta 2020), and our estimates show that women with and those without children are facing the largest increase in unemployment. The unemployment rate for some groups of mothers with young children grew by double digits between February and April 2020 (a 9 percentage point increase for mothers of children aged younger than 6 and an 11 percentage point increase for mothers of children 6 to 12). This increase is between 20 (for mothers with children aged less than six) and 51 (for mothers with children aged 6 to 12) percent larger than the growth in unemployment among fathers.

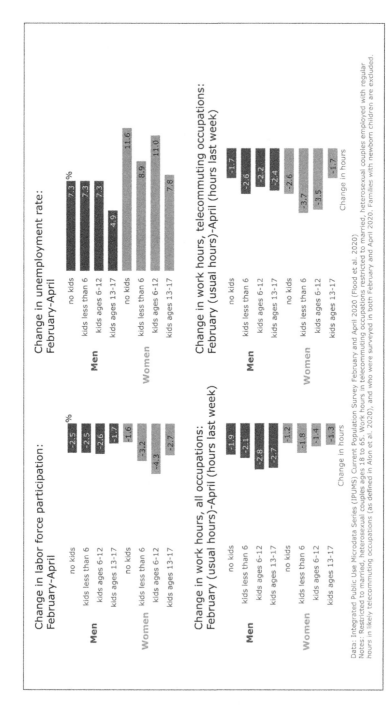

Figure 18.1 Change in labor force participation, unemployment, and work hours among married couples: February to April 2020.

Source: Flood et al. (2020).

Work Hours

Many employees have experienced work-hour reductions as a result of COVID-19. Among all workers, men experienced slightly larger reductions in work hours (however, this pattern reverses when controlling for stable respondent characteristics; see Collins et al. 2020). Among heterosexual couples of which both spouses are employed in occupations identified as telecommute-ready (Alon et al. 2020)—those who may have more control over hours worked—mothers have experienced the largest reductions in work hours. Mothers with young children scaled back by more than 3.5 hours per week between February and April 2020. Fathers scaled back by about 2.5 hours weekly.

Implications

These numbers spell bad news for the status of gender equality. During the COVID-19 pandemic, women are facing a "triple whammy": (1) as front-line workers at risk for contracting COVID-19, (2) as workers in industries experiencing greater economic distress, and (3) as caregivers shouldering increased domestic work due to school and daycare closures (Cooper and Mosseri, 2020). We bring robust evidence to show that women are more likely to be unemployed than men, and mothers of young children report higher unemployment rates and labor force exit rates compared with fathers. Even in households in which both parents remained employed and able to telecommute, our estimates show that mothers are reducing work time to a greater extent than fathers. The long-term implications are clear: the pandemic will likely exacerbate inequalities between women and men in occupational attainment, lifetime earnings, and economic independence. As cases continue to climb, governments must weigh the gendered consequences of COVID-19 to develop policies to support women's, particularly mothers', employment.

References

Alon, Titan M., Matthias Doepke, Jane Olmstead-Rumsey, and Michèle Tertilt. 2020. "The Impact of COVID-19 on Gender Equality." Working Paper 26947. Cambridge, MA: National Bureau of Economic Research. Retrieved July 24, 2020. www.nber.org/papers/w26947.pdf.

Collins, Caitlyn, Liana C. Landivar, Leah Ruppanner, and William J. Scarborough. 2020. "COVID-19 and the Gender Gap in Work Hours." *Gender, Work & Organization*. Retrieved July 24, 2020. https://onlinelibrary.wiley.com/doi/abs/10.1111/gwao.12506.

Cooper, Rae, and Sarah Mosseri. 2020. "Pandemic Has Impacted Upon Women Most Significantly." *The Sydney Morning Herald*, June 5. Retrieved July 24, 2020. www.smh.com.au/business/workplace/pandemic-has-impacted-women-most-significantly-20200604-p54ziu.html

Flood, Sarah, Miriam King, Renae Rodgers, Steven Ruggles, and J. Robert Warren. 2020. "Integrated Public Use Microdata Series, Current Population Survey: Version 7.0." Minneapolis, MN: IPUMS. Retrieved July 24, 2020. https://cps.ipums.org/cps/.

Gupta, Alisha Haridasani. 2020. "Why Some Women Call This Recession a 'Shecession'." *The New York Times*, May 9.

19 Visualizing the Geographic and Demographic Distribution of COVID-19

Patrick Denice, Kate H. Choi, Michael Haan, and Anna Zajacova

As communities, health agencies, and governments continue to deal with the coronavirus disease 2019 (COVID-19) pandemic, understanding how its impact varies over space and across population groups is crucial. But in Canada, two problems arise with such efforts. First, counts of COVID-19 cases are collected and released by Canada's health regions. These geographic areas are used by the provincial governments to administer and disperse health care resources, but they are too large and too heterogenous to meaningfully understand the impact of the pandemic on more local communities and specific subpopulations.

Second, the COVID-19 data are not tallied separately by race/ethnicity, socioeconomic status, or other demographic groups. Black Canadians, for example, constitute about 3.5 percent of the total population, with higher shares in cities such as Montreal (6.8 percent) and Toronto (7.5 percent), but it is not clear whether they are represented at disproportionately high rates among COVID-19 infections and deaths. In contrast, African Americans' overrepresentation among those affected by COVID-19 in the United States is well documented (Thebault, Tran, and Williams 2020). There are reasons to believe that this may or may not be the case in Canada. Despite Canada's national policy of multiculturalism (Brosseau and Dewing 2013), Black Canadians experience similar disadvantages and discrimination as their American counterparts, including in the labor market (Attewell, Kasinitz, and Dunn 2010). At the same time, Black Canadians generally report comparable or better health relative to white Canadians (Lebrun and LaVeist 2013; but see Veenstra and Patterson 2016).

In this visualization, we address both issues and provide an example of illustrating the spatial distribution of two demographic characteristics simultaneously. To examine the geographic spread of COVID-19 cases at a lower level of aggregation than the health region, we imputed COVID-19 infections for census subdivisions (akin to minor civil divisions, county divisions, or incorporated places in the United States). We excluded northern Canada (Yukon, the Northwest Territories, and Nunavut) given their sparse populations and low COVID-19 counts. We modeled the number of infections in a health region as a function of demographic factors including median

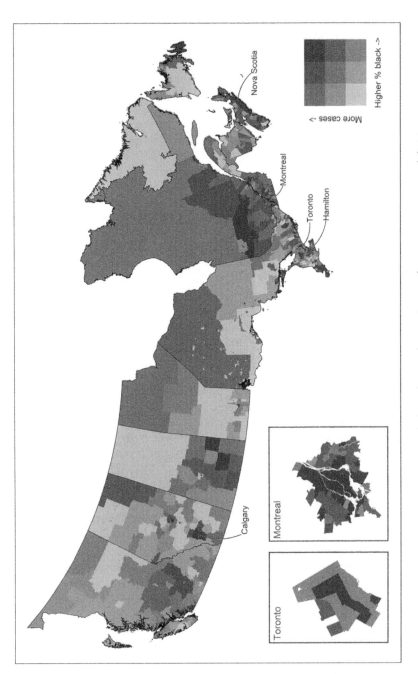

Figure 19.1 COVID-19 in Canada: percentage Black residents and COVID-19 infections across census subdivisions.

Note: Data are publicly available from the Public Health Agency of Canada and the 2016 Canadian census. This bivariate choropleth map illustrates the spatial distribution of the predicted count of coronavirus disease 2019 (COVID-19) infections and the percentage of residents who are Black across Canada's census subdivisions (*n* = 967). Provinces are outlined in black. The labeled cities (Calgary, Hamilton, and Montreal) and province (Nova Scotia) are discussed in the main text. Insets enlarge the census subdivisions in the Toronto and Montreal census metropolitan areas. Canada's northern provinces and territories are excluded.

after-tax income, percentage Black, percentage foreign born, percentage 65 years and older, and population size and density. We then used these results to allocate infections across each health region's constituent subdivisions. Absent individual-level demographic and COVID-19 data, and thus the ability to say whether Black Canadians are more or less likely to become infected by COVID-19, the choropleth map also shows where relatively high proportions of Black residents live.

Figure 19.1 maps the distribution of COVID-19 infections and the percentage of residents who are Black across Canada's census subdivisions. As expected, there are more cases in densely populated areas such as Montreal, Canada's second largest city. Its province, Quebec, has emerged has a "hotspot" for COVID-19 cases, and although some have speculated that this is due in part to the city's and province's relatively large Black population, we provide among the first evidence that this is the case. More generally, communities in which there are higher shares of Black residents also experience higher infection counts. These two measures are positively and moderately correlated ($r = .43$). This is not due simply to larger population centers or higher population density: dark purple areas—communities with high percentages of Black residents and high COVID-19 counts—are found in more and less densely populated areas. For instance, large cities such as Calgary (Canada's fourth largest) and Hamilton (a city near Toronto with population of more than half a million) as well as areas in Nova Scotia (a province with fewer than 1 million people overall) have both relatively high COVID-19 counts and relatively high shares of Black residents.

This data visualization illustrates the utility of bivariate choropleth maps for showing where and which communities are most affected by the present pandemic. In addition to highlighting the surprising similarities between Canada and the United States in terms of racial inequality (i.e., the vulnerability of communities with higher shares of Black residents in both countries), the information in this kind of map may prove useful to policymakers as they continue to craft effective and targeted responses to the mass health crisis.

References

Attewell, Paul, Philip Kasinitz, and Kathleen Dunn. 2010. "Black Canadians and Black Americans: Racial Income Inequality in Comparative Perspective." *Ethnic Racial Studies* 33(3):473–95.

Brosseau, Laurence, and Michael Dewing. 2013. "Canadian Multiculturalism." Publication No. 2009-20-E. Library of Parliament. Retrieved July 27, 2020. https://lop.parl.ca/staticfiles/PublicWebsite/Home/ResearchPublications/BackgroundPapers/PDF/2009-20-e.pdf.

Lebrun, Lydie A., and Thomas A. LaVeist. 2013. "Health Status among Black Canadians: Results from a National Survey." *Canadian Ethnic Studies* 45(1–2):143–55.

Thebault, Reis, Andrew Ba Tran, and Vanessa Williams. 2020. "The Coronavirus Is Infecting and Killing Black Americans at an Alarmingly High Rate." *The Washington Post.* Retrieved July 27, 2020. www.washingtonpost.com/nation/2020/04/07/coronavirus-is-infecting-killing-black-americans-an-alarmingly-high-rate-post-analysis-shows/?arc404=true.

Veenstra, Gerry, and Andrew C. Patterson. 2016. "Black-White Health Inequalities in Canada." *Journal of Immigrant and Minority Health* 18(1):51–57.

Part V

Latin America and Africa

The trail of the coronavirus next leads to Latin America, Africa, and India. Most countries in Latin America began adopting travel bans, prohibiting large public gatherings, issuing shelter-in-place orders, and closing schools, restaurants, and bars in mid-March 2020. Earlier, Brazil announced a public health emergency for COVID-19 only a few days after the World Health Organization's announcement of the disease as an international emergency at the end of January 2020. Latin America, however, did not report its first case until February 25 when a Brazilian national with the virus returned home from Italy. Afterwards, cases of infections skyrocketed in Brazil. By October, Brazil had over 5.3 million confirmed cases and over 156,000 deaths, third in the world in cases and second in deaths.

Various reasons have been suggested to explain why Brazil has been hit so hard by this disease. One issue has been leadership. President Jair Bolsonaro has been a strong advocate for maintaining an open economy during the pandemic. Despite testing positive for the virus himself in early July, Bolsonaro emphasized unemployment as a greater threat to Brazil than the virus. He has also been critical of scientific expertise leading to the termination of Brazil's Minister of Health in April after a disagreement over social distancing policies. A dispute with the President's promotion of hydroxychloroquine as an effective treatment led to the resignation of the next Minister of Health in May. The current Health Minister, an army general without medical experience, is serving on an interim basis (Barberia and Gomez 2020). Disagreements with state governors and mayors over the seriousness of the virus and social distancing measures have also become part of Brazil's politics (Duarte 2020). Mixed messaging from the government may have contributed to a lack of compliance with social distancing measures among Brazilians (Andreoni 2020).

Another major issue has been Brazil's significant inequality as 20 percent of its population lives in poverty (Malta et al. 2020). The virus has spread much more rapidly in poorer neighborhoods than wealthy neighborhoods in the same cities (McCoy and Traiano 2020). Black and mixed race Brazilians have faced disproportionally high death rates compared to whites, with a greater prevalence of obesity in these populations as well as less access to health care services. One of the best studies of the Brazilian situation is that of Pedro Baqui et al. (2020) who studied ethnic differences in hospital mortality. They found that *Pardo* (mixed ethnic ancestry) and Black Brazilians admitted to hospitals with COVID-19 had significantly higher mortality than White Brazilians. Of note is the finding that Pardo ethnicity was the second most important risk factor for death after age. Baqui et al. (2020:e1019) observe that their findings have serious social implications in that "Pardo and Black Brazilians tend to have less economic security, are less likely to be able to stay at home and work remotely, and comprise a substantial proportion of front-line health and care workers." The first reading in this section by Helen Ribeiro and her colleagues (2020) discusses the implications of this research.

Brazil's health infrastructure is also an issue. Even though Brazil has a universal health care system that is one of the strongest in Latin America, it had been plagued by chronic underfunding and shortages of medical staff prior to the pandemic (de Oliveira Andrade 2020). A great majority of the cities in Brazil do not have an intensive care unit (ICU) (Andreoni 2020). Among those patients treated in these units, those treated in a public hospital were almost twice as likely to die as those in a private hospital. Although COVID-19's pandemic effect on Brazil can be associated with its preexisting inequality, the disease seems to be exacerbating the problem as well. The World Bank estimated that an additional 7.2 million Brazilians would fall into poverty in 2020 without effective mitigation measures (World Bank 2020a).

Like much of Latin America, Mexico has struggled in its control of the COVID-19 pandemic. By October 2020, Mexico ranked tenth in the world for COVID infections and fourth in the world in COVID-related deaths. Some symptomatic Mexicans avoided hospitals since these were sites for dying. Mexico reported its first case of coronavirus on February 28, only three days after Brazil reported the first case in Latin America. As in the case of Brazil, the infected individual had recently returned from Italy. Mexico, like Brazil, was slow in responding.

Mexican President Andrés Manuel López Obrador took a limited approach in dealing with the virus by not placing travel restrictions or limiting mass gatherings (Semple 2020). Mexico did go into lockdown in late March, but López Obrador claimed the virus was under control and began to ease restrictions only weeks later even as deaths began to increase (McDonald 2020). In terms of an economic response to the pandemic, Mexico elected not to provide a major stimulus package and only issued a small increase in government spending to avoid accumulating more public debt despite a significant loss of jobs (Azam 2020).

The pandemic also put a significant strain on Mexico's already beleaguered health system. Mexico's spending on health care as a percentage of its gross domestic product (GDP) was among the lowest in Latin America and the Caribbean at 5% and well below the region's average of 8% prior to the pandemic (World Bank 2020b). Among the 36 states in the Organization for Economic Cooperation and Development (OECD), Mexico ranks 35th only above Turkey in the number of doctors and nurses per population (OECD 2020). It also ranked last among OECD countries in COVID testing per capita, indicating that its infection rates may be much higher than the official numbers (World Economic Forum 2020).

Given the relatively poor quality of much of Africa's health care and history of epidemics, the continent would seem to be a likely epicenter of coronavirus sickness and mortality. This has yet to happen, however, in most of Africa. The distinct exception is South Africa which was ranked twelfth in the world by late October 2020 with more than 712,000 cases and over 19,000 deaths. South Africa was considered the best-prepared of any country in sub-Saharan Africa for containing COVID-19 but did not do so. Schools and businesses were closed and the sale of alcohol banned, However, years of corruption, mismanagement, waste, and fraud weakened the health care delivery system as some $2.3 billion annually had been siphoned out of it over the years. Even the country's $26 billion economic relief package for COVID-19 was subject to corruption as several companies providing protective care for health care workers, medicines, and medical supplies engaged in massive overcharging.

Other than South Africa, the remaining African states have fared relatively well during the pandemic so far. Nigeria, the most populous African nation with some 201 million people, had fewer than 62,000 cases and only 1,129 deaths in October 2020. Africa does have the advantage of a relatively young population and considerable experience in dealing with recent pandemics such as Ebola. As discussed in the second reading by Jean Nachega and associates (2020), the Democratic Republic of the Congo is fighting three epidemics simultaneously: COVID-19, Ebola, and the measles. In the third reading, Wafaa El-Sadr and Jessica Justman (2020) point out that rather than being relieved or complacent, there nonetheless is considerable concern that the number of COVID-infected persons in Africa are likely similar to early drops of rain before a cloudburst. The 1.2 billion people living in Africa are described as being at tremendous risk and most African countries are not prepared to handle the pandemic.

Critical Thinking Questions

1. Why are the effects of COVID-19 in Brazil so deadly?
2. What has Mexico done to contain the pandemic?
3. Describe the situation in Africa with regard to COVID-19.

References

Anderoni, Manuela. "Coronavirus in Brazil: What You Need to Know." *New York Times* (June 18).

Azam, Ahmed. 2020. "Mexico's Leftist Leader Rejects Big Spending to Ease Virus's Sting." *New York Times* (June 8).

Baqui, Pedro, Ioana Bica, Valerio Marra, Ari Ercole, and Mihaela van der Schaar. 2020. "Ethnic and Regional Variations in Hospital Mortality from COVID-19 in Brazil: A Cross-sectional Observational Study." *Lancet Global Health* 8:e1018–26.

Barberia, Lorena G. and Eduardo G. Gomez. 2020. "Political and Institutional Perils of Brazil's COVID-19 Crisis." *Lancet* 396(10248):367–68.

de Oliveira Andrade, Rodrigo. 2020. "Covid-19 is Causing the Collapse of Brazil's National Health Service." *BMJ* 370:m3032.

Duarte, Tiago Ribeiro. 2020. "Ignoring Scientific Advice during the Covid-19 Pandemic: Bolsonaro's Actions and Discourse." *Tapuya: Latin American Science, Technology and Society.* https://doi.org/10.1080/25729861.2020.1767492

El-Sadr, Wafaa M. and Jessica Justman. 2020. "Africa in the Path of Covid-19." *New England Journal of Medicine* 383(3):e11–12.

Malta, Monica, et al. 2020. "Coronavirus in Brazil: The Heavy Weight of Inequality and Unsound Leadership." *EClinicalMedicine* 25:100472.

McCoy, Terrence and Heloisa Traiano. 2020. "One Disease. Two Brazils." *Washington Post* (August 10).

McDonald, Brent. 2020. "Mexico Is Reopening After Quarantine. Many Worry It's Too Early." *New York Times* (June 5).

Nachega, Jean B., Placide Mbala-Kingebeni, John Otshudiema, Alimuddin Zumla, and Jean-Jacques Muyembe Tam-Fum. 2020. "The Colliding Epidemics of COVID-19, Ebola, and Measles in the Democratic Republic of the Congo." *Lancet Global Health* (June 23). https://doi.org/10.1016/S2214-109X(20)30281-3

Organization for Economic Cooperation and Development. 2020. Beyond Containment: Health Systems Responses to COVID-19 in the OECD. www.oecd.org/coronavirus/policy-responses/beyond-containment-health-systems-responses-to-covid-19-in-the-oecd-6ab740c0/

Ribeiro, Helena, Viviana Mendes Lima, and Eliseu Alves Waldman. 2020. "In the COVID-19 Pandemic in Brazil, Do Brown Lives Matter?" *Lancet* 8:e976–77.

Semple, Kirk. 2020. "'We Call for Calm': Mexico's Restrained Response to the Coronavirus." *New York Times* (March 15).

World Bank. 2020a. COVID-19 in Brazil: Impacts and Policy Responses. www.worldbank.org/en/country/brazil/publication/covid-19-in-brazil-impacts-policy-responses.

World Bank. 2020b. Current Health Expenditure (% of GDP) – Latin America and Caribbean. https://data.worldbank.org/indicator/SH.XPD.CHEX.GD.ZS?locations=ZJ

World Economic Forum. 2020. These are the OECD Countries Testing Most for COVID-19. www.weforum.org/agenda/2020/04/these-are-the-oecd-countries-testing-most-for-covid-19/

World Health Organization. 2020. Coronavirus Disease (COVID-2019) Situation Reports. www.who.int/emergencies/diseases/novel-coronavirus-2019/situation-reports

20 In the COVID-19 Pandemic in Brazil, Do Brown Lives Matter?

Helena Ribeiro, Viviana Mendes Lima, and Eliseu Alves Waldman

In *The Lancet Global Health*, a pioneering study by Pedro Baqui and colleagues[1] confirms in Brazil findings observed in other countries hit hard by COVID-19: that mortality rates from the pandemic differ by geographical region and ethnicity, with disproportionate impact for Black populations and other ethnic minorities.[2,3] We can discuss these findings in the context of the social protests occurring in the past few months against structural racism and to the slogan "Black lives matter." However, in this Comment, we go beyond ethnicity, focusing on social and environmental determinants of health for about 50% of Brazilians.

Using COVID-19 hospital mortality data from SIVEP-Gripe (*Sistema de Informação de Vigilância Epidemiológica da Gripe*) dataset, Baqui and colleagues did a cross-sectional observational study to assess regional variations in patients with COVID-19 admitted to hospital by state and by two socioeconomically grouped regions (north and central-south). The ethnicity of patients was categorised according to the five categories used by the Brazilian Institute of Geography and Statistics: *Branco* (White), *Preto* (Black), *Amarelo* (East Asian), *Indígeno* (Indigenous), or *Pardo* (mixed ethnicity). The authors used mixed-effects Cox regression survival analysis to estimate the effects of ethnicity and comorbidity at an individual level in the context of regional variation.

Baqui and colleagues found that, compared with White Brazilians, Pardo and Black Brazilians who were hospitalised had significantly higher mortality risk (hazard ratio 1·45, 95% CI 1·33–1·58 for Pardo Brazilians; 1·32, 1·15–1·52 for Black Brazilians). Pardo ethnicity was the second most important risk factor after age for death. The authors also showed that, in the north region, hospitalised patients had higher risk of death from COVID-19 than those in the central-south region. Rio de Janeiro was an outlier, with mortality rates similar to those of northern states.

We add to their findings that incidence rates were also higher in northern regions.[4] Speculation that severe acute respiratory syndrome coronavirus 2 would have milder transmission in low latitudes has delayed actions in northern regions. However, historically, these areas face several challenges that directly affect their capacity to respond to the COVID-19 pandemic: shortages of doctors and intensivists; fragile epidemiological surveillance; poorer network of health services than in other regions; and fewer family health teams, hospital beds, and number of intensive care units (ICUs) per inhabitant than in other regions. Therefore, discussions regarding ethnicity and regional variations must be integrated, not only because northern states and Rio de Janeiro have higher proportions of Pardo and Black populations, but also because the root causes of higher mortality are overlapping. The percentage of low-income families living in subnormal housing, with higher average numbers of individuals per room, is more elevated in northern areas than in the central-south region and higher among Pardo and Black families than in White families. These conditions favour intense circulation of respiratory pathogens. Low-income neighbourhoods also have higher population density and low adherence to social distance measures. In these often hot and crowded neighbourhoods, the streets and sidewalks have cultural importance and become part of the living space. Additionally, lower schooling in northern regions and among Pardo and Black populations might jeopardise the comprehension of risks and measures proposed by sanitary authorities, as well as judgment of the right time to seek medical assistance. Additionally, in the north region, lower percentages of the urban population are served by piped water compared with those of other regions (69·5% in the north, 88·7% in the northeast, and 96% in southern regions).[5] This situation means that a substantial proportion of the northern urban population has difficulty in adhering to the simplest prevention recommendation of hygiene, such as washing hands.

The prevalence of comorbidities among Pardo and Black populations in Brazil is higher than among other ethnicities, including overweight and obesity,[6] risk factors for severity of symptoms of COVID-19.[2-4] Hypovitaminosis D is also more prevalent among Pardo and Black people in Brazil than among other ethnicities.[7] The lower the level of schooling, the higher the chances of obesity in Brazilian women.[6]

With soaring numbers of cases, cities in the northern region faced collapse of their health system, with worst cases occurring in Manaus, Fortaleza, and Natal. However, we note that phases of the epidemic vary within the country, and the northern region has probably reached the peak of the first wave of transmissions, whereas this might not be the case for other regions. The situation is dynamic, and Baqui and colleagues' research portrays a snapshot in a timeline. Additionally, substantial underreporting of deaths and cases of COVID-19 is occurring, related to low testing. This underreporting is more intense in the northern region, which might reinforce health inequities.

We draw attention to issues of mobility and historical shortages of doctors in villages and poverty areas, which are not discussed in Baqui and colleagues' study. In the Amazon, most people move around by boat through *igarapés* and rivers, and trips to cities with health equipment and medical doctors might take hours or even days. In Rio de Janeiro, mobility plays a role too. The poor, mostly Pardo and Black, live in shantytowns on steep slopes with no streets or health services, where ambulance access is difficult; or in suburbs with precarious and very crowded public transportation, facilitating transmission. In those cases, the delay to hospital admission might be fatal. Additionally, this population works mainly in unstable jobs with no payment for sick days, and thus are likely to postpone going to health services until disease symptoms are acute. Most doctors are White and might show less empathy for Pardo and Black patients. By contrast, the majority of non-medical health staff is composed of Pardo and Black people, who are more exposed to COVID-19 risks, as pointed out by Baqui and colleagues, sometimes without adequate protection equipment and tests to identify early contagion.

In Rio de Janeiro, but not exclusively, hospital equipment, beds, and ICUs were poorly managed, which left many people to die in inadequate places or at home. Irresponsibility and corruption have also played a role in this context. Therefore, there are people for whom and places where vulnerability and susceptibility[8] act together to exacerbate the risks of COVID-19, and this is compounded by a resistance of the Ministry of Health to account for ethnicity in its approach to the pandemic. Shedding light on these issues is a merit of Baqui and colleagues' study.

References

1. Baqui P, Bica I, Marra V, Ercole A, van der Schaar M. Ethnic and regional variations in hospital mortality from COVID-19 in Brazil: a cross-sectional observational study. *Lancet Glob Health* 2020; published online July 2. https://doi.org/10.1016/S2214-109X(20)30285-0.
2. Ravi K. Ethnic disparities in COVID-19 mortality: are co-morbidities to blame? *Lancet* 2020; published online June 19. https://doi.org/10.1016/S0140-6736(20)31423-9.
3. Haywood EGP, Burton J, Fort D, Seone L. Hospitalization and mortality among Black patients and White patients with COVID-19. *N Engl J Med* 2020; **382**: 2534–43.
4. Ministério da Saúde, Secretaria de Vigilância em Saúde. Boletim epidemiológico especial. Doença pelo Coronavírus COVID19. 2020. http://saude.gov.br/images/pdf/2020/June/18/Boletim-epidemiologico-COVID-2.pdf (accessed June 26, 2020).
5. Sistema Nacional de Informações sobre Saneamento. Diagnóstico dos serviços de água e esgotos—2018. 2019. https//snis.gov.br/diagnostico-anual-agua-e-esgotos/diagnostico-dos-servicos-de-agua-e-esgotos-2018 (accessed June 20, 2020).
6. Ferreira APS, Szwarcwald CL, Damacena GN. Prevalence of obesity and associated factors in the Brazilian population: a study of data from the 2013 National Health Survey. *Rev Bras Epidemiol* 2019; **22**: e190024.
7. Ribeiro H, de Santana KVdS, Oliver SL, et al. Does vitamin D play a role in the management of COVID-19 pandemic in Brazil? *Rev Saúde Púb* 2020; **54**: 53.
8. Diderichsen F, Hallqvist J, Whitehead M. Differential vulnerability and susceptibility: how to make use of recent development in our understanding of mediation and interaction to tackle health inequalities. *Int J Epidemiol* 2019; **48**: 268–274.

21 The Colliding Epidemics of COVID-19, Ebola, and Measles in the Democratic Republic of the Congo

Jean B. Nachega, Placide Mbala-Kingebeni, John Otshudiema, Alimuddin Zumla, and Jean-Jacques Muyembe Tam-Fum

The Democratic Republic of the Congo is facing major public health challenges due to a confluence of major outbreaks of Ebola virus disease, measles, and COVID-19.[1-4] The 10th Ebola outbreak in eastern DR Congo began on August 1, 2018, and as of May 28, 2020, there have been 3,406 Ebola virus disease cases with 2,243 deaths. The Ebola virus disease outbreak was well controlled in northeast DR Congo following a multisectoral response, but four new confirmed Ebola cases were detected in northwest DR Congo on June 1, 2020, and an outbreak response is underway.[4] Additionally, the DR Congo has been burdened with recurrent measles outbreaks: 133,802 cases in 2011, 88,381 cases in 2013, and 311,471 cases in 2019.[2] The first confirmed case of COVID-19 in DR Congo was diagnosed on March 10, 2020, and the government declared a state of emergency on March 24, 2020. A national multisectoral response committee instituted lockdown in the capital, Kinshasa, the epicentre of the epidemic in DR Congo, in which daily confirmed cases now average 100. As of June 16, 2020, 4,777 COVID-19 cases with 106 deaths have been reported from the DR Congo.[5]

Although the COVID-19 pandemic presents unique challenges that threaten the health, economy, and social fabric of DR Congo, several lessons learned from dealing with the devastating Ebola virus disease outbreaks have been invaluable and are guiding the ongoing COVID-19 public health response.[6] These responses include involvement of community leaders and institutions with communication to the public in local languages to explain the disease and its prevention strategies and disseminating messages in terms that are culturally understandable. Ebola virus disease control infrastructure, protocols, and staff have been repurposed and applied to the COVID-19 response. Multidisciplinary teams of nurses, doctors, medical students, and community health-care workers are implementing COVID-19 sensitisation, screening, and testing activities endorsed by the Ministry of Health and community and religious leaders.[7]

All COVID-19 testing by RT-PCR is done at the National Institute of Biomedical Research in Kinshasa. Efforts to decentralise testing to provinces and improve turnaround are underway using point-of-care testing with the

GeneXpert platform, but this remains challenging because of cost and supply constraints for severe acute respiratory syndrome coronavirus 2 testing cartridges. Several hospitals were identified as reference centres for the treatment of COVID-19, and intensive care units have been resourced with additional ventilators and oxygen supplies as part of the national plan. A clinical protocol has been developed by the Case Management Commission with support from technical partners. Bilateral and multilateral partnerships provided donations of medical equipment to hospitals, and clinical staff are being trained on COVID-19 case management. Patients with moderate and severe COVID-19 are hospitalised for supportive care, oxygen therapy, and anticoagulation as per WHO guidelines.[8]

The strong national commitment in DR Congo to the COVID-19 and Ebola virus disease epidemics provides hope that alignment of public health responses will prevent the high morbidity and mortality seen in South Africa. The DR Congo government understands the importance of strengthening its health systems through establishing effective partnerships with international stakeholders who leverage their unique areas of expertise to achieve tangible results. However, as with other African countries, major challenges for COVID-19 control remain. Mitigation measures such as travel bans and lockdowns in DR Congo are having negative socioeconomic effects on the population. Indeed, most citizens are unemployed and live below the poverty line in shanty towns or rural settings in overcrowded housing, which makes COVID-19 preventive measures, such as hand washing and social distancing, difficult. Also, the high prevalence of comorbidities, including chronic conditions such hypertension, diabetes, HIV and AIDS, and tuberculosis, add to the COVID-19 mortality risk.[9] Although attention has been focused on COVID-19 and Ebola virus disease, there have also been 369, 520 measles cases with 6,779 deaths in the past year, which illustrates that vaccination efforts have been suboptimal because of disruptions to immunisation campaigns and suggests that there are potential threats of resurgence of other vaccine-preventable infectious diseases.

DR Congo's early COVID-19 mitigation interventions have allowed the multisectoral response committee to gain time and prepare for the anticipated COVID-19 peak, but its response is being implemented in a fragile health system that faces challenges, including the coexisting Ebola virus disease and measles outbreaks. The World Bank provided US$300 million to support the 2018–2020 Ebola virus disease response strategy, and it should ensure that additional assistance includes support for primary health care and regular supply of essential medicines, vaccines, and technical assistance.[10] Although urgent measures are required to slow the spread of COVID-19 and tackle the renewed threat of Ebola virus disease, every effort must be made by stakeholders to ensure that prevention programmes for measles or other infectious diseases, including transporting vaccinations for children, are not compromised.

References

1. Nsio J, Kapetshi J, Makiala S, et al. 2017 outbreak of Ebola virus disease in northern Democratic Republic of Congo. *J Infect Dis* 2020; **221:** 701–06.
2. Ilunga Kalenga O, Moeti M, Sparrow A, Nguyen VK, Lucey D, Ghebreyesus TA. The ongoing Ebola epidemic in the Democratic Republic of Congo, 2018–2019. *N Engl J Med* 2019; **381:** 373–83.
3. WHO. Measles and Rubella Surveillance Data. 2020. www.who.int/immunization/monitoring_surveillance/burden/vpd/surveillance_type/active/measles_monthlydata/en/ (accessed June 7, 2020).
4. The Washington Post. New Ebola outbreak declared in Congo city that last saw the virus in 2018. 2020. www.washingtonpost.com/world/africa/new-ebola-outbreak-declared-in-congo-city-that-last-saw-the-virus-in-2018/2020/06/01/33a9f958-a3ff-11ea-898e-b21b9a83f792_story.html (accessed June 7, 2020).
5. WHO. Coronavirus disease (COVID-2019) situation reports. 2020. www.who.int/docs/default-source/coronaviruse/situation-reports/20200615-covid-19-sitrep-147.pdf?sfvrsn=2497a605_4 (accessed June 16, 2020).
6. Mobula LM, Samaha H, Yao M, et al. Recommendations for the COVID-19 response at the national level based on lessons learned from the Ebola virus disease outbreak in the Democratic Republic of the Congo. *Am J Trop Med Hyg* 2020; published online May 19. https://doi.org/10.4269/ajtmh.20-0256.
7. Nachega JB, Grimwood A, Mahomed H, et al. From easing lockdowns to scaling-up community-based COVID-19 screening, testing, and contact tracing in Africa – shared approaches, innovations, and challenges to minimize morbidity and mortality. *Clin Infect Dis* 2020; published online May 31. https://doi.org/10.1093/cid/ciaa695.
8. WHO. Clinical Management of COVID-19. 2020. www.who.int/publications-detail/clinical-management-of-covid-19 (accessed May 31, 2020).
9. Mehtar S, Preiser W, Lakhe NA, et al. Limiting the spread of COVID-19 in Africa: one size mitigation strategies do not fit all countries. *Lancet Glob Health* 2020; published online April 28. https://doi.org/10.1016/S2214-109X(20)30212-6.
10. Wadman M. World Bank dedicates $300 million to Ebola response. 2019. www.sciencemag.org/news/2019/07/world-bank-dedicates-300-million-ebola-response (accessed June 7, 2020).

22 Africa in the Path of COVID-19

Wafaa M. El-Sadr and Jessica Justman

In South Sudan, all schools and churches have been closed to promote social distancing. In South Africa, President Cyril Ramaphosa declared a three-week total lockdown of his country's 57 million citizens. In Uganda, pop star Bobi Wine's newly recorded song "Sensitise to Sanitise" is playing on radios throughout the country to raise awareness about reducing coronavirus transmission. At the large regional hospital in Kisumu, Kenya, teams of health workers have set up tents to provide information on COVID-19 and to take visitors' temperatures and log their travel histories before they enter the hospital. The coronavirus is coming to Africa, and with creative actions, large and small, Africans are aiming to meet it head on.

As the COVID-19 pandemic sweeps the globe, causing tens of thousands of deaths and massive economic disruption, Africa has so far been largely spared the kind of impact that has thrown China, the United States, and Europe into chaos. As of April 13, there were about 14,000 confirmed cases on the African continent, as compared with 160,000 in Italy and more than 560,000 in the United States.[1,2] But rather than inviting relief or complacency, the numbers from Africa are like the early drops of rain before the clouds open up. Despite the slow arrival of COVID-19, a storm is building, and the 1.2 billion people living in Africa are at tremendous risk.

Most African countries remain woefully unprepared for what's coming. Kenya, for example, has only 200 intensive care beds for its entire population of 50 million. Compare that to the United States, which has 34 beds for every 100,000 people.[3] Countries from Mali to Liberia have only a few ventilators for millions of people. In urban communities throughout Africa, health facilities tend to be overcrowded and understaffed, while in rural areas, poor roads and unreliable transport make it difficult for people to access care. Advanced health care is sorely lacking in nearly every country.

But the obstacles are not limited to care and treatment of people who are sick. In many communities, people live together in close quarters, which makes social distancing, a critical prevention strategy, more difficult. Millions of people live without access to clean running water, which makes frequent handwashing all but impossible.[4] Adding to these concerns, winter is coming to the Southern Hemisphere, where most of Africa lies, and some experts worry that drier, colder weather may increase viral activity.

Confronting epidemics is not new to Africans, and their experience may prove to be an advantage. Responding to infectious diseases for generations has sensitized governments and communities to the dangers and to the need for rapid, proactive measures to save lives. Moreover, a substantial number of countries in Africa have benefited from previous global initiatives to strengthen health systems to address HIV, malaria, tuberculosis, and Ebola.[5] In addition, the Africa Centers for Disease Control has accelerated its work to enhance diagnostic and surveillance capacity on the continent. As a result, health infrastructures are less fragile than they have been in the past.

The biggest advantage, of course, is time. Heads of state, ministries of health, hospitals, clinics, and community health organizations are taking immediate action. As the pandemic makes its first inroads, several countries have vigorously pursued containment efforts involving identifying, assessing, and isolating people with suspected cases and close contacts of each infected person. Countries are also mobilizing virtual learning networks to disseminate information to health and community workers. From Angola to Zimbabwe, governments are putting in place mitigation measures by closing borders, shuttering markets, suspending internal flights, and instituting limits or outright bans on social gatherings.

But despite these intensive preparations, we should have no illusions that Africa can confront this threat alone. Coordinated global support is essential in the face of the COVID-19 pandemic, and the time to act is now. We believe that during the next few weeks, countries around the world should take concrete steps to assist Africa in staying ahead of the curve, even as they confront their own epidemics. These steps may include donations of coronavirus test kits, personal protective equipment, ventilators, and other life-support equipment or, at a minimum, ensuring that African countries are not priced out of the market for these commodities. Support is urgently needed for real-time COVID-19 surveillance systems and for surveys to determine the scope of the epidemic and to inform decisions about how to respond. Funding and technical support are also needed to run national information campaigns to promote safe behaviors and to counter the stigma that often arises against the people thought to be causing the epidemic. Vulnerable populations, particularly the poor and people engaged in the informal economy, will need to be supported during periods when movement of people is restricted. Finally, it is critically important that resources and attention not be diverted from the continent's ongoing threats from other infectious diseases, such as HIV, tuberculosis, and malaria.

When HIV spread like wildfire across the African continent, it took decades for the world to mobilize a response. Tens of millions of people were infected and many millions died as the epidemic took root—and it persists to this day. Epidemics know no borders, and success in controlling the epidemic in any one country will be limited if epidemics continue to rage elsewhere. Today, we have the chance to avoid a repeat of history. Africans are doing their part. Now is the time for us to do ours.

References

1. Center for Systems Science and Engineering (CSSE) at Johns Hopkins University. COVID-19 dashboard (https://coronavirus.jhu.edu/map.html).
2. Africa Centres for Disease Control and Prevention. COVID-19 dashboard (https://africacdc.org/covid-19/).
3. Wallace DJ, Angus DC, Seymour CW, Barnato AE, Kahn JM. Critical care bed growth in the United States: a comparison of regional and national trends. Am J Respir Crit Care Med 2015;191:410–6.
4. World Health Organization. Key facts from JMP 2015 report. 2015 (www.who.int/water_sanitation_health/publications/JMP-2015-keyfacts-en-rev.pdf).
5. Mwisongo A, Nabyonga-Orem J. Global health initiatives in Africa—governance, priorities, harmonisation and alignment. BMC Health Serv Res 2016;16:Suppl 4:212.

Part VI

Resolution

This final section deals with steps toward resolution. Everything comes to an end. As we know from history, plagues and epidemics diminish or stop at some point, and social life returns to a changed normal (Cantor 2001; Hempel 2018; Oldstone 2010). The ultimate resolution is an effective future vaccine which scores of scientists in several countries are rushing to develop, test, manufacture, and distribute on a worldwide basis. Whether a cure will be discovered and COVID-19 will be stopped by a vaccine as if it hit a wall and disappears, or whether it will return every year like flu season and needs to be contained on an annual basis is not known at this time.

This final section contains two readings, one by Bo Yan and his colleagues (2020) comparing the differing approaches of four countries—Sweden, China, France, and Japan—toward coping with the pandemic before the discovery of a vaccine. Each of these countries, as elsewhere in the world, had to rely on nonpharmaceutical interventions against COVID-19—namely, strategies to modify social behavior. The responses to the same threat were dependent on the distinctive institutions and cultural orientation of each country, and there was no One-Size-Fits-All strategy. Instead, the distinct strategies adopted by each nation were described as nudge (Sweden), mandate (China), decree (France), and boost (Japan).

The second and concluding reading for this book is a *New York Times* article by Gina Kolata (2020) on how the end of the COVID-19 pandemic will be decided. Kolata points out that pandemics typically have two types of endings. One is medical, which occurs when the incidence of new cases and mortality rates fall, and the social, when fear about the disease weakens. That is, a pandemic can end not because a cure has been found but because people grow tired of being afraid of it and learn to live with it. Consequently, the COVID-19 pandemic may end socially before it ends medically. The Kolata chapter discusses these two options and asks the question: "For whom does the epidemic end, and who gets to say?" As economic problems grow, more people may desire to end restrictions. A fundamental tension exists in society between allowing people to make a living on the one hand and protecting them from infection on the other. The former is seen in U.S. states where politicians have opted for early reopenings and the latter in warnings by public health officials that such measures are premature.

The Vaccine

In the meantime, the devastating loss of life and economic damage created by the COVID-19 pandemic spurred an intense race to develop a vaccine. Research programs in China, the United States, and Europe emerged as the first contenders. Although the entire world would benefit from an effective vaccine, this race is highly competitive among both pharmaceutical companies and national governments. The country that vaccinates its population first could fully reopen its economy and potentially gain an advantage over others (Sanger et al. 2020). An effective vaccine could also enhance profits and reputations for the organizations bringing it to the market. A Chinese vaccine could help restore China's standing as a dependable partner in protecting public health.

By July 2020, multiple vaccine developers showed promising results in early human trials. A vaccine developed by Oxford University and Astra-Zeneca (a British-Swedish firm) and one developed by CanSino Biologics (a Chinese firm) published peer-reviewed results of their successful early trials (Kilpatrick 2020). Another vaccine produced by Pfizer (an American firm) and BIoNTech (a German firm) published positive results in August. Moderna (an American firm) is also considered a front-runner in vaccine development and moved into Phase 3 trials by August. Surprisingly, Russia became the first country to approve a vaccine for delivery despite not conducting Phase III final-stage clinical trials. The Russian announcement was met with alarm by health experts as they viewed widespread administration of such an untested vaccine as risky and potentially dangerous (Zimmer 2020).

Although the world has been desperately hoping for a quick vaccine, concerns have been raised that the race for one has become too politicized, and safety and effectiveness may be compromised for political gain. The United States named its vaccine development program "Operation Warp Speed," which raised concerns about whether speed was the priority in a process that can take years to complete, although a vaccine seems likely in 2021. The fact 2020 was an election year for the American presidency and the possibility that the United States may rush to approve a vaccine before the November election exacerbated these concerns (LaFraniere et al. 2020). In Russia, which accelerated the development process beyond safety protocols, politics were involved as Premier Vladimir Putin had seen declining approval ratings due to the economic damage caused by the pandemic and a surprisingly unassertive response (Kramer 2020). China has faced political pressure as well in competing against the United States and Europe in the vaccine race because of the pandemic's origin in that country.

Even if an effective vaccine is developed, administering the vaccine could be a problem. A poll by NPR/PBS News Hour/Marist College found in early August that 35 percent of Americans would not take the vaccine (Marist Poll 2020). This poll is consistent with several previous polls, which likewise suggest that many Americans would not take any vaccine (Hoffman 2020). The numbers typically range from 20 to 30 percent saying no with a good number of people expressing uncertainty. The reasons for skepticism about a vaccine have been varied, including a lack of trust in for-profit pharmaceutical companies, the U.S. government, and doctors, along with greater faith in natural remedies as an alternative, as well as the existence of various conspiracy theories about the spread of the virus and the vaccine process (Hoffman 2020). If these poll numbers are correct, it could be problematic for even an effective vaccine to put an end to the pandemic. It takes immunity for at least 70 percent of the population to achieve herd immunity (D'Souza and Dowdy 2020), while about 85 to 95 percent immunity is needed to protect almost everyone in a community depending on the disease (Reich 2016). Once a vaccine becomes available, if a third of Americans (or a similar number in another country) do not take the vaccine, then a good part of the population will continue to be vulnerable to the disease and both public health and the economy could continue to be adversely affected by COVID-19.

According to sociologist Jennifer Reich (2016:14), research on unvaccinated children in the United States divides them into two categories. One group consists of those that are unvaccinated because of a lack of consistent access to professional health care, are more likely to be a racial minority, have an unwed mother without a college degree, and live in a low-income household. The other group is unvaccinated because of parental choice and more likely to be white, have a college-educated and married mother, middle-class affluence, and clustered in geographic regions. These anti-vaccination groups are global, not just in the United States, and involves nearly 100 million individuals partitioned into interconnected clusters across cities, countries, continents, and languages capable of challenging existing viewpoints and influencing the undecided (Johnson et al. 2020). This group goes unvaccinated because they or their caretakers believe vaccines may not work and can damage the health of their children since vaccination involves administering a virus as a foreign substance into the body of their children. As COVID-19 affects older people much worse than younger individuals generally, there may be resistance on the part of young adults and parents with young children to participate in public health vaccination programs.

Social Class

From a sociological perspective, a topic that has not been addressed in the research literature to date is social class. In virtually all epidemics and pandemics, the lower social classes suffer the worst outcomes. For example, some 40 percent of the peasant population in small English villages died during the bubonic plague in the 1340s; some of these villages simply disappeared from written records (Cantor 2001). In the Italian states during the same period, the privileged classes abandoned towns for their villas in the countryside, where they secluded themselves in luxury to avoid the black death. The late historian Barbara Tuchman (1978:98) aptly described this situation over 40 years ago in her prize-winning book, *A Distant Mirror: The Calamitous 14th Century*:

> Flight was the chief recourse of those who could afford it or arrange it. The rich fled to their country places like Boccaccio's young patricians of Florence, who settled in a pastoral place "removed on every side from the roads" with "wells of cool water and vaults of rare wine." The urban poor died in their burrows "and only the stench of their bodies informed their neighbors of their death." That the poor were more heavily afflicted than the rich was clearly remarked on at the time, in the north as in the south.

Similarly, in 2020, some seven centuries later, many of the affluent left New York City and other sites with a concentration of COVID-19, to go where the likelihood of being infected by the virus was significantly less. Of course, it is obvious to state that the poor who have less of the good things in life and more of the bad, including health, are more likely to have the most cases of the coronavirus and the highest mortality. This is because the lower- and working-classes have *less* access to quality health care, along with fewer jobs that provide regularly occurring, sustaining monthly incomes and the capability of being performed remotely from home with access to quality digital services. These classes have *more* comorbid health problems, jobs in which it is challenging to self-isolate, and work and live in crowded dwellings and neighborhoods. Being able to social distance in these circumstances, as Clyde Yancy (2020) points out, is a privilege. Yancy (2020:1892) observes that "COVID-19 has become the herald event that now fully exposes the deep and chronic social wounds in U.S. communities."

Another class-related social problem is kindergarten through 12th grade education. Many such schools have a hybrid format (mixed face-to-face/ remote) or only remote instruction. Having to learn remotely by electronic means requires having access to and competency in using computers in a supportive home environment. Affluent families are better able to marshal the resources for online education. They also have been more likely to form educational "pods" within their neighborhoods with small groups of families or just their own family for home schooling, sometimes employing tutors, or a combination of home and online instruction (Bueno 2020). In such cases, the parents are typically college-educated and motivated to give their children the best education possible. Class-based gaps in educational achievement are likely to widen under such circumstances.

Since the 1980s, the wealth gap in the United States and the world has been increasing evermore. According to French economist Thomas Piketty (2014:247), income equality in the United States is on the rise with the income of the top 10 percent of earners (the "upper class" of breadwinners) increasing from acquiring 35 percent of all income in 2010 to 45 percent in 2030; conversely, the bottom 50 percent in income ("the lower class" of breadwinners) will see their proportion of the nation's total income fall from 25 percent to 20 percent over the same period. The "middle class" of earners are also predicted to experience a decrease of about 40 percent of all income in 2010 to 35 percent in 2030. This illustrates the continuing trend in income inequality where the rich get even richer and the poor even poorer in the next decade. This estimate, however, was before the pandemic. What it signifies is that those at the bottom of society will find it even more difficult to buffer the economic effects of the virus and take longer to recover. The coronavirus is not the great social equalizer.

An applicable theory in medical sociology explaining the relationship between social class and the COVID-19 pandemic is fundamental cause theory. According to Jo Phelan and Bruce Link (Phelan and Link 2013; Phelan, Link, and Tehranifar 2010), social class or socioeconomic status (SES) is a fundamental cause of health and disease in that class position involves access to resources that can be used to avoid risks or minimize the consequences of a disease if a person does become ill. The theory's core thesis is that a superior collection of flexible resources permits higher SES persons to avoid disease and death in varying situations. Consequently, greater resources produce better health, while inequalities in resources cause persistent inequalities in health and mortality. The socioeconomic resources a person has or does not have in relation to avoiding disease are money, knowledge, status, power, and beneficial social connections. These resources are flexible because they can be used in multiple circumstances. Flexible resources influence individual health behaviors with respect to whether people know about, have access to, can afford, and are motivated to engage in health-promoting practices, as well as determining access to jobs, neighborhoods, and social networks that vary dramatically in the amount of risk and protection they provide. Resources and the ability to use them are most effective for preventable causes of mortality such as COVID-19. This theory helps us understand the mechanisms that account for the virus having its most potent effects among persons on the lower rungs of the social ladder.

Societal Adjustments

It is clear there will be changes in society regardless of the form of resolution. There will likely be an economic recession featuring higher unemployment than usual and failed businesses, an oversupply of workers because of businesses failures causing growth in wages to stagnate or decrease, a worldwide decline in gross national product (GNP) productivity, a decrease in global trade, serious damage to housing markets, banking and other financial services, and manufacturing, and especially severe damage to hospitality industries such as hotels, travel and tourism, entertainment venues like movie theaters and playhouses, shopping malls as more people shop online, and sports. Some restaurants and bars will likely close permanently and motion picture theatres may become extinct, like mid-20th century drive-in movies, as viewers come to prefer streaming films at home. Professional and college sports teams will need to adjust to diminished attendance and revenues. Some college football teams and squads in other fall sports canceled their 2020 seasons.

The academic side of higher education is suffering as enrollments and revenues decline, some students defer admission to a future date when they can be on campus, dorms are underutilized, and the preponderance of instruction goes on online. Faculty numbers will likely decrease or stagnate as hiring freezes are initiated, salaries cut, pension plans not supported, and positions eliminated. There is also a rebellion against the high cost of a university education with students and parents objecting to paying high tuition prices for an education that is increasingly moving online ("glorified Skype") instead of being conducted face-to-face on a campus with its specialized educational facilities, opportunities for interaction and learning, and immersion in college life (Hubler 2020). Reductions of fees and rebates are being demanded, requests for financial aid increased, and leaves of absences requested because of what appears to be a substandard educational experience. Educational institutions without substantial financial reserves will likely be forced to close, especially already struggling private colleges with small enrollments. Furthermore, once students were back on some reopened campuses, there were several instances of newly confirmed COVID-19 cases further complicating the capability of continuing. The University of North Carolina at Chapel Hill was the first university to suspend in-person undergraduate classes after multiple coronavirus clusters among students both on and off campus were reported after two weeks of classes. All classes were shifted to online remote learning. This occurred after 177 students tested positive for the virus and another 349 were quarantined because of exposure to an infected person.

Full recovery in the United States and elsewhere around the world will take time and perhaps not be the same normal as before the virus.

References

Bueno, Carycruz. 2020. "Bricks and Mortar vs. Computers and Modems: The Impacts of Enrollment in K–12 Virtual Schools." https://papers.ssrn.com/sol3/papers.cfm?abstract_id=3642969.

Cantor, Norman F. 2001. *In the Wake of the Plague*. New York: Simon & Shuster.

D'Souza, Gypsyamber and David Dowdy. 2020. "What is Herd Immunity and How Can We Achieve It with COVID-19?" Johns Hopkins School of Public Health. www.jhsph.edu/covid-19/articles/achieving-herd-immunity-with-covid19.html.

Hempel, Sandra. 2018. *The Atlas of Disease*. London: White Lion.

Hoffman, Jan. 2020. "Mistrust of a Coronavirus Vaccine Could Imperil Widespread Immunity." *New York Times* (July 18).

Hubler, Shawn. 2020. "As Colleges Move Classes Online, Families Rebel Against the Cost." *New York Times* (August 16).

Johnson, Neil F., Nicolas Velásquez, Nicholas Johnson Restrepo, Rhys Leahy et al. 2020. "The Online Competition between Pro- and Anti-vaccination Views." *Nature* 582:230–33.

Kilpatrick, David D. 2020. "Three Coronavirus Vaccine Developers Report Promising Initial Results." *New York Times* (July 20).

Kolata, Gina. 2020. "How Pandemics End." *New York Times* (May 10).

Kramer, Andrew E. 2020. "Russia Approves Coronavirus Vaccine Before Completing Tests." *New York Times* (August 11).

LaFraniere, Sharon, Katie Thomas, Noah Weiland, Peter Baker and Annie Karni. 2020. "Scientists Worry About Political Influence Over Coronavirus Vaccine Project." *New York Times* (August 2).

Marist Poll. 2020. "NPR/PBS News Hour/Marist Poll Results: Election 2020, Trump, & the Issues." *Maristpoll.Marist.edu.* http://maristpoll.marist.edu/npr-pbs-newshour-marist-poll-results-election-2020-trump-the-issues/#sthash.FoTXpgjw.dpbs.

Oldstone, Michael B. A. 2010. *Viruses, Plagues and History.* Oxford, UK: Oxford University Press.

Phelan, Jo C., Bruce G. Link, and Parisa Tehranifar. 2010. "Social Conditions as Fundamental Causes of Health Inequalities: Theory, Evidence, and Policy Implications." *Journal of Health and Social Behavior* 51(extra issue):S28–S40.

Phelan, Jo C. and Bruce G. Link. 2013. "Fundamental Cause Theory," Pp. 105–26 in William Cockerham (ed.), *Medical Sociology on the Move: New Directions in Theory.* Dordrecht: Springer.

Piketty, Thomas. 2014. *Capitalism in the Twenty-First Century.* Cambridge, MA: Belknap Press of Harvard University.

Reich, Jennifer A. 2016. *Calling the Shots: Why Parents Reject Vaccines.* New York: New York University.

Sanger, David E., David D. Kirkpatrick, Sui-Lee Wee, and Katrin Bennhold. 2020. "Search for Coronavirus Vaccine Becomes a Global Competition." *New York Times* (March 19).

Tuchman, Barbara W. 1978. *A Distant Mirror: The Calamitous 14th Century.* New York: Random House.

Yan, Bo, Xiaomin Zhang, Long Wu, Heng Zhu and Bin Chen. 2020. "Why Do Countries Respond Differently to COVID-19? A Comparative Study of Sweden, China, France, and Japan." *American Review of Public Administration* 50(6–7):762–69.

Yancy, Clyde W. "COVID-19 and African Americans." *JAMA* 323(19):1891–92.

Zimmer, Carl. 2020. "'This Is All Beyond Stupid.' Experts Worry About Russia's Rushed Vaccine." *New York Times* (August 12).

23 Why Do Countries Respond Differently to COVID-19? A Comparative Study of Sweden, China, France, and Japan

Bo Yan, Xiaomin Zhang, Long Wu, Heng Zhu, and Bin Chen

Since December 2019, COVID-19 has become a global pandemic, quickly spreading to more than 200 countries and territories around the world. Changing individuals' behavior is critical to containing and mitigating the COVID-19 pandemic because the virus can spread via human-to-human transmission (Bavel et al., 2020). By March 2020, national governments had employed a series of nonpharmaceutical interventions (NPIs), including isolation, quarantine, and social distancing, as well as community containment, to combat the transmission of the virus (Wilder-Smith & Freedman, 2020). Yet, there are noticeable country-to-country variations in regard to the scale and scope of these NPIs. Oxford University created a stringency index to track and compare the strictness of government policy interventions across countries (Hale et al., 2020). The Oxford index reveals that governments' responses to COVID-19 exhibit significant nuances and heterogeneity, especially with respect to policy interventions regarding containment and closure. Why do national governments respond differently to COVID-19? Many factors may shape government response strategies; for example, the severity of the pandemic in that country and the country's health care capacity (Kandel et al., 2020; Pillemer et al., 2015). We discuss how two critical contextual factors, institutional arrangements and national cultural orientation, impact the formation and adoption of four distinct national COVID-19 response strategies: a nudge strategy in Sweden, a mandate strategy in China, a decree strategy in France, and a boost strategy in Japan. We chose these four countries because their divergent COVID-19 response strategies have gained worldwide attention and sparked a global debate, despite the fact that all of them are unitary states with identical levels of Health Emergency Preparedness, as ranked by World Health Organization (WHO) in 2018.[1]

Two Critical Contextual Factors: Institutional Arrangements and National Cultural Orientation

Understanding context is critical to analyzing and designing public policy (Geva-May, 2002). In addition to problem-specific factors, such as different types of crisis (Christensen et al., 2016), a multitude of contextual factors, such as cultural orientation, economic development level, and political institution, influence national governments' policymaking (Berkman et al., 2005; Carayannopoulos, 2017; Weible et al., 2020). Given that COVID-19 is a transboundary virus that can spread via human-to-human transmission, we argue that national government response strategies are contingent not only upon the state's domination and control, but also upon citizens' compliance and voluntary support (Migdal, 2009).

The exercising of state power depends on both structural features within the political system and cultural factors in the broader environment (Jessop, 2010). We thus focus on two critical contextual factors, institutional arrangements and cultural orientation, to explain why four distinct response strategies were adopted by the chosen four countries.

Institutional Arrangements: Decentralized Versus Centralized Regimes

Institutional arrangements refer to the systems and processes that countries use to structure authority, attention, information flows, and relationships in addressing policy problems (May, 2015). They can be either formal government organizational structures or informal norms that are in place in a country for the sake of arranging and undertaking policy work. These formal system processes provide governments at all levels (central and local) with a framework within which to formulate, adopt, and implement policies. Informal institutional structures include the general public, nongovernmental organizations, and private sector groups that are not official institutions.

One formal institutional arrangement key to understanding different COVID-19 response strategies is the degree to which power and authority are centralized versus decentralized in a country. The extent of decentralization versus centralization varies even across unitary states. Centralized states emphasize the authority of the central government and blur the responsibilities between central-local ties, making it easier to adopt and implement policies in a top-down fashion (León & Orriols, 2019; Wimmer, 2018). In contrast, decentralized states share power with the governments at different levels and clarify the responsibilities among multiple tiers. Actual authority is put into the hands of local authorities when it comes to policy decision-making (Goel et al., 2017). Therefore, in a decentralized regime, either policy blockages or bargaining may set limits on the choice of policy strategy (Clune, 1993). Centralized countries with strong top-down mandates and a homogeneous governance structure, such as China and France, may find it easier to implement more stringent response policy measures nation-wide, whereas decentralized countries, such as Sweden and Japan, prefer to provide recommended measures and lax restrictions on individuals.

National Cultural Orientation: Loose Versus Tight Cultures

Culture is generally understood as the shared meaning and values that distinguish one group of people from another (Hofstede et al., 2010). Culture, as a multi-dimensional construct, can be studied at individual, organizational, group, regional, and even national levels. We are interested in national cultural orientation along a tightness-looseness continuum, capturing two key components: the strength of social norms and the degree of sanctioning within societies (Gelfand et al., 2011).

People living in different cultural contexts have strikingly different senses of the self, of others, and of the interdependence of the two (Markus & Kitayama, 1991). In a society with a tight culture, citizens are more likely to comply with government interventions (Gaenslen, 1986; Gelfand, 2012). They attach importance to group solidarity and orders (Poole, 2019), so as to attend to others and be harmoniously interdependent with each other. Furthermore, culture is instrumental to fostering people's normative commitments and psychological beliefs. Gelfand et al. (2011) have illustrated that the tightness-looseness cultural orientation can impact individuals' adherence to social norms and subsequently influence their perception of responsibility in state-citizen interactions (Gelfand et al., 2011; Trnka & Trundle, 2014). As suggested by behavioral public administration studies (Tummers, 2019; F. Zhang et al., 2018), the adoption of policy measures across different countries by and large depends on the public's attitudes, subjective norms, perceived behavioral control, and willingness to cooperate in regard to containing the pandemic (X. Zhang et al., 2020).

Asian countries, such as China and Japan, are mostly associated with a tight culture, as a result of Confucius's legacy. In these countries, a societal consensus has generally been reached to comply with the containment and closure measures during the COVID-19 crisis. In contrast, people in nations with a loose culture show less tolerance for behavioral intervention, value individuals' own preferences, and preserve the self through self-regulation and self-responsibility (Gelfand, 2012; Markus & Kitayama, 1991). National culture in both France and Sweden views the individual as an independent, self-contained, autonomous entity who comprises a unique configuration of internal attributes; thus, these countries encourage individual flexibility and risk-taking, consistent with these loose cultural values (Luria et al., 2015; Markus & Kitayama, 1991).

In Figure 23.1, we group together the four countries under study along vertical and horizontal dimensions. The vertical dimension concerns institutional arrangements and ranges from "decentralized regime" at the top of the figure to "centralized regime" at the bottom. The horizontal dimension is concerned with national cultural orientation, moving from "loose

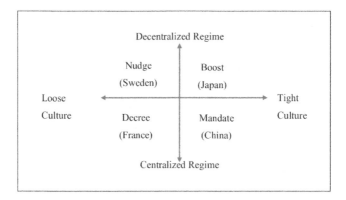

Figure 23.1 Two critical contextual factors shaping COVID-19 response strategies.

culture" on the left of the figure to "tight culture" on the right. This simple framework reflects fundamental differences in institutional arrangements and cultural values. Sweden is a country with a more decentralized regime and looser culture, whereas China is a nation with a more centralized regime and tighter culture. The other opposing pair includes France, with a more centralized regime but looser culture, and Japan with a more decentralized regime but tighter culture.

On the basis of the scale and scope of policy interventions aiming to affect individuals' behaviors, the countries' response strategies can be further classified into nudge, mandate, decree, and boost categories. Accordingly, we posit that the two critical contextual factors jointly shape these countries' COVID-19 response strategies, which are nudge in Sweden, mandate in China, decree in France, and boost in Japan.

A Comparison of Stringency in COVID-19 Response Strategies Across Four Countries

NPIs targeting individual, community, and environmental levels, including social distancing measures and other behavioral modifications, are the interventions available to mitigate the spread of COVID-19 (Katz et al., 2019). Governments have adopted a number of policy measures aiming to alter the public's behaviors, including school and workplace closures, the cancelation of public events, restrictions on gathering sizes, shutting down public transport, stay-at-home orders, restrictions on internal movement and international travel, and public information campaigns. Yet, there are a great deal of variations in regard to the scale, scope, and strictness of these measures across countries.

The Oxford COVID-19 Government Response Tracker (OxCGRT) provides a systematic approach to tracking and comparing how government

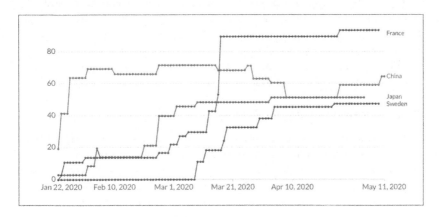

Figure 23.2 Four government response stringency indexes, January 22 to May 11, 2020.

Table 23.1 Key information about response strategies across four countries.

Countries	Critical turning points	Response stringency index at stable stages
China	January 23, 2020, and January 26, 2020	About 60–70
Japan	February 25, 2020	About 40–50
France	March 17, 2020	About 85–95
Sweden	March 9, 2020, and March 19, 2020	About 35–45

COVID-19 responses have evolved over time (Hale et al., 2020). The data involved were collected from publicly available sources and updated in real time by a research team based at Oxford University. The research team constructed a composite index to update the stringency of governments' responses across countries, longitudinally.

According to the OxCGRT, the trajectories of the stringency of policy interventions across the four countries are not synchronous. As shown in Figure 23.2, the stringency indexes regarding the response strategies are evolving over time, contingent upon the different stages of the pandemic outbreak. To compare their policy interventions on the same benchmark, we chose to focus our attention on the steady phase.

Table 23.1 displays information regarding the critical turning points and corresponding stringency indices of the four countries' COVID-19 response strategies at stable stages. Among the four selected countries, France has the highest stringency index (85–95), followed by China (60–70), Japan (40–50), and Sweden (35–45).

The Oxford stringency index does not provide information on how well policies are enforced or to capture institutional and cultural contextual factors. We thus collected data from publicly available sources, such as government press releases and briefings, as well as news articles, to engage in an inquiry regarding how institutional and cultural factors have shaped different countries' distinct response strategies.

"Nudge" Response Strategy in Sweden

Sweden's COVID-19 response is a good example of a nudge strategy, which is designed to change behaviors without prohibiting options or imposing upon individuals' freedom of choice, so as to steer people in a particular direction (Hertwig & Grüne-Yanoff, 2017; Tummers, 2019). It ranks the weakest on the stringency index among the four countries. Sweden's COVID-19 response has been singled out as controversial for not imposing a full lockdown, as seen in most of Europe, to contain the pandemic. The Swedish authorities made it clear that managing the COVID-19 pandemic would not be a sprint but a marathon—a long-term undertaking.[2] Thus, policies need to be designed on a level that is acceptable to the people over a long period of time.

Although a temporary ban on all nonessential travel to Sweden was put in place on March 19, closure-related measures and restrictions on internal movement have not been fully implemented. Swedish gyms, schools, restaurants, and shops have all remained open throughout the spread of the pandemic. There have been no regulations regarding citizens' mobility. There are some recommendations regarding public health efforts, such as social distancing rules in restaurants, working online, and restricting the sizes of gatherings. The Swedish strategy to contain COVID-19 has relied on the voluntary social distancing and self-restraint of its citizens, who have received daily briefings and instructions concerning individually targeted self-protection techniques from the Swedish Public Health Agency and press conferences held by state epidemiologists, the Prime Minister, and other government representatives (Nygren & Olofsson, 2020).

Sweden is, by tradition, a unitary but conspicuously decentralized country in which the central government exercises only ministerial functions. Most public tasks are fulfilled by the two-tier elected local government structure, in which municipalities fulfill a broad scope of responsibilities, including education, social services, and public utilities (Wollmann, 2004). At the national level, Sweden's strategy focuses more on recommendations than requirements, to induce the public to modify their behaviors voluntarily to combat COVID-19. The key here is the sense of individuals' self-responsibility and high level of trust in Swedish society; these elements are highlighted in a loose culture.

"Mandate" Response Strategy in China

In contrast to Sweden, China's COVID-19 response strategy represents a mandate strategy, which involves authority-based coercive forces and social consensus. Since the COVID-19 outbreak was officially declared in China, policy interventions have been undertaken to mitigate the pandemic and prevent the persistence of the virus across the population (Kraemer et al., 2020). Besides the lockdown measures that took effect in Wuhan on January 23, by January 26, as many as 30 provinces had successively launched first-level responses to the major public health emergency.

The Chinese authorities nationally invoked wartime narratives to mobilize the public and emphasized group solidarity to contain the spread of COVID-19. The Chinese response to COVID-19 has featured the complete lockdown of cities with major outbreaks and mandatory social distancing for all populations (S. Zhang, et al., 2020). Specifically, all residents were restricted to staying at home in quarantine. The state delegated the power of monitoring the behavior of residents to massive grassroots community-based organizations. In addition, the vast majority of public places, such as shopping centers, schools, restaurants, and cinemas, were closed on a national scale. With the leadership of the central government, mandatory interventions have been imposed on the whole society. On the whole, citizens in China have demonstrated strong levels of obedience and a cooperative willingness to maintain social stability, which are key features of a tight culture.

Just as the Chinese President, Xi Jinping, declared fighting the virus a people's war, the Chinese authorities mobilized people to support the government's strict control of human mobility in the fight against COVID-19. China features tight cultural values and so Chinese individuals are willing to submit themselves to authority such as this with few complaints. The adoption of mandatory policy interventions to adjust individuals' behavior in China is partly due to its authority-based consensus, which was reached under a centralized regime.

"Decree" Response Strategy in France

Although both the mandate and decree strategies emphasize the prohibition and limitation of unwanted behavior, there are some distinctions between them (Keeler, 1993; Nasir & Turner, 2013; Zhao, 2009). The decree strategy in France is legally based in this sense.

France was the first country in Europe to detect COVID-19, on January 24. Yet, the largest-ever gathering of Smurfs, Yellow Vest protests, and local elections were still continuing in March. During the initial stages of the outbreak, the public in France emphasized liberty and continued life as usual. Meanwhile, the authorities enacted soft measures to mitigate the spread of COVID-19. As the virus began to spread with unprecedented speed, France was in danger of a serious COVID-19 outbreak in mid-March. Correspondingly, the response strategy to the spread of the pandemic changed from mitigation to suppression.

President Emmanuel Macron employed wartime rhetoric to describe the crisis ("We are at war") when he declared a nationwide lockdown in his

March 16 television address.[3] The whole of French society, including hospitals, the military, and the public, have been mobilized in an attempt to defeat COVID-19. France's confinement measures continued until May 11, which was the turning point in the fight against the pandemic.

The authorities imposed restrictions on individual freedom of movement in accordance with the decree.[4] Since the lockdown was instituted, residents have been instructed to stay at home, apart from for essential activities, such as shopping for food, seeking medical care, and exercising. Those who go out are required to obtain a written note explaining why. Moreover, if COVID-19 lockdown rules are violated, the individuals concerned can be fined an amount between €135 and €3,750, according to the severity of the violation. In addition, airport screenings, quarantines, bans on major events, and the closure of public places, including schools, workplaces, restaurants, and public transport, were put into place simultaneously.

France is a unitary and highly centralized state in which major public tasks are performed by the central state, acting through central ministries (Wollmann, 2004). Once the pandemic worsened on a national scale, the French authorities were able to transform policy interventions to quickly cope with the pandemic. Considering the relatively loose cultural orientation in regard to the French public's acceptance and compliance, the response strategy in France is a more coercive, legal-based one, aiming to change citizens' behaviors.

"Boost" Response Strategy in Japan

A boost strategy tends to foster people's competence in regard to making choices by altering their external environments and through the presentation of information (Bradt, 2019; Hertwig & Grüne-Yanoff, 2017). These features have manifested in Japan's policy interventions in their battle against the COVID-19 virus. The Japanese government first issued *Basic Policies for Novel Coronavirus Disease Control* on February 25, 2020, which has been revised four times since its release,[5] especially after the state of emergency took effect in six designated prefectures (Saitama, Chiba, Tokyo, Kanagawa, Osaka, Hyogo, and Fukuoka) on April 7.

Although Japan has a unitary government system, subnational governments have gained a fair amount of autonomy by law in the policymaking process (Jacobs, 2003). Thus, Japan has so far not enforced mandatory policy interventions, partly because the central government cannot enforce closures or fine citizens for breaking rules. Even after the areas under a state of emergency were expanded to all 47 prefectures on April 16, the Japanese government did not take compulsory measures, such as a lockdown (city blockade), which were otherwise implemented in other countries. Furthermore, the declared emergency is more of a symbolic gesture than a move that actually involves the delegation of extra power to local governments. For instance, specific to the COVID-19 crisis, local policy interventions guiding individuals' behavior in Tokyo and Hokkaido were issued much earlier than the national government's recommendations in the state of emergency.

The basic COVID-19 response strategy in Japan includes three pillars: early detection, intensive care and securing medical services, and the behavioral modification of citizens. The Japanese authorities released guidelines on "Three Cs" (closed spaces with insufficient ventilation, crowded conditions with people, and conversations at a short distance) to provide the public with vital information about how to avoid infectious environments, to guide and educate the public in terms of eliciting their cooperation during the COVID-19 pandemic (Hayasaki, 2020; Shaw et al., 2020). The risk of the occurrence of infection clusters is particularly high when the Three Cs overlap. Therefore, governments in Japan recommended that residents avoid the Three Cs, with the aim of reducing human-to-human contact. The relatively less stringent index assigned to Japan is largely attributed to its decentralized regime and tight cultural orientation (Table 23.2).

Table 23.2 COVID-19 response strategies in Sweden, China, France, and Japan.

Countries	Narrative	Response	Scope	Containment and closure measures
Sweden	Marathon	Mild and advisory	Subnational—	• Requirements regarding international travel control and the cancelation of public events • Recommendations regarding the restriction of internal movement • No measures regarding the closure of schools, workplaces, and public transport
China	War	Drastic and mandatory	National	• Lockdowns in cities with major outbreaks • Requirements regarding the closure of schools, workplaces, and public transport; restrictions on internal movement; international travel control; and the cancelation of public events • Grassroots organizations monitor individuals' behavior

(Continued)

Table 23.2 (Continued)

Countries	Narrative	Response	Scope	Containment and closure measures
France	War	Drastic and required	National	• Nationwide lockdown based on a decree • Requirements regarding the closure of schools, workplaces, and public transport; restrictions on internal movement; international travel control; and the cancelation of public events • Limitations regarding individual mobility (certification and penalties)
Japan	Emergency	Mild and recommended	Subnational	• Recommendations regarding the closure of schools and workplaces, public information campaigns, restrictions on internal movement, and the cancelation of public events • Requirements regarding international travel control • No measures regarding the closure of public transport • The behavioral modification of citizens (avoid the Three Cs and implement self-restraint)

No One-Size-Fits-All Strategy

As countries around the world are continuing their efforts to tackle the coronavirus, what can we learn from a brief reflection on the divergent response strategies applied to the four countries examined here? We suggest that there is no one-size-fit-all strategy that can be used to combat COVID-19 on a global scale. Although the experiences of the four countries examined in the present study can provide lessons for other countries, their distinct trajectories are contextually dependent and depend upon reflections regarding how pandemic response strategies have interacted with the response of the population, are shaped by institutional arrangements, and are informed by national cultural orientations. Our comparative analysis reaffirms the joint role of institutional and cultural contexts in the shaping of governmental policymaking.

Notes

1. The World Health Statistics 2018 indicate that international health regulations (IHR) capacity and health emergency preparedness are similar in Sweden (93), China (100), France (89), and Japan (100). According to the 2019 Global Health Security Index, these four countries were all ranked as the most prepared countries in regard to the "Sufficient and Robust Health System to Treat the Sick and Protect Health Workers" indicator.
2. Swedish Foreign Minister Ann Linde believes that the country's coronavirus response has been pragmatic, not libertarian. Retrieved from www.politico.eu/article/sweden-coronavirus-leader-ann-linde-defends-approach-shrugs-off-far-right-embrace/.
3. France became the third European country to implement a lockdown. Retrieved from: www.cidrap.umn.edu/news-perspective/2020/03/france-orders-lockdown-slow-covid-19-spread.
4. On March 16, 2020, France published a decree (No. 2020-260) regulating movement as part of the fight against the spread of the COVID-19 virus. Retrieved from: www.mwe.com/it/insights/covid-19-checklist-for-publicly-listed-companies-in-france/.
5. *Basic Policies for Novel Coronavirus Disease Control* in Japan has been revised 4 times, February 25, March 27, April 7, and April 16. Retrieved from: www.mhlw.go.jp/stf/seisakunitsuite/bunya/newpage_00032.html.

References

Bavel, J. J. V., Baicker, K., Boggio, P. S., Capraro, V., Cichocka, A., Cikara, M., . . . Willer, R. (2020). Using social and behavioural science to support COVID-19 pandemic response. *Nature Human Behaviour, 4*(5), 460–471.

Berkman, A., Garcia, J., Muñoz-Laboy, M., Paiva, V., & Parker, R. (2005). A critical analysis of the Brazilian response to HIV/AIDS: Lessons learned for controlling and mitigating the epidemic in developing countries. *American Journal of Public Health, 95*(7), 1162–1172.

Bradt, J. (2019). Comparing the effects of behaviorally informed interventions on flood insurance demand: An experimental analysis of "boosts" and "nudges." *Behavioural Public Policy*, 1–31. Advance online publication. https://doi.org/10.1017/bpp.2019.31

Carayannopoulos, G. (2017). Whole of government: The solution to managing crises? *Australian Journal of Public Administration, 76*(2), 251–265.

Christensen, T., Lægreid, P., & Rykkja, L. H. (2016). Organizing for crisis management: Building governance capacity and legitimacy. *Public Administration Review, 76*(6), 887–897.

Clune, W. H. (1993). The best path to systemic educational policy: Standard/centralized or differentiated/decentralized? *Educational Evaluation and Policy Analysis, 15*(3), 233–254.

Gaenslen, F. (1986). Culture and decision making in China, Japan, Russia, and the United States. *World Politics, 39*(1), 78–103.

Gelfand, M. J. (2012). Culture's constraints: International differences in the strength of social norms. *Current Directions in Psychological Science, 21*(6), 420–424.

Gelfand, M. J., Raver, J. L., Nishii, L., Leslie, L. M., Lun, J., Lim, B. C., . . . Yamaguchi, S. (2011). Differences between tight and loose cultures: A 33-nation study. *Science, 332*(6033), 1100–1104.

Geva-May, I. (2002). Cultural theory: The neglected variable in the craft of policy analysis. *Journal of Comparative Policy Analysis, 4*(3), 243–265.

Goel, R. K., Mazhar, U., Nelson, M. A., & Ram, R. (2017). Different forms of decentralization and their impact on government performance: Micro-level evidence from 113 countries. *Economic Modelling, 62*, 171–183.

Hale, T., Angrist, N., Kira, B., Petherick, A., Phillips, T., & Webster, S. (2020). *Variation in government responses to Covid-19 Version 5.0*. Blavatnik School of Government Working Paper. University of Oxford.

Hayasaki, E. (2020). Covid-19: How Japan squandered its early jump on the pandemic. *BMJ (Clinical Research Ed.), 369*, m1625.

Hertwig, R., & Grüne-Yanoff, T. (2017). Nudging and boosting: Steering or empowering good decisions. *Perspectives on Psychological Science, 12*(6), 973–986.

Hofstede, G., Hofstede, G. J., & Minkov, M. (2010). *Cultures and organizations: Software for the mind* (3rd ed.). New York: McGraw-Hill.

Jacobs, A. J. (2003). Devolving authority and expanding autonomy in Japanese prefectures and municipalities. *Governance, 16*(4), 601–623.

Jessop, B. (2010). Redesigning the state, reorienting state power, and rethinking the state. In K. T. Leicht & J. C. Jenkins (Eds.), *Handbook of politics: State and society in global perspective* (pp. 41–61). New York: Springer.

Kandel, N., Chungong, S., Omaar, A., & Xing, J. (2020). Health security capacities in the context of COVID-19 outbreak: An analysis of international health regulations annual report data from 182 countries. *The Lancet, 395*(10229), 1047–1053.

Katz, R., Vaught, A., & Simmens, S. J. (2019). Local decision making for implementing social distancing in response to outbreaks. *Public Health Reports, 134*(2), 150–154.

Keeler, J. T. S. (1993). Opening the window for reform: Mandates, crises, and extraordinary policy-making. *Comparative Political Studies, 25*(4), 433–486.

Kraemer, M. U. G., Yang, C.-H., Gutierrez, B., Wu, C.-H., Klein, B., Pigott, D. M., . . . Scarpino, S. V. (2020). The effect of human mobility and control measures on the COVID-19 epidemic in China. *Science, 368*(6490), 493–497.

León, S., & Orriols, L. (2019). Attributing responsibility in devolved contexts. Experimental evidence from the UK. *Electoral Studies, 59*, 39–48.

Luria, G., Cnaan, R. A., & Boehm, A. (2015). National culture and prosocial behaviors: Results from 66 countries. *Nonprofit and Voluntary Sector Quarterly, 44*(5), 1041–1065.

Markus, H., & Kitayama, S. (1991). Culture and the self: Implications for cognition, emotion, and motivation. *Psychological Review, 98*(2), 224–253.

May, P. J. (2015). Implementation failures revisited: Policy regime perspectives. *Public Policy and Administration, 30*(3–4), 277–299.

Migdal, J. S. (2009). Researching the state. In A. S. Zuckerman & M. I. Lichbach (Eds.), *Comparative politics: Rationality, culture, and structure* (2nd ed., pp. 162–192). Cambridge: Cambridge University Press.

Nasir, K. M., & Turner, B. S. (2013). Governing as gardening: Reflections on soft authoritarianism in Singapore. *Citizenship Studies, 17*(3–4), 339–352.

Nygren, K. G., & Olofsson, A. (2020). Managing the COVID-19 pandemic through individual responsibility: The consequences of a world risk society and enhanced ethopolitics. *Journal of Risk Research*, 1–5. Advance online publication. https://doi.org/10.1080/13669877.2020.1756382

Pillemer, F. M., Blendon, R. J., Zaslavsky, A. M., & Lee, B. Y. (2015). Predicting support for non-pharmaceutical interventions during infectious outbreaks: A four region analysis. *Disasters*, *39*(1), 125–145.

Poole, E. G. (2019). How institutional culture trumps tier effects: Evidence from government responsiveness to FOI requests. *Journal of Public Administration Research and Theory*, *29*(2), 210–226.

Shaw, R., Kim, Y-k, & Hua, J. (2020). Governance, technology and citizen behavior in pandemic: Lessons from COVID-19 in East Asia. *Progress in Disaster Science*, *6*, 1–10.

Trnka, S., & Trundle, C. (2014). Competing responsibilities: Moving beyond neoliberal responsibilisation. *Anthropological Forum*, *24*(2), 136–153.

Tummers, L. (2019). Public policy and behavior change. *Public Administration Review*, *79*(6), 925–930.

Weible, C. M., Nohrstedt, D., Cairney, P., Carter, D. P., Crow, D. A., Durnová, A. P., . . . Stone, D. (2020). COVID-19 and the policy sciences: Initial reactions and perspectives. *Policy Sciences*, *53*, 225–241.

Wilder-Smith, A., & Freedman, D. O. (2020). Isolation, quarantine, social distancing and community containment: Pivotal role for old-style public health measures in the novel coronavirus (2019-Ncov) outbreak. *Journal of Travel Medicine*, *27*, taaa020. https://doi.org/10.1093/jtm/taaa020

Wimmer, A. (2018). *Nation building: Why some countries come together while others fall apart*. Princeton, NJ: Princeton University Press.

Wollmann, H. (2004). Local government reforms in Great Britain, Sweden, Germany and France: Between multi-function and single-purpose organisations. *Local Government Studies*, *30*(4), 639–665.

Zhang, F., Welch, E. W., & Miao, Q. (2018). Public organization adaptation to extreme events: Mediating role of risk perception. *Journal of Public Administration Research and Theory*, *28*(3), 371–387.

Zhang, S., Wang, Z., Chang, R., Wang, H., Xu, C., Yu, X., . . . Cai, Y. (2020). COVID-19 containment: China provides important lessons for global response. *Frontiers of Medicine*, *14*, 215–219.

Zhang, X., Wang, F., Zhu, C., & Wang, Z. (2020). Willingness to self-isolate when facing a pandemic risk: Model, empirical test, and policy recommendations. *International Journal of Environmental Research and Public Health*, *17*(1), 197.

Zhao, D. (2009). The mandate of heaven and performance legitimation in historical and contemporary China. *American Behavioral Scientist*, *53*(3), 416–433.

24 How Pandemics End

Gina Kolata

An infectious outbreak can conclude in more ways than one, historians say. But for whom does it end, and who gets to decide?

When will the COVID-19 pandemic end? And how?

According to historians, pandemics typically have two types of endings: the medical, which occurs when the incidence and death rates plummet, and the social, when the epidemic of fear about the disease wanes. "When people ask, 'When will this end?,' they are asking about the social ending," said Dr. Jeremy Greene, a historian of medicine at Johns Hopkins.

In other words, an end can occur not because a disease has been vanquished but because people grow tired of panic mode and learn to live with a disease. Allan Brandt, a Harvard historian, said something similar was happening with COVID-19: "As we have seen in the debate about opening the economy, many questions about the so-called end are determined not by medical and public health data but by sociopolitical processes."

Endings "are very, very messy," said Dora Vargha, a historian at the University of Exeter. "Looking back, we have a weak narrative. For whom does the epidemic end, and who gets to say?"

In the Path of Fear

An epidemic of fear can occur even without an epidemic of illness. Dr. Susan Murray, of the Royal College of Surgeons in Dublin, saw that firsthand in 2014 when she was a fellow at a rural hospital in Ireland.

In the preceding months, more than 11,000 people in West Africa had died from Ebola, a terrifying viral disease that was highly infectious and often fatal. The epidemic seemed to be waning, and no cases had occurred in Ireland, but the public fear was palpable.

"On the street and on the wards, people are anxious," Dr. Murray recalled recently in an article in The New England Journal of Medicine. "Having the wrong color skin is enough to earn you the side-eye from your fellow passengers on the bus or train. Cough once, and you will find them shuffling away from you."

The Dublin hospital workers were warned to prepare for the worst. They were terrified, and worried that they lacked protective equipment. When a young man arrived in the emergency room from a country with Ebola patients, no one wanted to go near him; nurses hid, and doctors threatened to leave the hospital.

Dr. Murray alone dared treat him, she wrote, but his cancer was so advanced that all she could offer was comfort care. A few days later, tests confirmed that the man did not have Ebola; he died an hour later. Three days afterward, the World Health Organization declared the Ebola epidemic over.

Dr. Murray wrote: "If we are not prepared to fight fear and ignorance as actively and as thoughtfully as we fight any other virus, it is possible that fear can do terrible harm to vulnerable people, even in places that never see a single case of infection during an outbreak. And a fear epidemic can have far worse consequences when complicated by issues of race, privilege, and language."

Black Death and Dark Memories

Bubonic plague has struck several times in the past 2,000 years, killing millions of people and altering the course of history. Each epidemic amplified the fear that came with the next outbreak.

The disease is caused by a strain of bacteria, Yersinia pestis, that lives on fleas that live on rats. But bubonic plague, which became known as the Black Death, also can be passed from infected person to infected person through respiratory droplets, so it cannot be eradicated simply by killing rats.

Historians describe three great waves of plague, said Mary Fissell, a historian at Johns Hopkins: the Plague of Justinian, in the sixth century; the medieval epidemic, in the 14th century; and a pandemic that struck in the late 19th and early 20th centuries.

The medieval pandemic began in 1331 in China. The illness, along with a civil war that was raging at the time, killed half the population of China. From there, the plague moved along trade routes to Europe, North Africa and the Middle East. In the years between 1347 and 1351, it killed at least a third of the European population. Half of the population of Siena, Italy, died.

"It is impossible for the human tongue to recount the awful truth," wrote the 14th-century chronicler Agnolo di Tura. "Indeed, one who did not see such horribleness can be called blessed." The infected, he wrote, "swell beneath the armpits and in their groins, and fall over while talking." The dead were buried in pits, in piles.

In Florence, wrote Giovanni Boccaccio, "No more respect was accorded to dead people than would nowadays be accorded to dead goats." Some hid in their homes. Others refused to accept the threat. Their way of coping, Boccaccio wrote, was to "drink heavily, enjoy life to the full, go round singing and merrymaking, and gratify all of one's cravings when the opportunity emerged, and shrug the whole thing off as one enormous joke."

That pandemic ended, but the plague recurred. One of the worst outbreaks began in China in 1855 and spread worldwide, killing more than 12 million in India alone. Health authorities in Bombay burned whole neighborhoods trying to rid them of the plague. "Nobody knew if it made a difference," the Yale historian Frank Snowden said.

It is not clear what made the bubonic plague die down. Some scholars have argued that cold weather killed the disease-carrying fleas, but that would not have interrupted the spread by the respiratory route, Dr. Snowden noted. Or perhaps it was a change in the rats. By the 19th century, the plague was being carried not by black rats but by brown rats, which are stronger and more vicious and more likely to live apart from humans.

"You certainly wouldn't want one for a pet," Dr. Snowden said.

Another hypothesis is that the bacterium evolved to be less deadly. Or maybe actions by humans, such as the burning of villages, helped quell the epidemic.

The plague never really went away. In the United States, infections are endemic among prairie dogs in the Southwest and can be transmitted to people. Dr. Snowden said that one of his friends became infected after a stay at a hotel in New Mexico. The previous occupant of his room had a dog, which had fleas that carried the microbe. Such cases are rare, and can now be successfully treated with antibiotics, but any report of a case of the plague stirs up fear.

One Disease That Actually Ended

Among the diseases to have achieved a medical end is smallpox. But it is exceptional for several reasons: There is an effective vaccine, which gives lifelong protection; the virus, Variola major, has no animal host, so eliminating the disease in humans meant total elimination; and its symptoms are so unusual that infection is obvious, allowing for effective quarantines and contact tracing.

But while it still raged, smallpox was horrific. Epidemic after epidemic swept the world, for at least 3,000 years. Individuals infected with the virus developed a fever, then a rash that turned into pus-filled spots, which became encrusted and fell off, leaving scars. The disease killed three out of 10 of its victims, often after immense suffering. In 1633, an epidemic among Native Americans "disrupted all the native communities in the northeast and certainly facilitated English settlement in Massachusetts," said Harvard historian Dr. David S. Jones. William Bradford, leader of the Plymouth colony, wrote an account of the disease in Native Americans, saying the broken pustules would effectively glue a patient's skin to the mat he lay on, only to be torn off. Bradford wrote: "When they turn them, a whole side will flay off at once as it were, and they will be all of a gore blood, most fearful to behold."

The last person to contract smallpox naturally was Ali Maow Maalin, a hospital cook in Somalia, in 1977. He recovered, only to die of malaria in 2013.

Forgotten Influenzas

The 1918 flu is held up today as the example of the ravages of a pandemic and the value of quarantines and social distancing. Before it ended, the flu killed 50 million to 100 million people worldwide. It preyed on young to middle-aged adults—orphaning children, depriving families of breadwinners, killing troops in the midst of World War I.

In the autumn of 1918, Victor Vaughan, a prominent doctor, was dispatched to Camp Devens near Boston to report on a flu that was raging there. He saw "hundreds of stalwart young men in the uniform of their country, coming into the wards of the hospital in groups of 10 or more," he wrote. "They are placed on the cots until every bed is full, yet others crowd in. Their faces soon wear a bluish cast, a distressing cough brings up blood stained sputum. In the morning the dead bodies are stacked up in the morgue like cord wood."

The virus, he wrote, "demonstrated the inferiority of human inventions in the destruction of human life."

After sweeping through the world, that flu faded away, evolving into a variant of the more benign flu that comes around every year.

"Maybe it was like a fire that, having burned the available and easily accessible wood, burns down," Dr. Snowden said.

It ended socially, too. World War I was over; people were ready for a fresh start, a new era, and eager to put the nightmare of disease and war behind them. Until recently, the 1918 flu was largely forgotten.

Other flu pandemics followed, none so bad but all nonetheless sobering. In the Hong Kong flu of 1968, 1 million people died worldwide, including 100,000 in the United States, mostly people older than 65. That virus still circulates as a seasonal flu, and its initial path of destruction—and the fear that went with it—is rarely recalled.

How will COVID-19 end?
Will that happen with COVID-19?

One possibility, historians say, is that the coronavirus pandemic could end socially before it ends medically. People may grow so tired of the restrictions that they declare the pandemic over, even as the virus continues to smolder in the population and before a vaccine or effective treatment is found.

"I think there is this sort of social psychological issue of exhaustion and frustration," the Yale historian Naomi Rogers said. "We may be in a moment when people are just saying: 'That's enough. I deserve to be able to return to my regular life.'"

It is happening already; in some states, governors have lifted restrictions, allowing hair salons, nail salons and gyms to reopen, in defiance of warnings by public health officials that such steps are premature. As the economic catastrophe wreaked by the lockdowns grows, more and more people may be ready to say "enough."

"There is this sort of conflict now," Dr. Rogers said. Public health officials have a medical end in sight, but some members of the public see a social end.

"Who gets to claim the end?" Dr. Rogers said. "If you push back against the notion of its ending, what are you pushing back against? What are you claiming when you say, 'No, it is not ending.'"

The challenge, Dr. Brandt said, is that there will be no sudden victory. Trying to define the end of the epidemic "will be a long and difficult process."

Author Index

Subject Index

Made in the USA
Coppell, TX
07 February 2022

73122973R00155